W9-DDP-457

COLLEGE

ALGEBRA

by **HENRY L. RIETZ**

Late of the University of Iowa

and **ARTHUR R. CRATHORNE**

Late of the University of Illinois

SIXTH EDITION
Revised by J. WILLIAM PETERS

University of Illinois

HENRY HOLT AND COMPANY New York

Copyright © 1909, 1919, 1929, 1939, 1951, 1958
by Henry Holt and Company, Inc.;
Copyright 1936 by Henry L. Rietz
and Arthur R. Crathorne
Library of Congress Catalog Card Number 58-6322
Printed in the United States of America
27453-0918

October, 1958

PREFACE TO THE SIXTH EDITION

The majority of students who study College Algebra plan to use that subject as a tool in other fields. They need to know the fundamental definitions and facts of algebra; to see, in so far as they are able, the reason behind the processes; and to develop a facility in the manipulation of mathematical symbols. The aim in revising this text has been to meet these objectives.

While there are many high schools that give excellent preparation in elementary algebra, there are still many students entering college who need to review the basic facts and techniques of their high school courses. In the first seven chapters of this text, an extensive review of these topics of high school algebra has been given, while at the same time new material has been introduced to interest and stimulate the student in his study. Chapter 1 is intended for those teachers who prefer to begin the course with a discussion of the number system and the elementary operations of algebra. On the other hand, many instructors prefer to start with Chapter 2 and refer to special topics in Chapter 1 when those topics are pertinent to a specific problem. Throughout the book, frequent reference is made to statements in Chapter 1, so that the student will understand when the facts of that chapter are being applied.

The plan of this edition is the same as for the fifth edition. The first fourteen chapters are centered on the development of the number system and the solution of equations. Logarithms are introduced immediately after the chapter on exponents, and many problems further on in the text require the use of logarithms in their solution. However, two changes should be mentioned. In Chapter 7, a more extensive treatment of imaginary numbers has been given. In Chapter 8, the development of the rules for obtaining the characteristic of the common logarithm of a number has been based on the expression of the number in scientific notation.

The latter part of the text is devoted to the discussion of progressions, permutations, combinations, probability, series, and other traditional topics.

Many of the exercises and problems have been revised, and an effort has been made to arrange them in order of increasing difficulty. Occasionally there are problems that appear to demand lengthy computation and that do not yield simple answers which students expect in their mathematics courses. Usually these are exercises lifted from problems in other fields with which I have seen my students struggling. I feel that the student must be made aware of the fact that problems may not always have pat answers. At the end of each group of exercises, there is usually one problem to tax the ingenuity of the better student. Answers to odd-numbered exercises are given in the back of the text.

In preparing this revision, I have leaned heavily on the suggestions of those persons who have used the previous edition of the text. For their suggestions and criticisms, I am deeply grateful. I am especially indebted to Professors H. J. Miles and W. A. Ferguson for their advice and encouragement.

J. W. P.

Urbana, Illinois
June 1957

PREFACE TO THE FIRST EDITION

THIS book is designed primarily for use as a textbook in the freshman year of colleges and technical schools. Special attention is directed to the following features:

(1) The method of reviewing the algebra of the secondary schools.

(2) The selection and omission of material.

(3) The explicit statement of assumptions upon which the proofs are based.

(4) The application of algebraic methods to physical problems.

For the majority of college freshmen, a considerable period of time elapses between the completion of the high school algebra and the beginning of college mathematics. The review of the secondary school algebra is written for these students. This part of the book is, however, more than a hasty review. While the student is reviewing a first course, he is at the same time making a distinct advance by seeing the subject-matter from new viewpoints, which his added maturity enables him to appreciate. For example, the functional notation, graphs, and determinants are introduced and used to advantage in the review. The extensions of the number concept receive fuller treatment than is usual in a college algebra. The various classes of numbers from positive integers to complex numbers are treated in the order in which they are demanded by the equation.

The application of algebra in the more advanced courses in mathematics has been an important factor in determining the subject-matter. Not only are some of the topics usually treated in the traditional course in algebra entirely omitted, but in each chapter the material is restricted to the development of those

v

central points which experience has shown to be essential. While a complete discussion of limits and infinite series does not properly belong in a course in algebra, it has been thought best to include an introduction to these subjects which covers in considerable detail only the theory necessary to a discussion of the comparison and ratio tests. From the experience of the authors, a great deal is gained by thus taking a very elementary first course in limits and series.

While it is out of place in a book of this character to attempt a critical study of fundamentals, great care has been taken to point out just what is proved and what is assumed in so far as a first-year student can be expected to appreciate the necessity of assumptions.

Without trying to teach physics or engineering, many problems are introduced in which the principles of algebra are applied to physical problems, but no technical knowledge is assumed on the part of the student. Rules for the mechanical guidance of students in solving problems have been used sparingly.

The authors take great pleasure in acknowledging their indebtedness to their colleagues in the mathematical and engineering departments of the University of Illinois. We are indebted to Professors Haskins and Young for suggestions during the preparation of the manuscript as well as for a critical reading of the manuscript; to Professors Townsend, Goodenough, Miller, Wilczynski, Dr. Lytle, and to Professor Kuhn of Ohio State University for suggestions upon the manuscript; to Professor Watson for some of the practical problems; and again to Professor Goodenough for assistance in seeing the book through the press.

H. L. RIETZ
A. R. CRATHORNE

CONTENTS

CONTENTS

CONTENTS

Chapter 9 — QUADRATIC EQUATIONS

Chapter 10 — SYSTEMS OF EQUATIONS INVOLVING QUADRATICS

Chapter 11 — INEQUALITIES

CONTENTS

CONTENTS

SERIES OF POSITIVE TERMS

SERIES WITH BOTH POSITIVE AND NEGATIVE TERMS

GREEK ALPHABET

Letters	Names	Letters	Names	Letters	Names
A α	Alpha	I ι	Iota	P ρ	Rho
B β	Beta	K κ	Kappa	Σ σ ς	Sigma
Γ γ	Gamma	Λ λ	Lambda	T τ	Tau
Δ δ	Delta	M μ	Mu	Υ υ	Upsilon
E ϵ	Epsilon	N ν	Nu	Φ ϕ	Phi
Z ζ	Zeta	Ξ ξ	Xi	X χ	Chi
H η	Eta	O o	Omicron	Ψ ψ	Psi
Θ θ	Theta	Π π	Pi	Ω ω	Omega

A LIST OF SIGNS AND SYMBOLS

$+$, read *plus*. $-$, read *minus*.

$\times$, or $\cdot$, read *times*.

$\div$, read *divided by*.

$=$, read *is equal to*.

$\equiv$, read *is identical with*.

$\neq$, read *is not equal to*.

$\rightarrow$, read *approaches*.

$<$, read *is less than*.

$>$, read *is greater than*.

$\leqq$, read *is less than or equal to*.

$\geqq$, read *is greater than or equal to*.

$a!$ read *factorial a*.

( )   Parentheses.

[ ]   Brackets.   Signs of aggregation. These signs are used

{ }   Braces.   to collect together symbols which are to be

$\overline{}$ Vinculum.   treated in operations as one symbol.

| Bar.

a_r, read *a subscript r*, or *a sub r*.

x', x'' ..., read *x prime, x second* ... respectively.

$\lim x$, read *limit of x*.

$x \rightarrow \infty$, read *x becomes infinite*, or *x increases beyond bound*.

$\log_a n$, read *logarithm of n to the base a*.

$|a|$, read *absolute value of a*.

a^n, read *a to the nth power*, or *a exponent n*.

$\sqrt{a}$, read *square root of a*.

$\sqrt[n]{a}$, read *nth root of a*.

$f(x)$, $\phi(x)$, etc., read "f" *function of x*, "ϕ" *function of x*, etc.

$P(n, r)$ read *number of permutations of n things taken r at a time*.

$C(n, r)$ read *number of combinations of n things taken r at a time*.

(x, y), read *point whose coördinates are x and y*.

1 | THE NUMBER SYSTEM

1. The Rational Numbers

The first acquaintance that an individual has with numbers is the process of counting the objects of a group. The numbers he uses for this purpose are the **positive integers.** They are an ordered set of numbers, that is, 1 comes before 2, 2 before 3, 3 before 4, and so on. There is no largest positive integer, for no matter how large an integer is chosen, another larger by one unit can be found.

Early in his career, an individual learns to perform four fundamental operations with positive integers, namely, addition, subtraction, multiplication, and division. In arithmetic and algebra, these processes are to be applied only a finite number of times in any single problem. The sum of two positive integers and the product of two positive integers are always positive integers. Difficulties arise when the inverse processes, subtraction and division, are applied to positive integers.

The problem of subtracting equal positive integers, $5 - 5$ for instance, leads to the introduction of the new number 0 (read zero). The problem of subtracting a larger positive integer from a smaller one leads to the introduction of the **negative integers,** -1, -2, -3, and so on. For example, we say $5 - 7 = -2$. These negative integers have a number of practical uses, even though the word "negative" is not used in the applied problem. Negative numbers are encountered in problems of finance if an individual's assets are less than his liabilities. They are also met in reading thermometers when the temperature falls below zero.

The quotient of one positive integer by another yields a positive

1

integer only if the divisor happens to be a factor of the dividend. For example, 6 divided by 3 is 2, since 3 is a factor of 6. The problem of dividing 2 by 3 leads to the introduction of a new number called a rational fraction.

A **rational fraction** is the quotient of two integers.

The totality of positive and negative integers, zero, and the positive and negative rational fractions is called the system of **rational numbers**.

2. The Irrational Numbers

One of the problems of plane geometry is to find the diagonal of a square when the length of a side is known. If the square has sides of length one unit, the square of the length of the diagonal is 2 units. The problem now resolves itself into the arithmetic problem of finding a number x so that when x is multiplied by itself the product is 2. It can be shown that no rational number has this property. Therefore a new number, $\sqrt{2}$ (read square root of 2), is introduced into the number system.

Again in plane geometry, it is stated that the ratio of the circumference of a circle to its diameter is constant. This constant is designated by π (read pi). The number, π, cannot be represented by the quotient of two integers; that is, π is not a rational number.

Numbers like $\sqrt{2}$ and π, which cannot be represented as the quotient of two integers, are called **irrational**. Such numbers are used extensively by carpenters, surveyors, engineers, technicians, and scientists.

3. The Real Numbers

The totality of the rational and irrational numbers is called the system of **real numbers**. The real numbers may be represented by the points of a straight line. Let $X'X$ be this line (Fig. 1). Choose a point O on this line and call it the origin. Adopt some unit of measurement OA.

FIG. 1.

Beginning at O and proceeding in both directions, apply the unit of measure to mark OX and OX' at equal intervals, thus forming a scale of indefinite length of which a part is shown in Figure 1. The positive and negative integers may then conveniently be represented by the points marking the intervals. Similarly, corresponding to any fraction $\dfrac{a}{b}$ (a and b integers), there can be constructed a point on $X'X$ such that the fraction denotes the distance and the direction of the point from O. In fact, we assume that by means of this scale we are able to represent graphically all real numbers, and we can say, to any point P on the line, there corresponds a number which indicates the distance and direction of the point P from O; and conversely, we assume that to every real number there corresponds a point on this line.

Since the real numbers form an ordered array of entities, two numbers A and B may be equal to each other, or A may be greater than B, or A may be less than B. The terms "greater than" and "less than", which are common to everyday life, are easily misunderstood when used in the technical sense of algebra. For this reason we define these terms with respect to the relative position of the points representing A and B on the line $X'X$.

The real number A is said to be **equal** to the real number B if the points representing A and B coincide.

Illustration: The real numbers $\dfrac{2}{3}, \dfrac{8}{12}, \dfrac{14}{21}$, are all represented by the same point and hence these three numbers are equal to each other.

The real number A is said to be **greater than** the real number B (written $A > B$) if the point representing A falls to the right of the point representing B.

The real number A is said to be **less than** the real number B (written $A < B$) if the point representing A falls to the left of the point representing B.

Illustrations: $\quad 4 > 0, -3 < -2, \dfrac{22}{7} > \pi.$

Exercise. Arrange the following numbers in ascending order of magnitude: $3, -2, \sqrt{3}, 1, -\dfrac{25}{13}, \sqrt{2}, 1.414, \sqrt[3]{3}, -\dfrac{7}{2}.$

4. Operations with Real Numbers

Having introduced the real numbers, we now proceed to apply the operations of addition, subtraction, multiplication, and division to these numbers. The student has probably been performing these operations in arithmetic and algebra without being conscious of the fundamental assumptions which underlie the processes. We shall now proceed to a formal statement of the assumptions made concerning these processes.

In algebra, a letter is used to represent a number. The value of the letter is the number which it represents. In the following, let a, b, c, . . ., represent any real numbers.

The operations of **addition** and **multiplication** of numbers are subject to the following laws I–IX:

I. *The sum of two numbers is a uniquely determined number.*

That is, given a and b, there is one and only one number c such that $a + b = c$.

II. *Addition is commutative.*
That is, $a + b = b + a$.

Illustrations: $3 + 5 = 5 + 3$, $4x + 5x = 5x + 4x$.

III. *Addition is associative.*
That is, $a + b + c = (a + b) + c = a + (b + c)$.

Illustration: $10 + 3 + 7 = (10 + 3) + 7 = 10 + (3 + 7)$.

IV. *If equal numbers be added to equal numbers, the sums are equal numbers.*
That is, if $a = b$,
and $c = d$,
then $a + c = b + d$.

V. *The product of any two numbers is a uniquely determined number.*

That is, given a and b, there is one and only one number c such that $ab = c$. In this case, a and b are said to be **factors** of c.

VI. *Multiplication is commutative.*
That is, $ab = ba$.

VII. *Multiplication is associative.*
That is, $abc = (ab)c = a(bc)$.

VIII. *Multiplication is distributive with respect to addition.*
That is, $a(b + c) = ab + ac$.

Illustration: $4(x + 2y + 4z) = 4x + 8y + 16z$.

IX. *If equal numbers be multiplied by equal numbers, the products are equal numbers.*

That is, if $\qquad\qquad a = b$,
and $\qquad\qquad\qquad c = d$,
then $\qquad\qquad\qquad ac = bd$.

The following laws X and XI are definitions of subtraction and division, and enable us to give meanings to the symbols 0, $-a$, $\dfrac{a}{b}$, 1, and $\dfrac{1}{b}$.

X. *Given a and b, there is one and only one number x, such that* $x + b = c$.

Subtraction is the process of finding the number x in the equation $x + b = c$. The process is designated by the symbol $x = c - b$. The number x is called the **remainder** or the **difference** when b is subtracted from c.

By X, the number x in $x + b = c$ exists when $b = c$. In this case, the number x is called **zero,** and is written 0. In symbols,

$$0 + b = b. \qquad\qquad (1)$$

From X and the definition of 0, there exists a number x, such that $x + b = 0$. In this case, x and b are said to be the negatives of each other, and x is represented by the symbol $(-b)$. If b is a positive number, x is a **negative** number; and conversely, if b is a negative number, then x is a positive number. In symbols,

$$(-b) + b = 0 \qquad\qquad (2)$$

gives a definition of $(-b)$.

XI. *Given a and b* $(b \neq 0)$,* *there is one and only one number x, such that* $bx = a$.

Division is the process of finding the number x in $bx = a$. In other words, to divide a by b is to find a number x, called the **quotient** of a divided by b, such that b multiplied by x gives a. This quotient is often written $\dfrac{a}{b}$, and, when thus written, is called

---

* The sign $\neq$ stands for "is not equal to".

a **fraction.** If a and b are integers, it is called a **rational fraction.** In dividing a by b, the number a is called the **dividend** and b the **divisor,** just as in arithmetic. Likewise, in the fraction $\frac{a}{b}$, a is called the **numerator** and b the **denominator.**

By XI, the number x in $bx = a(b \neq 0)$ exists when $b = a$, so that $ax = a$. In this case, the number x is called **unity** and is written 1, that is,

$$a \cdot 1 = a \quad \text{and} \quad \frac{a}{a} = 1. \tag{3}$$

Further, by XI and the definition of 1, there exists a number x which satisfies $bx = 1$ $(b \neq 0)$. This value of x is called the **reciprocal** of b and is written $\frac{1}{b}$. Thus

$$b \cdot \frac{1}{b} = 1. \tag{4}$$

It should be noted that, by means of XI, a meaning is given to unity and to the reciprocal of any number other than zero in a manner analogous to that by which a meaning is given to zero and the negative numbers by means of X.

It is not to be inferred that these laws I–XI are entirely independent of one another, but rather that they constitute convenient assumptions for the purpose of this course in algebra. Although further assumptions are made later in the course, the principles I–XI enable us to prove many important propositions of algebra, and the wide application of algebra depends upon the fact that many changes in the physical world take place in accordance with these laws.

5. Properties of the Number 0

The number 0 obeys a number of special laws which are listed below.

I. *The sum, $a + 0$, is equal to a.*

II. *The difference between a and 0 is a, and the difference between 0 and a is $- a$.*

That is, $\qquad\qquad a - 0 = a,$
and $\qquad\qquad\qquad 0 - a = - a.$

III. *The product of 0 and any number a is 0.*

That is, $a \cdot 0 = 0$.

IV. *If the product ab is zero, then either a or b is 0.*

Illustration: If $(x - 3)(x - 2) = 0$, then either $x = 3$ or $x = 2$.

V. *The quotient $\dfrac{0}{a}$ is equal to 0 when a is not 0.*

Illustrations: $\dfrac{0}{27} = 0, \quad \dfrac{0}{1203} = 0.$

Division by zero is excluded not only from algebra, but from all mathematics and the applications of mathematics. The reasons for this seemingly drastic exclusion are contained in the following discussion.

Case I. If the divisor is 0 and the dividend is not 0, then $\dfrac{a}{0} = b$ means that $a = 0 \cdot b$, according to the definition of division. But from rule III above, $0 \cdot b = 0$, and hence $a = 0$, which contradicts the hypothesis that the dividend is not zero. Since we want no contradictions in our number system, we shall have to exclude division by zero in this case.

Case II. If both dividend and divisor are zero, then $\dfrac{0}{0} = b$ means that $0 = 0 \cdot b$, and this statement is true for all values of b. We demand a unique result for our problems in division and hence this case must be rejected too.

6. Properties of Negative Numbers

The negative numbers were defined in Article **4**. We now list some properties of negative numbers that enable us to perform the operations of addition, subtraction, multiplication, and division on these numbers.

I. *There exists a number, $-a$, such that $a + (-a) = 0$.*

II. *The symbol $-(-a)$ is equal to a.*

Illustration: $-(-2) = 2.$

III. *The symbol $a - b$ is equal to $-(b - a)$.*

Illustration: $(3 - 5) = -(5 - 3).$

IV. *The sum $b + (-a)$ is equal to $b - a$.*

Illustrations: $5 + (-3) = 5 - 3 = 2$,
$$3 + (-5) = 3 - 5 = -(5 - 3) = -2.$$

V. *The difference $b - (-a)$ is equal to $b + a$.*

Illustrations: $3 - (-5) = 3 + 5 = 8$,
$$(-5) - (-3) = (-5) + 3 = 3 + (-5) = -2.$$

VI. *The product of two numbers of like sign is positive; the product of two numbers of unlike sign is negative.*

That is, $\quad (-a)(-b) = ab$,
and $\quad a(-b) = -ab$.

Illustrations: $(-2)(-3) = 2 \cdot 3 = 6$,
$$2(-3) = -(2 \cdot 3) = -6.$$

VII. *The quotient of two numbers of like sign is positive; the quotient of two numbers of unlike sign is negative.*

That is, $\quad \dfrac{-a}{-b} = \dfrac{a}{b}$, and $\dfrac{-a}{b} = \dfrac{a}{-b} = -\dfrac{a}{b}$.

Illustrations: $\dfrac{-6}{-3} = \dfrac{6}{3} = 2$,

$$\dfrac{-6}{3} = \dfrac{6}{-3} = -\dfrac{6}{3} = -2.$$

7. Properties of Fractions

The following rules enable us to perform the four fundamental operations with fractions.

I. *The two fractions $\dfrac{a}{b}$ and $\dfrac{c}{d}$ are equal if $ad = bc$.*

II. *The value of a fraction is not changed by multiplying or dividing both the numerator and the denominator by the same number, providing that number is not zero.*

That is, $\quad \dfrac{a}{b} = \dfrac{ax}{bx}, x \neq 0$;

or $\quad \dfrac{a}{b} = \dfrac{a \div x}{b \div x}, x \neq 0$.

Illustrations:
$$\frac{3}{5} = \frac{3 \cdot 4}{5 \cdot 4} = \frac{12}{20},$$
$$\frac{9}{12} = \frac{9 \div 3}{12 \div 3} = \frac{3}{4}.$$

III. *Changing the sign of either numerator or denominator of a fraction is equivalent to changing the sign of the fraction.*

That is,
$$\frac{-a}{b} = -\frac{a}{b} = \frac{a}{-b}.$$

Illustration:
$$\frac{-5}{8} = -\frac{5}{8} = \frac{5}{-8}.$$

IV. *Adding two fractions having a common denominator gives a fraction whose numerator is the sum of the numerators and whose denominator is the common denominator.*

That is,
$$\frac{a}{c} + \frac{b}{c} = \frac{a+b}{c}.$$

Likewise,
$$\frac{a}{c} - \frac{b}{c} = \frac{a-b}{c}.$$

Illustrations:
$$\frac{7}{5} + \frac{3}{5} = \frac{10}{5} = 2,$$
$$\frac{7}{5} - \frac{3}{5} = \frac{4}{5}.$$

V. *The sum or the difference of any two fractions may be found by first reducing both fractions to the same common denominator. For this purpose it is convenient to use the least common denominator.*

Illustrations:
$$\frac{3}{4} - \frac{2}{3} = \frac{3 \cdot 3}{4 \cdot 3} - \frac{2 \cdot 4}{3 \cdot 4} = \frac{9-8}{12} = \frac{1}{12}.$$
$$\frac{5}{12} - \frac{11}{30} = \frac{5}{2 \cdot 2 \cdot 3} - \frac{11}{2 \cdot 3 \cdot 5}$$
$$= \frac{5 \cdot 5}{2 \cdot 2 \cdot 3 \cdot 5} - \frac{11 \cdot 2}{2 \cdot 2 \cdot 3 \cdot 5}$$
$$= \frac{25}{60} - \frac{22}{60} = \frac{3}{60} = \frac{1}{20}.$$

VI. *The product of two fractions is a fraction whose numerator is the product of the numerators of the given fractions and whose denominator is the product of the denominators of the given fractions.*

That is,
$$\frac{a}{c} \cdot \frac{b}{d} = \frac{ab}{cd}.$$

VII. *The quotient of the fraction $\frac{a}{b}$ by the fraction $\frac{c}{d}$ is a fraction whose numerator is the product of $\frac{a}{b}$ and the least common denominator of the given fractions and whose denominator is the product of $\frac{c}{d}$ and the least common denominator of the given fractions.*

That is,
$$\frac{\frac{a}{b}}{\frac{c}{d}} = \frac{\frac{a}{b} \cdot bd}{\frac{c}{d} \cdot bd} = \frac{ad}{bc}.$$

It is from this result that one obtains the often quoted rule, "To divide two fractions invert the denominator and multiply".

Illustration:
$$\frac{\frac{5}{12}}{\frac{11}{30}} = \frac{\frac{5}{2 \cdot 2 \cdot 3} \cdot 2 \cdot 2 \cdot 3 \cdot 5}{\frac{11}{2 \cdot 3 \cdot 5} \cdot 2 \cdot 2 \cdot 3 \cdot 5} = \frac{25}{22}.$$

8. Exponents

It is convenient to have a symbol for the indicated product of a number by itself r times. Accordingly, we define a^r (read a to the r-th power) as the product of a by itself r times. The number a is called the **base** and the positive integer r is called the **exponent** of the **power** to which a is raised. As a consequence of this definition, we have the following three **laws of exponents.**

I. *The product of a^r by a^s is a^{r+s}.*

That is,
$$a^r \cdot a^s = a^{r+s}.$$

Since a^r is the product of a by itself r times and a^s is the product of a by itself s times, it follows that $a^r \cdot a^s$ is the product of a by itself $r + s$ times.

Illustration: $a^2 \cdot a^3 = (a \cdot a)(a \cdot a \cdot a) = a^5.$

II. *The quotient of a^r by a^s is a^{r-s} if $r > s$; and the quotient of a^r by a^s is $\frac{1}{a^{s-r}}$ if $r < s$.*

Illustrations:
$$\frac{a^5}{a^3} = \frac{a \cdot a \cdot a \cdot a \cdot a}{a \cdot a \cdot a} = a^2.$$

$$\frac{a^3}{a^5} = \frac{a \cdot a \cdot a}{a \cdot a \cdot a \cdot a \cdot a} = \frac{1}{a^2}.$$

III. *The s-th power of a^r is a to the power rs.*

That is, $\qquad (a^r)^s = a^{rs}$

Illustration: $\qquad (a^2)^3 = a^2 \cdot a^2 \cdot a^2 = a^6.$

2 POLYNOMIALS

9. Introduction

In this chapter our chief interest is to review the processes of adding, subtracting, multiplying, and dividing certain algebraic expressions called **polynomials.**

Expressions like

$$2x^3 + 3x - 5$$

and

$$4x^2y - 3x^2 - 7xy + y^2 - 8x$$

are called polynomials. The first is a polynomial in x, the second a polynomial in x and y.

Every polynomial in x consists of a sum or difference of **terms** in which the exponents of x are positive integers and x appears neither in the denominator nor under a radical sign. Similarly, a polynomial in x and y consists of a sum or difference of terms in which the exponents of x and y are positive integers and neither letter occurs in the denominator nor under a radical sign.

The first of the above polynomials consists of three terms, while the second had five terms. A polynomial which consists of a single term is called a **monomial,** one which consists of two terms a **binomial,** one which consists of three terms a **trinomial.**

In the polynomial $2x^3 + 3x - 5$, the numbers $2, 3, -5$ are called the **coefficients** of the terms. The coefficients of the terms of a polynomial may be any real numbers. For instance,

$$\sqrt{2}x^2 - \frac{3}{5}x + 2$$

is a polynomial of three terms, where the coefficient of x^2 is $\sqrt{2}$, the coefficient of x is $-\dfrac{3}{5}$, and the constant term is 2.

The expressions $x^2 - 2\sqrt{x} + 7$ and $2x - \dfrac{5}{x}$ are not polynomials. Why?

10. Identities

The expressions $2x - 8$ and $2(x - 4)$ are equal to each other no matter what value is assigned to x, and the statement *

$$2x - 8 \equiv 2(x - 4)$$

is called an identity.

Similarly, $x^2 - 4$ and $(x - 2)(x + 2)$ are equal to each other for all values of x and

$$x^2 - 4 \equiv (x - 2)(x + 2)$$

is an identity.

Again, $\qquad \dfrac{1}{1 - x} \equiv 1 + \dfrac{x}{1 - x}, \; x \neq 1,$

is an identity.

Thus an identity is an equation which is true for all values of the symbols for which the expressions are defined.

Two expressions may be equal for some values of the symbols without being identical. Thus, for $x = 2$ and for $x = -5$, the expressions $x^2 + 2x - 1$ and $9 - x$ are equal, but they are equal for no other values of x. Hence

$$x^2 + 2x - 1 = 9 - x$$

is not an identity. It is called a **conditional equation.**

Frequently in our problems, the work will be made easier by replacing expressions by identical expressions which are simpler.

11. Use of Parentheses

In order to group terms together, we use **parentheses.** It should be remembered that parentheses may be removed with or without change of sign of each term included, according as the sign $-$ or $+$ precedes the parenthesis.

Thus, $\qquad a - (b - c) \equiv a - b + c,$

and $\qquad a + (b - c) \equiv a + b - c.$

Parentheses may also be inserted in accordance with the same rules.

---

* The symbol $\equiv$ is read "is identically equal to".

Thus $25 - x^2 + 2xy - y^2 \equiv 25 - (x^2 - 2xy + y^2)$,
and $ax - ay + bx - by \equiv (ax - ay) + (bx - by)$.

Expressions often occur with more than one pair of parentheses. When one pair occurs within another pair, other symbols besides ( ) are used as follows: [ ] called **brackets**, { } called **braces**, and — called the **vinculum**. All these symbols of grouping may be removed by first removing the innermost pair according to the rule for a single pair; next, the innermost pair of all that remain, and so on.

Illustration: $2a - \{3b - 5[a + 4(b - 2)] - 6\}$
$\equiv 2a - \{3b - 5[a + 4b - 8] - 6\}$
$\equiv 2a - \{3b - 5a - 20b + 40 - 6\}$
$\equiv 2a - 3b + 5a + 20b - 40 + 6$
$\equiv 7a + 17b - 34.$

Sums and differences of polynomials may be expressed as sums and differences of expressions enclosed in parentheses. Thus the sum of $2x^2 - 3x + 7$ and $3x^2 + 5x - 2$ is expressed as

$$(2x^2 - 3x + 7) + (3x^2 + 5x - 2) \equiv 5x^2 + 2x + 5;$$

and the difference of the same two polynomials is expressed as

$$(2x^2 - 3x + 7) - (3x^2 + 5x - 2) \equiv - x^2 - 8x + 9.$$

EXERCISES

Remove the parentheses and other signs of grouping from the expressions in the first eight exercises.

1. $(a - 2b) + (b - 3c) - (c - 4a)$.
2. $3(x - y + z) - 2[(x - y) - (2y + z)]$.
3. $(a + b + 2c) - (a + 2b - c) + (2a + b - c)$.
4. $(a - 2) - [(3a - 5) - (7 - 2a)]$.
5. $c(a + b - c) + b(a - b + c) - a(a - \overline{b + c})$.
6. $\{4(x - y) - 2[x - (y + z)] + 3(z - y)\} - 2(3x - 2y)$.
7. $2(q^2 + 3q - 5) - (3q^2 - \overline{4}) - q(1 - q) + 21$.
8. $3\{12y - 5[2x - 3(x - \overline{5 + y})] + 50\}$.

In each of the following four expressions, enclose terms involving x, y, and z in parentheses preceded by a minus sign.

9. $25 - 4y^2 + 12xy - 9x^2$.
10. $a - 2b + 3c - x + 2y - 3z$.

11. $36 - 9x^2 + 9y^2$.

12. $x^2 + 64 + y^2 - 2xy$.

13. Find the value of the expression

$$- p + q - \{r - [(p - q + r) - (r - \overline{p + q})]\}$$

when $p = 3, q = -2, r = 1$.

14. Find the value of the expression

$$[2(x + 1) - 3(2 - x)] - [x(1 - x) + x(x - 2)]$$

when $x = 2$.

15. Find the sum and difference of the polynomials

$$3x^2 - 4xy + 2y^2 - 3y - 5 \text{ and } 2x^2 + 3xy + 5x - 10.$$

16. Find the sum and difference of the polynomials

$$a - 2b + 3c - 10 \text{ and } -a + 2b - 3c + 5.$$

Fill out the parentheses in the following:

17. $5a - 6b + 2 - (\ ) \equiv a - b$.

18. $3x^2 - 2xy + 5y^2 - (\ ) \equiv y^2 - x^2$.

12. The Product of Two Polynomials

The product of two polynomials follows directly from the application of the distributive law, the rules of signs, and the laws of exponents discussed in Chapter 1. The process will be illustrated by the following example.

Example: Find the product of $(2x - 3y)$ and $(x^2 - 2xy + 5y^2)$.

Solution: According to the distributive law (Art. **4**), the product may be written

$$2x(x^2 - 2xy + 5y^2) - 3y(x^2 - 2xy + 5y^2),$$

and applying the same law a second time, we have

$$2x \cdot x^2 - 2x \cdot 2xy + 2x \cdot 5y^2 - 3y \cdot x^2 + 3y \cdot 2xy - 3y \cdot 5y^2.$$

Upon multiplying the coefficients together and using the laws of exponents (Art. **8**), we have

$$2x^3 - 4x^2y + 10xy^2 - 3x^2y + 6xy^2 - 15y^3.$$

After like quantities are collected, we have the result:

$$2x^3 - 7x^2y + 16xy^2 - 15y^3.$$

The discussion on page 15 illustrates the rule:

To multiply two polynomials, multiply the multiplicand by each term of the multiplier and add the products.

The work is usually put in the more compact form:

$$
\begin{array}{r}
x^2 - 2xy + 5y^2 \\
2x\ - 3y \\
\hline
2x^3 - 4x^2y + 10xy^2 \\
-\ 3x^2y +\ 6xy^2 - 15y^3 \\
\hline
2x^3 - 7x^2y + 16xy^2 - 15y^3.
\end{array}
$$

A number of type products occur so frequently in mathematics that they should be committed to memory. The student should verify that the following list of identities is correct and then memorize them.

$$(x - y)(x + y) \equiv x^2 - y^2.$$
$$(x + a)(x + b) \equiv x^2 + (a + b)x + ab.$$
$$(x + y)^2 \equiv x^2 + 2xy + y^2.$$
$$(x - y)^2 \equiv x^2 - 2xy + y^2.$$
$$(x + y)^3 \equiv x^3 + 3x^2y + 3xy^2 + y^3.$$
$$(x - y)^3 \equiv x^3 - 3x^2y + 3xy^2 - y^3.$$
$$(x - y)(x^2 + xy + y^2) \equiv x^3 - y^3.$$
$$(x + y)(x^2 - xy + y^2) \equiv x^3 + y^3.$$
$$(x + y + z)^2 \equiv x^2 + y^2 + z^2 + 2xy + 2xz + 2yz.$$

ORAL EXERCISES

Find the following products:

1. $(2x - 3)(2x + 3)$.
2. $(x + 2)(x + 5)$.
3. $(x - 2)(x + 5)$.
4. $(2x + 3y + z)^2$.
5. $(x - 2)^3$.
6. $(2x + 3)(3x - 2)$.
7. $(2x + 5)^3$.
8. $(2x - 3)(4x^2 + 6x + 9)$.
9. $(4x + 9y)^2$.
10. $(5 - x)(3 + x)$.
11. $(x - 2y + 4z)^2$.
12. $(x^2 + 3)^2$.

Use the identities of Article **12** to evaluate the following:

13. $(42)^2 = (40 + 2)^2$.
14. $(58)(62)$.
15. $(32)(37)$.
16. $(26)(37)$.

13. The Quotient of Two Polynomials

The method of dividing one polynomial by another will be illustrated by the following three examples. The first is the quotient of a monomial by a monomial, the second the quotient of a polynomial of more than one term by a monomial, and the third the quotient of two general polynomials. The rules of signs for division and the laws of exponents are of fundamental importance in problems of division.

Example 1. Find the quotient of $12a^3b^2c^4$ by $4a^2b^3c^4$.

Solution: $\dfrac{12a^3b^2c^4}{4a^2b^3c^4} = \dfrac{12}{4} \cdot \dfrac{a^3}{a^2} \cdot \dfrac{b^2}{b^3} \cdot \dfrac{c^4}{c^4} = 3a \cdot \dfrac{1}{b} \cdot 1 = \dfrac{3a}{b}.$

Example 2. Find the quotient of $12a^5b^3 - 4a^2b + 3ab^2$ by $6a^3b^2$.

Solution:
$$\frac{12a^5b^3 - 4a^2b + 3ab^2}{6a^3b^2}$$
$$= \frac{12a^5b^3}{6a^3b^2} - \frac{4a^2b}{6a^3b^2} + \frac{3ab^2}{6a^3b^2}$$
$$= 2a^2b - \frac{2}{3ab} + \frac{1}{2a^2}.$$

Example 3. Divide $a^4 + 2b^4 + a^2b^2$ by $a^2 + b^2 - ab$.

Solution: First arrange the divisor and dividend in descending powers of one of the quantities in a form similar to the following:

$$
\begin{array}{llll}
(divisor) & (dividend) & & (quotient) \\
a^2 - ab + b^2 \,\big|\, a^4 & + a^2b^2 & + 2b^4 \,\big|\, a^2 + ab + b^2 \\
\quad\quad\quad a^4 - a^3b + a^2b^2 & & \\
\hline
\quad\quad\quad\quad\quad a^3b & + 2b^4 & \\
\quad\quad\quad\quad\quad a^3b - a^2b^2 + ab^3 & & \\
\hline
\quad\quad\quad\quad\quad\quad\quad a^2b^2 - ab^3 + 2b^4 & \\
\quad\quad\quad\quad\quad\quad\quad a^2b^2 - ab^3 + \; b^4 & \\
\hline
\quad\quad\quad\quad\quad\quad\quad\quad\quad\quad\quad b^4 &
\end{array}
$$

Use the first term of the divisor as a trial divisor and divide it into the first term of the dividend, getting the quotient a^2. Multiply the divisor by a^2 and subtract this product from the dividend. Again divide the first term of the divisor into the first term of this remainder and get ab. Multiply the divisor by ab and subtract this product from the first remainder. Continue this process until the first term of the remainder is no longer divisible by the first term of the divisor.

In the above example, the quotient is $a^2 + ab + b^2$ with a remainder of b^4.

Find the following products:

1. $2xy^2(5x^2 - 3xy + 4y^2)$.

2. $-3ab(ab - 3a + 2b - 5)$.

3. $(a - 2b^2)(2a^2 - b)$.

4. $(x^2 - y^2)(x^2 + y^2)$.

5. $(a + 2b)(a^2 - 4b^2)$.

6. $(2x - y)(4x^2 + 2xy + y^2)$.

7. $(3x - 4y)(9x^2 - 24xy + 16y^2)$.

8. $(2a + b - 3c)(a - b + 2c)$.

9. $(3a - b + 2c)^2$.

10. $(3x^2 - 2xy + 4y^2)(x^2 + 2xy + y)$.

Find the following quotients:

11. $6ab^3 \div 2ab^2$.

12. $12x^2y^3 \div 3x^3y^2$.

13. $(x - 2y)(x + 2y) \div 2(x - 2y)$.

14. $(a - 2b)^3 \div 2(2b - a)$.

15. $(6a^2 - 13ab + 6b^2) \div (3a - 2b)$.

16. $(6x^2 - 20y^2 - 7xy) \div (3x + 4y)$.

17. $(x^2 - 4y^2 - 9z^2 + 12yz) \div (x + 2y - 3z)$.

18. $(x^4 - xy^6 + x^2y^4 - y^8) \div (x - y^2)$.

19. $(x^3 - 3x + 2x^2 - 5) \div (x + 3)$.

20. $(3y^5 - 10y^3 + 2y) \div (y + 2)$.

21. $(7x^3y + 16xy^3 + 3x^4 - 8y^4 - 8x^2y^2) \div (3xy + x^2 - 2y^2)$.

22. $(4ab - 2ac - 4bc + a^2 + 4b^2 + c^2) \div (2b - c + a)$.

14. Factoring

In Article **12**, we found the product of two or more polynomials. Now let us discuss the reverse process, given a polynomial, find its factors. The identities of Article **12** will be invaluable in this work. Below are listed some of the rules for factoring polynomials.

I. *First remove factors common to each term.*

That is, $$ax + ay \equiv a(x + y).$$

Illustrations: $ab^2 - 2a^2b \equiv ab(b - 2a),$
$$(a - b)^2 - 2(a - b) \equiv (a - b)[(a - b) - 2],$$
$$x^3 - 5x^2y + 6xy^2 \equiv x(x^2 - 5xy + 6y^2).$$

After all factors common to each term are removed, the remaining expression will be a binomial, a trinomial, or a polynomial of more than three terms. We then proceed according to the appropriate one of the following rules.

II. *To factor binomials of the type $a^n \pm b^n$, where n is a positive integer.*

1. $a^2 - b^2 \equiv (a - b)(a + b)$.
2. $a^{2r} - b^{2r} \equiv (a^r - b^r)(a^r + b^r)$.
3. $a^2 + b^2$ **cannot be factored at the present stage.**
4. $a^3 - b^3 \equiv (a - b)(a^2 + ab + b^2)$.
5. $a^3 + b^3 \equiv (a + b)(a^2 - ab + b^2)$.

If n is a positive odd integer, the following two rules hold:

6. $a^n - b^n \equiv (a-b)(a^{n-1}+a^{n-2}b+a^{n-3}b^2 + \cdots + ab^{n-2}+b^{n-1})$.
7. $a^n + b^n \equiv (a+b)(a^{n-1}-a^{n-2}b+a^{n-3}b^2 - \cdots - ab^{n-2}+b^{n-1})$.

Illustration 1. $\quad 8x^3 - 18xy^2 \equiv 2x(4x^2 - 9y^2)$
$$\equiv 2x(2x - 3y)(2x + 3y).$$

Illustration 2. $\quad 8 - 125y^3 \equiv (2)^3 - (5y)^3$
$$\equiv (2 - 5y)(4 + 10y + 25y^2).$$

Illustration 3. $\quad 32x^5 + y^{10} \equiv (2x)^5 + (y^2)^5$
$$\equiv (2x + y^2)(16x^4 - 8x^3y^2 + 4x^2y^4 - 2xy^6 + y^8).$$

Illustration 4. $\quad (a - 2b)^2 - (2a - b)^2$
$$\equiv [(a - 2b) + (2a - b)][(a - 2b) - (2a - b)]$$
$$\equiv (3a - 3b)(- a - b)$$
$$\equiv - 3(a - b)(a + b).$$

III. *To factor trinomials.*

1. Perfect trinomial square.

$$a^2 \pm 2ab + b^2 \equiv (a \pm b)^2.$$

2. Trinomial of the form

$$x^2 + (a + b)x + ab \equiv (x + a)(x + b).$$

3. Trinomial of the form $ax^2 + bx + c$.

Trinomials of this type can be factored easily if a, b, c are integers and $b^2 - 4ac$ is the square of an integer.

Illustration 1. $4x^2 - 12xy + 9y^2 \equiv (2x - 3y)^2$.

Illustration 2. $x^2 - 7x + 12 \equiv (x - 3)(x - 4)$.

Illustration 3. $2x^2 - 3x - 35$ can be factored because

$$9 - 4(2)(-35) = (17)^2.$$

We must then find numbers a, b, c, d, such that

$$(ax + b)(cx + d) \equiv 2x^2 - 3x - 35.$$

Obviously a and c have like signs, and b and d have opposite signs. Possible values for a and c are ± 1, ± 2. Possible values for b and d are ± 1, ± 5, ± 7, ± 35. By trial and error the desired factors are found to be $(2x + 7)(x - 5)$.

Illustration 4. The trinomial $x^2 + 2x + 3$ cannot be factored at this stage, since $4 - 4(1)(3)$ is not the square of an integer.

IV. *Factors of a polynomial of more than three terms.*

1. Factors found by grouping the terms.

$$ax + ay + by + bx \equiv a(x + y) + b(x + y)$$
$$\equiv (x + y)(a + b).$$

2. Perfect trinomial square.

$$a^2 + b^2 + c^2 + 2ab + 2ac + 2bc \equiv (a + b + c)^2.$$

3. Cube of a binomial.

$$a^3 \pm 3a^2b + 3ab^2 \pm b^3 \equiv (a \pm b)^3.$$

Illustration 1. $2x^2 - 18y^2 + 3x + 9y$
$$\equiv 2(x^2 - 9y^2) + 3(x + 3y)$$
$$\equiv 2(x - 3y)(x + 3y) + 3(x + 3y)$$
$$\equiv (x + 3y)(2x - 6y + 3).$$

Illustration 2.

$$8x^3 + 36x^2y + 54xy^2 + 27y^3$$
$$\equiv (2x)^3 + 3(2x)^2(3y) + 3(2x)(3y)^2 + (3y)^3$$
$$\equiv (2x + 3y)^3;$$

or
$$8x^3 + 36x^2y + 54xy^2 + 27y^3$$
$$\equiv (8x^3 + 27y^3) + 18xy(2x + 3y)$$
$$\equiv (2x + 3y)(4x^2 - 6xy + 9y^2) + 18xy(2x + 3y)$$
$$\equiv (2x + 3y)(4x^2 + 12xy + 9y^2)$$
$$\equiv (2x + 3y)^3.$$

Illustration 3.

$$4x^2 + 9y^2 + 25 + 12xy - 20x - 30y$$
$$\equiv (2x)^2 + (3y)^2 + (-5)^2 + 2(2x)(3y) + 2(2x)(-5) + 2(3y)(-5)$$
$$\equiv (2x + 3y - 5)^2;$$

or $4x^2 + 9y^2 + 25 + 12xy - 20x - 30y$

$$\equiv (4x^2 + 12xy + 9y^2) - (20x + 30y) + 25$$
$$\equiv (2x + 3y)^2 - 10(2x + 3y) + 25$$
$$\equiv (2x + 3y - 5)^2.$$

ORAL EXERCISES

Factor the following:

1. $2x^2 - 6xy$.

2. $9a^2 - 25b^2$.

3. $8x^3 - y^3$.

4. $x^2 + x - 12$.

5. $12x^2 - x - 1$.

6. $4x^2 - 4xy + y^2$.

7. $a^3b - ab^3$.

8. $xy - 8y - 5x + 40$.

9. $x^3 + 125$.

10. $a^4 - b^4$.

11. $2x^2 - 5xy - 12y^2$.

12. $6x^2 - 11xy + 4y^2$.

13. $x^2 - y^2 + 2x + 2y$.

14. $x^3 - y^3 - x^2 - xy - y^2$.

15. $u^7 - v^7$.

16. $(2x - 5)^2 - 6(2x - 5) + 9$.

WRITTEN EXERCISES

Factor the following:

1. $a^4b - 8ab^4$.

2. $2xy^2 - 5x^2y - 12x^3$.

3. $x^6 - y^6$.

4. $x^8 - y^8$.

5. $x^7 - y^7$.

6. $x^7 + y^7$.

7. $6x^2 - 11xy + 4y^2$.

8. $125x^3 + 8y^3$.

9. $(2x - 1)^2 - (x + 2)^2$.

10. $(2x - 1)^3 - (x + 2)^3$.

11. $2x^2 + 9x - 35$.

12. $12x^2 + 11x - 15$.

13. $2a^3 + 8ab^2$.

14. $4x^4 - 5x^2y^2 - 9y^4$.

15. $(x + 2y)^2 - 5(x + 2y) + 6$.

16. $14 + (2x - y) - 3(2x - y)^2$

17. $a^4 - a^3b + ab^3 - b^4$.

18. $12(3x + 2)^3(2x - 1)^2 + 4(3x + 2)^4(2x - 1)$.

19. $3x^2(x - 1)^2(3x + 2) + 2x^3(x - 1)(3x + 2) + 3x^3(x - 1)^2$.

20. $a^2 + 16b^2 + 9 - 6a - 24b + 8ab$.

21. $a^2 + 16b^2 + 16 - 10a - 40b + 8ab$.

22. $x^2 - 100 - 25y^2 + 100y$.

23. $y^2 - v^2 + x^2 - u^2 - 2xy - 2uv$.

24. $(a + b)^4 - (a - b)^4$.

25. $(a + b)^4 - (a^4 - b^4)$.

26. $(x - y)^3 + (x + y)^3$.

27. $125a^3 - 27b^3 - 225a^2b + 135ab^2$.

28. $x^6 - 4x^4 - 4x^2 + 16$.

29. $x^6 + 35x^3 + 216$.

30. $x^4y - 7x^2y^2 + 12y^3$.

15. Lowest Common Multiple

The **lowest common multiple** (L.C.M.) of two or more polynomials is the product of all their different **prime** factors, each taken the greatest number of times that it occurs in any one of the polynomials.

Example. Find the L.C.M. of $a^2 + a - 6$, $4 - a^2$, and $a^2 - 4a+4$.

Solution: Separate each polynomial into its prime factors:

$$a^2 + a - 6 \equiv (a + 3)(a - 2),$$
$$4 - a^2 \equiv (2 + a)(2 - a) = -(a + 2)(a - 2),$$
$$a^2 - 4a + 4 \equiv (a - 2)^2.$$

The different prime factors are $(a + 2)$, $(a + 3)$, and $(a - 2)$. The greatest number of times each of these prime factors occurs in any one expression is once for $(a + 2)$, once for $(a + 3)$, and twice for $(a - 2)$. Hence

$$\text{L.C.M.} = (a + 2)(a + 3)(a - 2)^2.$$

EXERCISES

Find the L.C.M. of each of the following sets of expressions.

1. 8, 18, 20.

2. 30, 36, 40.

3. $15ab^2c^3$, $24a^3bc^2$, $36ac^2$.

4. $a^{2n}b^nc$, a^nbc^{2n}, $ab^{2n}c^n$, where n is a positive integer.

5. $a^2 + 5a - 6$, $a^2 + a - 2$, $a^2 + 8a + 12$.

6. $2a^2 - 3a - 2$, $6a^2 - 5a - 4$, $10a - 3a^2 - 8$.

7. $x^4 - y^4$, $x^3 + x^2y - xy^2 - y^3$, $y^2 - 2xy + x^2$.

8. $x^3 - x^2y - xy^2 + y^3$, $x^3 + x^2y - xy^2 - y^3$.

9. $9y - 2y^2 - 9$, $3y^2 - y^3$, $9y - 6y^2 + y^3$.

10. $x^2 - 3x + 2$, $x^2 + 3x + 2$, $x^3 + 2x^2 - x - 2$.

11. $x^{2n} - 9$, $x^{2n} - 3x^n$, $x^{2n} - x^n - 6$.

12. $(x - 1)^2(x - 3)^3$, $(3 - x)^2(x + 2)^4$, $(1 - x)(x + 2)^3$.

3 | RATIONAL FRACTIONS

16. Definitions

A **rational fraction** is the quotient of two polynomials. For example,

$$\frac{2(x+3)}{x^2 - 3x + 2}$$

is a rational fraction. In our work we shall drop the adjective "rational" and speak of the expression as a fraction.

A fraction is said to be in lowest terms if the numerator and denominator contain no **common** factors. To reduce a fraction to **lowest terms,** divide the numerator and the denominator by their common factors. It is assumed that none of these factors may be zero. (Art. **7**, rule II).

Illustration: Reduce the fraction $\dfrac{2x^2 - 5x + 2}{4x^2 - 4x + 1}$

to lowest terms.

Solution: First write the numerator and denominator in factored form and then divide by the common factors.

$$\frac{2x^2 - 5x + 2}{4x^2 - 4x + 1} = \frac{(x-2)(2x-1)}{(2x-1)(2x-1)} = \frac{x-2}{2x-1}.$$

17. Addition and Subtraction of Fractions

To add or subtract two or more fractions, we proceed in accordance with rules IV and V of Article **7**. That is, we reduce all the fractions occurring in the problem to the same **common denominator** and add or subtract the numerators of the fractions so found. The sum or difference is then reduced to its lowest terms.

It is convenient to choose the **least common denominator** for the common denominator of the fractions to be added or subtracted.   The least common denominator is the least common multiple of the denominators appearing in the problem.

Illustration: Combine into a single fraction

$$\frac{8x + 4y}{x^2 - 4y^2} - \frac{5x - y}{2x^2 + 5xy + 2y^2} + \frac{5}{2y - x}.$$

Solution: The factors of the denominators are:

$$x^2 - 4y^2 \equiv (x + 2y)(x - 2y),$$
$$2x^2 + 5xy + 2y^2 \equiv (2x + y)(x + 2y),$$
$$2y - x \equiv -(x - 2y).$$

The least common denominator is $(2x + y)(x + 2y)(x - 2y)$.   A single fraction equivalent to the given one is

$$\frac{(8x + 4y)(2x + y) - (5x - y)(x - 2y) - 5(2x + y)(x + 2y)}{(2x + y)(x + 2y)(x - 2y)}$$

$$= \frac{x^2 + 2xy - 8y^2}{(2x + y)(x + 2y)(x - 2y)}$$

$$= \frac{x + 4y}{(2x + y)(x + 2y)}.$$

ORAL EXERCISES

Reduce the following fractions to lowest terms:

1. $\dfrac{30}{42}$.

2. $\dfrac{x^3}{xy + 2x^2}$.

3. $\dfrac{36xy^2z^3}{14x^2yz}$.

4. $\dfrac{x - y}{y - x}$.

5. $\dfrac{(a + 2b)(x + 3y)^2}{(a + 2b)(x + 3y)}$.

6. $\dfrac{x^2 - 5x + 6}{x^2 - x - 2}$.

7. Which fraction is larger, $\dfrac{5}{12}$ or $\dfrac{10}{21}$?

Combine into a single fraction:

8. $\dfrac{2}{9} + \dfrac{5}{8} - \dfrac{7}{12}$.

9. $\dfrac{1}{a^2} + \dfrac{1}{b^2} - \dfrac{2}{ab}$.

WRITTEN EXERCISES

Reduce the following fractions to lowest terms:

1. $\dfrac{a^2 - b^2}{3a^2 + 3ab}$.

2. $\dfrac{a^2 + ab}{a^3 + a^2b + ab^2 + b^3}$.

3. $\dfrac{x^4 - y^4}{x^6 - y^6}$.

6. $\dfrac{(6x - x^2 - 5)(3x^2 - 8x - 3)}{(25 - x^2)(1 - 9x^2)}$.

4. $\dfrac{128 - 8x^2}{16x^2 + 4x^3}$.

7. $\dfrac{8x^2 - 14x + 3}{6x + 5x^2 - 6x^3}$.

5. $\dfrac{a^3 + a^2b - ab^2 - b^3}{(ab + b^2)(a - b)^2}$.

8. $\dfrac{x^3 - 9x^2y + 27xy^2 - 27y^3}{(2y + x)^2 - (y - 2x)^2}$.

Combine into a single fraction:

9. $\dfrac{1}{b - c} + \dfrac{1}{c - a} + \dfrac{1}{a - b}$.

10. $y - 3 + \dfrac{4}{y + 2}$.

11. $\dfrac{-5}{2x} + \dfrac{7}{6x - 12} - \dfrac{7}{3x^2 - 6x}$.

12. $\dfrac{x - 4y}{x^2 + 13xy + 30y^2} - \dfrac{x + 10y}{x^2 - xy - 12y^2}$.

13. $\dfrac{x}{(x - y)(x - z)} + \dfrac{y}{(y - x)(y - z)} + \dfrac{z}{(z - x)(z - y)}$.

14. $\dfrac{1}{(a - b)(a - c)} + \dfrac{1}{(b - a)(b - c)} + \dfrac{1}{(c - a)(c - b)}$.

15. $\dfrac{a - 2}{1 - 3a + 2a^2} + \dfrac{a - 3}{4a - 1 - 3a^2}$.

16. $\dfrac{ab(a - b)}{a^3 - a^2b - ab^2 + b^3} - \dfrac{ab + 2b^2}{a^2 - ab - 2b^2}$.

18. Multiplication and Division of Fractions

To find the product of two or more fractions, we find a fraction whose numerator is the product of the numerators of the given fractions and whose denominator is the product of the denominators of the given fractions. The result is then expressed in lowest terms. This is in accordance with rule VI of Article **7**.

By rule VII, Article **7**, the quotient of two fractions is a fraction whose numerator is the product of the dividend and the least common denominator of the given fractions and whose denominator is the product of the divisor and the least common denominator of the given fractions. The essential fact is that the quotient is obtained by multiplying the dividend and the divisor by the same quantity. Instead of choosing the least common denominator of the given fractions for this multiplier, we might have chosen some other quantity that would simplify the indicated quotient. A second obvious choice for this multiplier would be the reciprocal of the divisor. The following example will illustrate each of these methods.

Example: Find the quotient $\dfrac{a^4 - b^4}{(a - b)^2} \div \dfrac{a^2 + b^2}{a^2 - ab}$.

Solution 1. The least common denominator of the given fractions is $a(a - b)^2$. Then, by rule VII, Article **7**, the quotient is

$$\dfrac{\dfrac{a^4 - b^4}{(a - b)^2} \cdot a(a - b)^2}{\dfrac{a^2 + b^2}{a^2 - ab} \cdot a(a - b)^2}$$

$$= \dfrac{a(a - b)(a + b)(a^2 + b^2)}{(a - b)(a^2 + b^2)}$$

$$= a(a + b).$$

Solution 2. If the dividend and divisor of the indicated quotient of the two fractions are each multiplied by the reciprocal of the divisor, we have

$$\dfrac{\dfrac{a^4 - b^4}{(a - b)^2} \cdot \dfrac{a^2 - ab}{a^2 + b^2}}{\dfrac{a^2 + b^2}{a^2 - ab} \cdot \dfrac{a^2 - ab}{a^2 + b^2}}$$

$$= \dfrac{\dfrac{(a - b)(a + b)(a^2 + b^2)}{(a - b)^2} \cdot \dfrac{a(a - b)}{a^2 + b^2}}{1}$$

$$= a(a + b).$$

ORAL EXERCISES

Give the reciprocal of each of the following:

1. $\dfrac{7}{3}$.

2. 1.9.

3. $\dfrac{x + y}{x - y}$.

4. $\dfrac{1}{2} + \dfrac{1}{3}$.

5. What number has no reciprocal? What numbers are equal to their reciprocals?

Perform the indicated operations:

6. $\dfrac{24}{35} \cdot \dfrac{15}{28}$.

8. $\dfrac{3x^2y}{z^3} \cdot \dfrac{y^2z}{9x}$.

7. $\dfrac{24}{35} \div \dfrac{15}{28}$.

9. $\dfrac{3x^2y}{z^3} \div \dfrac{y^2z}{9x}$.

WRITTEN EXERCISES

Perform the indicated operations:

1. $\left(\dfrac{2}{9} + \dfrac{3}{4}\right) \div \dfrac{5}{12}$.

6. $\dfrac{2}{9} \cdot \left(\dfrac{3}{4} \div \dfrac{5}{12}\right)$.

2. $\dfrac{2}{9} + \left(\dfrac{3}{4} \div \dfrac{5}{12}\right)$.

7. $\dfrac{2}{9} \div \left(\dfrac{3}{4} \cdot \dfrac{5}{12}\right)$.

3. $\dfrac{2}{9} \div \left(\dfrac{3}{4} + \dfrac{5}{12}\right)$.

8. $\left(\dfrac{2}{9} \div \dfrac{3}{4}\right) \cdot \dfrac{5}{12}$.

4. $\left(\dfrac{2}{9} \div \dfrac{3}{4}\right) + \dfrac{5}{12}$.

9. $\left(\dfrac{2}{9} \div \dfrac{3}{4}\right) \div \dfrac{5}{12}$.

5. $\left(\dfrac{2}{9} \cdot \dfrac{3}{4}\right) \div \dfrac{5}{12}$.

10. $\dfrac{2}{9} \div \left(\dfrac{3}{4} \div \dfrac{5}{12}\right)$.

11. $\dfrac{16x^2 - 9}{3y^2 - 15y} \div \dfrac{4x + 3}{6y}$.

12. $\dfrac{a^2 + 11a + 28}{a^2 - 6a - 27} \div \dfrac{a^2 + 9a + 14}{19a - a^2 - 90}$.

13. $\dfrac{x^3 - 3x^2y + 3xy^2 - y^3}{x^3 - y^3} \div \dfrac{x^2 - y^2}{x^3 + 2x^2y + 2xy^2 + y^3}$.

14. $\dfrac{x^2}{x^3 + x^2y + xy^2 + y^3} \cdot \dfrac{x + y}{x^2 - xy} \cdot \dfrac{x^4 - y^4}{y - x}$.

15. $\dfrac{6x^2 - 5x + 1}{4x^3 - x} \div \dfrac{3x^2 - 2x - 1}{2x^2 - 3x + 1}$.

16. $\left(\dfrac{1}{a} - \dfrac{1}{b}\right) \div \dfrac{a^2 - b^2}{ab}$.

17. $\left(\dfrac{a^2 + b^2}{b} + a\right) \div \left(\dfrac{1}{b^3} - \dfrac{1}{a^3}\right)$.

18. $(14a^2 - 11ab - 15b^2) \div \left(7 - \dfrac{5a + 3b}{a}\right)$.

19. Complex Fractions

A **complex fraction** is one that has a fraction in the numerator or denominator or in both numerator and denominator. The rules for the simplification of arithmetical fractions apply to algebraic fractions no matter how complicated the numerator or denominator may be.

The main principle is that the value of a fraction is not changed by multiplying numerator and denominator by the same expression. As illustrated by the following examples and exercises on complex fractions, a simplification is often brought about if we multiply by the lowest common denominator of the fractions which are in the numerator and denominator of the complex fraction.

Example 1. Simplify the complex fraction

$$\frac{\dfrac{2}{3} - \dfrac{1}{2}}{\dfrac{3}{4} - \dfrac{5}{12}}.$$

Solution: Since 12 is the lowest common denominator of the fractions in the numerator and denominator of the given fraction, we multiply the numerator and denominator of the given fraction by 12. We have

$$\frac{\dfrac{2}{3} - \dfrac{1}{2}}{\dfrac{3}{4} - \dfrac{5}{12}} = \frac{12\left(\dfrac{2}{3} - \dfrac{1}{2}\right)}{12\left(\dfrac{3}{4} - \dfrac{5}{12}\right)} = \frac{8 - 6}{9 - 5} = \frac{2}{4} = \frac{1}{2}.$$

Example 2. Simplify the complex fraction

$$\frac{\dfrac{1}{b} + \dfrac{1}{a + b}}{\dfrac{1}{a} - \dfrac{1}{a - b}}.$$

Solution: The lowest common denominator of all the simple fractions appearing in the given expression is $ab(a^2 - b^2)$. Hence we have

$$\frac{\dfrac{1}{b} + \dfrac{1}{a + b}}{\dfrac{1}{a} - \dfrac{1}{a - b}} = \frac{ab(a^2 - b^2)\left(\dfrac{1}{b} + \dfrac{1}{a + b}\right)}{ab(a^2 - b^2)\left(\dfrac{1}{a} - \dfrac{1}{a - b}\right)}$$

$$= \frac{a(a^2 - b^2) + ab(a - b)}{b(a^2 - b^2) - ab(a + b)}$$

$$= -\frac{a(a - b)(a + 2b)}{b^2(a + b)}.$$

EXERCISES

Simplify the following complex fractions:

1. $\dfrac{\dfrac{3}{8} + \dfrac{2}{3}}{\dfrac{5}{6}}$.

2. $\dfrac{3 - \dfrac{1}{2}}{2 - \dfrac{1}{3}}$.

3. $\dfrac{a + \dfrac{1}{b}}{b + \dfrac{1}{a}}$.

4. $\dfrac{\dfrac{1}{x+y} - \dfrac{1}{x-y}}{\dfrac{1}{x+y} + \dfrac{1}{x-y}}$.

5. $\dfrac{\dfrac{x-y}{x+y} - \dfrac{x+y}{x-y}}{\dfrac{x-y}{x+y} + \dfrac{x+y}{x-y}}$.

6. $\dfrac{\dfrac{1}{a-1} - 1}{1 + \dfrac{1}{1-a}}$.

7. $\dfrac{\dfrac{1}{x-2} - \dfrac{1}{x+7}}{\dfrac{4}{14 - 5x - x^2}}$.

8. $\dfrac{16x^2 - \dfrac{9}{y^2}}{4y - \dfrac{3}{x}}$.

9. $\dfrac{1 - \dfrac{1}{x} + \dfrac{1}{x^2}}{x + \dfrac{1}{x^2}}$.

10. $\dfrac{\dfrac{x+y}{1 - \dfrac{y}{x}} - 2x}{3 + \dfrac{2x}{y-x}}$.

MISCELLANEOUS EXERCISES AND PROBLEMS

Evaluation of Formulas Involving Fractions

1. The present value P at simple interest of a sum S due in n years at interest rate i per year is given by the formula

$$P = \frac{S}{1 + ni}.$$

Find P when $S = \$1000$, $n = \dfrac{1}{2}$, $i = .05$.

2. The speed v in feet per second of a projectile of weight w pounds and diameter d inches is given by

$$\frac{1}{v} = \frac{1}{v_0} + \frac{td^2}{7000w}$$

where v_0* is muzzle speed with which the shell is projected, and t is the number of seconds after leaving the muzzle.   Find v when $v_0 = 2750$, $t = 5$, $d = 14$, $w = 1200$.

3. $H = \dfrac{v}{825}\left(T - \dfrac{wv^2}{g}\right).$

Find H when $T = 390$, $w = 0.7$, $g = 32.2$, and $v = 88$.

4. $T = \dfrac{\left(P + \dfrac{a}{v^2}\right)(v - b)}{R}.$

Find T when $a = 1322$, $b = 0.01969$, $R = 36.24$, $v = 1.590$, $P = 11100$.

5. The specific gravity S of a floating body is given by the expression

$$S = \frac{w_1}{w_1 + (w_2 - w_3)}$$

where w_1 is the weight of the body in air, w_2 is the weight of a sinker in water, and w_3 is the weight in water of the body with sinker attached.

Determine the specific gravity of a body when by physical measurements it is found that

$$w_1 =   17.36$$
$$w_2 = 193.7$$
$$w_3 = 186.8$$

6. One cubic centimeter of mercury at x degrees centigrade increases in volume when heated to y degrees by an amount given by the following formula:

$$\frac{\dfrac{A(y - x)}{100}}{1 + \dfrac{Ax}{100}},$$

where $A = 0.018$.   Find the increase in volume when the temperature is raised from $11°$ to $127°$.

7. To correct a barometer reading for temperature the following amount is subtracted from the reading:

$$B\frac{m(t - 32) - s(t - 62)}{1 + m(t - 32)},$$

*A letter with a subscript, say a_r, is read, "a sub r".

where B is the barometer reading in inches, t the temperature in degrees Fahrenheit, $m = 0.00010$, $s = 0.00001$. What is the corrected reading of the barometer when the temperature is 86 and the barometer reads 30.15?

8. Let P be the day of the month, q the number of the month in the year, counting January and February as the 13th and 14th months of the preceding year, N the year, and

$$n = \left[\frac{N}{100}\right] - \left[\frac{N}{400}\right] - 2.$$

If

$$P + 2q + \left[\frac{3(q+1)}{5}\right] + N + \left[\frac{N}{4}\right] - n$$

be divided by 7, the remainder will be the day of the week of a given date where Sunday counts as the first day. The expressions in brackets mean the largest integer contained in the enclosed number. Verify this formula for the present date.

9. The formula for the horsepower H.P. of an automobile engine is given by

$$\text{H.P.} = \frac{Planc}{(24)(33000)},$$

where P is the pressure in pounds per square inch, l is the length of stroke of the piston in inches, a is the area of the end of the piston in square inches, n is the number of revolutions of the flywheel per minute, c is the number of cylinders in the engine. How many H.P. are developed by a six-cylinder engine if P is 74, l is 5.5, a is 15.56, and n is 1250?

4 FUNCTIONS AND THEIR GRAPHS

20. The Function Idea

By means of the formula $C = 2\pi r$, the circumference, C, of a circle may be calculated if the radius, r, is known. The symbols 2 and π are called **constants**; they always have the same value. The symbols C and r are called **variables**; they have different values for different circles. Since the radius of a circle is always a positive real number, we may assign various positive real values to r and calculate the circumferences of the corresponding circles. We would thus be able to form the following table.

r	C
0.5 in.	3.1416 in.
1.0 "	6.2832 "
1.5 "	9.4248 "
2.0 "	12.5664 "
2.5 "	15.7080 "
3.0 "	18.8496 "

Since for each value that may be assigned to r, a value of C can be determined, we say that C is a **function** of r.

Consider a further example from the field of physics. The distance that a freely falling body dropped from rest travels in time t is given by the formula $s = \dfrac{1}{2} gt^2$, where g is a constant. The constant g is somewhat different from the constants in the previous example, in that it changes as one moves from point to point on the surface of the earth. Its value also depends on the units of measurement chosen for time and distance. If t is measured in

32

seconds and s is measured in feet, then in the neighborhood of Chicago g has the value 32.2 feet per second per second. Again we call s and t variables, and if we assign positive real values to t we may calculate the corresponding values of s and form the following table.

t	s
0.5 sec.	4.0 feet
1.0 "	16.1 "
1.5 "	36.2 "
2.0 "	64.4 "
2.5 "	100.6 "
3.0 "	144.9 "

Since for each value that we assign to t a value of s can be determined, we say that s is a function of t.

Consider the expression $x(a - x)$, where a is a constant. In this example, a may have the value 5 in one problem; in a second problem it may have the value -1; in a third problem it may have the value $\frac{1}{4}$, and so on. The symbol a then has a fixed value for a given problem. The symbol x may be assigned any real value in any one problem. It is called a variable. As different values are assigned to x, the corresponding values of the expression $x(a - x)$ may be calculated. In this example it will be simpler to assign to x values which are multiples of a. Then the following table may be formed for the values of x between $x = -4a$ and $x = 4a$.

x	$x(a - x)$
$-4a$	$-20a^2$
$-3a$	$-12a^2$
$-2a$	$-6a^2$
$-a$	$-2a^2$
0	0
a	0
$2a$	$-2a^2$
$3a$	$-6a^2$
$4a$	$-12a^2$

Since for each value that we assign to x a value of the expression $x(a - x)$ can be found, we say that the expression is a function of x.

The above three examples are illustrations of types of relationships that abound in many fields. In each example, the words "constant," "variable," and "function" appeared. Before proceeding further, we should state the definitions of these terms precisely.

A **constant** is a symbol that represents the same number throughout a given problem.

A **variable** is a symbol that in a given problem may represent any value in a given range.

In this definition, the phrase "in a given range" needs some explanation. In finding the circumferences of the circles in the first example, only positive real values were assigned to the variable r. The range of the variable r in this problem is then all the positive real numbers. Again in the second example, the range of the variable t is all the positive real numbers. In the third example, the variable x ranged through all the real numbers, both positive and negative. If one is required to tabulate corresponding values of x and y for the function $y = \sqrt{x - 4}$, the range of variation of x is restricted to those values of x greater than 4.

If two variables x and y are so related that when a value is assigned to x, a corresponding value of y can be determined, then y is said to be a **function** of x. The variable x is called the **independent variable,** while y is called the **dependent variable.**

This definition implies that by some means or other a table showing the corresponding values of the variables x and y can be made. The values of y may be found by use of a mathematical formula, but it frequently happens that the desired mathematical formula is not known and recourse must be made to some other method to build the table. A scientist might retire to his laboratory and after repeated experiment produce the table he seeks. In some fields it is necessary to record a vast amount of statistical data before such a table may be arrived at.

EXERCISES

1. The area of a square is a function of what variable?

2. The postage required on a piece of first class mail is a function of what variable?

3. The cost of a long distance person-to-person telephone call between New York and Chicago is a function of what variable?

4. The cost of a railroad ticket good in coaches only is a function of what variable?

5. The annual premium on a $10,000 ordinary life insurance policy with a given company is a function of what variable?

6. A man borrows $1,000 and agrees to repay the loan, principal and interest, by making equal payments at the end of each month for one year. The monthly payment is a function of what variable?

7. The pressure of a gas kept enclosed in a container at constant temperature is a function of what variable?

21. Functional Notation

The symbols $f(x)$, $g(x)$, $\phi(x)$, . . . are used to represent functions of the variable x. For example, let $f(x)$ represent $x^4 + 3x^2 - 2x + 10$. The symbol $f(x)$ is read "the f function of x." Similarly "$\phi(y)$" is read "the ϕ function of y," (pronounced "phi function of y").

To illustrate further, suppose that in a discussion

$$f(x) = 3x^2 - 2x + 1,$$
then
$$f(2) = 3 \cdot 2^2 - 2 \cdot 2 + 1 = 9,$$
and
$$f(a) = 3a^2 - 2a + 1.$$

Similarly, if
$$g(x) = x^2 + 4x,$$
then
$$g(b) = b^2 + 4b,$$
and
$$g(3) = 3^2 + 4 \cdot 3 = 21,$$
$$g(-2) = (-2)^2 + 4(-2) = -4.$$

These illustrations bring out an important point in the functional notation, namely: If the same functional symbol, say $g(\ )$, be used more than once in a discussion, it stands in each case for the same operation or set of operations on the number or expression contained in the parentheses of the functional symbol.

EXERCISES

1. If $f(x) = 8 - 4x$, find $f(-1), f(0), f(1), f(2), f(3)$.

2. If $f(t) = t^4 - 2t^2 + 4$, find $f(2), f(0), f\left(\dfrac{1}{2}\right), f\left(-\dfrac{1}{2}\right), f(a), f(-a)$.

3. If $g(y) = \dfrac{y^2 - 2y + 1}{3y^2 + y + 3}$, find $g(0)$, $g(1)$, $g\left(\dfrac{1}{x}\right)$, $g(x+1)$, $g(y+1)$.

4. If $\phi(x) = \dfrac{x-1}{x+1}$, show that $\phi\left(\dfrac{1}{x}\right) = -\phi(x)$.

5. If $T(l) = 2\pi\sqrt{\dfrac{l}{g}}$, show that $T(4l) = 2T(l)$.

6. If $f(x) = a^x$, show that $\dfrac{f(x)}{f(y)} = f(x - y)$.

7. If $f(x) = \dfrac{x}{x - 1}$, find $f(a) + f\left(\dfrac{1}{a}\right)$.

8. If $y = f(x) = \dfrac{x}{x - 1}$, show that $f(y) = x$.

9. If $f(x) = \dfrac{x - 1}{x + 1}$, find $f[f(x)]$.

10. If $f(x) = \dfrac{x - 1}{x}$ and $F(x) = \dfrac{x}{x + 1}$, find $F[f(x)]$ and $f[F(x)]$.

11. If $s(n) = 1 + 3 + 5 + \cdots + (2n - 1)$, find $s(5)$. Write out the sum for $s(n + 1)$.

12. If $s(n) = \dfrac{1}{1 \cdot 2} + \dfrac{1}{2 \cdot 3} + \cdots + \dfrac{1}{n(n + 1)}$, find $s(4)$. Write out the sum for $s(n + 1)$.

22. System of Coordinates

Let $X'X$ and $Y'Y$ be any two straight lines meeting at right angles. Let them be considered as two number scales with the point of intersection as the zero point of each. The lines $X'X$ and $Y'Y$ are called the **coordinate axes.** Their intersection is called the **origin** and is designated by O. The line $X'X$ is called the X-axis or the **axis of abscissas,** and the line $Y'Y$ is called the Y-axis or the **axis of ordinates.** The coordinate axes divide the plane into four parts called **quadrants** which are conveniently numbered, I, II, III, IV as in Figure 2.

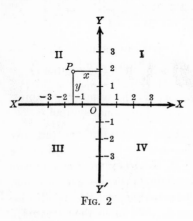

FIG. 2

Let P be any point in the plane. Through P draw two lines, one perpendicular to the Y-axis, the other perpendicular to the X-axis. Let x represent the distance from the Y-axis to the point and let y represent the distance from the X-axis to the point. If

P lies to the right of the Y-axis, x is positive; if P lies to the left of the Y-axis, x is negative. If P lies above the X-axis, y is positive; while if P lies below the X-axis, y is negative. Thus, for each point P in the plane, there exists one and only one pair of real numbers x and y, where x represents the distance from the Y-axis to the point and y represents the distance from the X-axis to the point. The pair of numbers, x and y, are called the **co-ordinates** of the point. The number x is called the **abscissa** of the

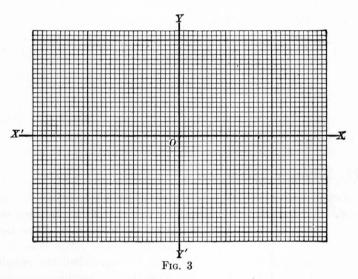

Fig. 3

point and y is called the **ordinate** of the point. The symbol (x, y) denotes a point whose abscissa is x and whose ordinate is y. The symbol $P(x, y)$ is sometimes used and is read "the point whose coordinates are x and y."

If we are given any two real numbers, we can find one and only one point P which has the first number for its abscissa and the second number for its ordinate. If, for example, the numbers are 2 and -5, we measure from the origin, in the positive direction, a distance 2 on the X-axis and at this point we erect a perpendicular and measure downward a distance 5. We have then located a point whose abscissa is 2 and whose ordinate is -5.

When a point is located in the manner described above, it is said to be **plotted**. In plotting points and obtaining the geometrical pictures we are about to make, it will be convenient to use coordinate paper, which is made by ruling off the plane into equal squares with the sides parallel to the axes (Fig. 3). Then the side of a square may be taken as the unit of length. To plot a point, count off from the origin along the X-axis the number of divisions required to represent the abscissa and from the point thus determined count off the number of divisions parallel to the Y-axis required to represent the ordinate. It is often more convenient to take more than one division for a unit of length, or to make one division represent several units.

EXERCISES

1. Construct a pair of coordinate axes and plot the following points: $(5, -3)$; $(-3, 5)$; $(0, 5)$; $(-1, -8)$; $(2, 0)$; $(0, 0)$; $(3\frac{1}{2}, -5\frac{1}{4})$; $(-7, -9)$; $(-9, -7)$.

2. What can be said about the ordinates of all points on the X-axis? What can be said about the abscissas of all the points on the Y-axis?

3. In what quadrant are both coordinates negative? In which quadrant is the abscissa positive and the ordinate negative?

4. Plot the points $(5, 5)$ and $(-2, -2)$. What can be said about the coordinates of all points on the line joining these two points?

5. Plot the points $(-3, 9)$ and $(5, -15)$. What can be said about the coordinates of all points on the line joining these two points?

6. The vertices of a right triangle are $A(3, 0)$, $B(6, 0)$ and $C(6, 4)$. Draw the triangle and find the length of each side.

7. The vertices of a right triangle are $A(4, 2)$, $B(-11, 2)$ and $C(-11, -6)$. Draw the triangle and calculate the length of the hypotenuse.

8. Plot the points $(4, -6)$ and $(-8, 3)$ and find the length of the line joining them.

9. Plot the points $(5, -9)$ and $(-3, 6)$ and find the length of the line joining them.

10. Plot the points $(-5, 2)$ and $(7, 10)$ and find the coordinates of the mid-point of the line segment joining them.

11. A line segment is bisected by the point $(-1, -2)$. If one end of the line segment is $(-5, -9)$, find the coordinates of the other end.

12. Plot the points $(0, 5)$, $(1, 2\sqrt{6})$, $(2, \sqrt{21})$, $(3, 4)$, $(4, 3)$, and $(5, 0)$. Find the distance from the origin to each point. On what kind of curve do the given points lie? What relation must the coordinates of all points on this curve satisfy?

23. Graph of a Function

If $y = f(x)$, then a table showing the corresponding values of x and y may be formed as in Article **20**. Each pair of corresponding values of x and y may be thought of as the coordinates of a point in a plane. The points may be plotted on a set of rectangular coordinate axes and then connected by a smooth curve. This curve is a pictorial representation of the function and is called the **graph** of the function. The graph of $f(x)$ gives a picture of the changes in $f(x)$ as x changes.

Example. Obtain the graph of $\dfrac{3}{2}x + 4$ for values of x between -5 and $+5$.

Let $f(x) = \dfrac{3}{2}x + 4$. The object is to present a picture which will exhibit the values of $f(x)$ which correspond to assigned values of x. Any assigned value of x with the corresponding value of $f(x)$ determines a point whose abscissa is x and whose ordinate is $f(x)$.

Assuming values for x and computing the corresponding values for $f(x)$, we obtain the following table.

x	0	1	2	$2\frac{1}{2}$	3	4	5	-1	$-1\frac{1}{2}$	-2	-3	-4	-5	$-\frac{1}{2}$	$\frac{1}{2}$	$1\frac{1}{2}$
$f(x)$	4	$\frac{11}{2}$	7	$\frac{31}{4}$	$\frac{17}{2}$	10	$\frac{23}{2}$	$\frac{5}{2}$	$\frac{7}{4}$	1	$-\frac{1}{2}$	-2	$-\frac{7}{2}$	$\frac{13}{4}$	$\frac{19}{4}$	$\frac{25}{4}$

These corresponding values are plotted as coordinates of points in Figure 4.

Example. Draw a graph of the function $(x - 2)(x - 3)$.

It should first be noticed that if $x > 3$, the function is always positive. Further, as x increases beyond 3, each factor increases and the value of the function continually increases. Similarly for values of $x < 2$, each factor is negative and the value of the function is positive. If x decreases from 2, each factor continually decreases

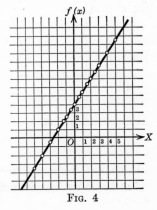

Fig. 4

and the product of the two factors continually increases. Hence the interesting part of the graph of this function is in the neighborhood of the points where $x = 2$ and $x = 3$. On that basis, let us make a table showing the values of the function corresponding to the values of x from $x = 0$ to $x = 5$.

x	0	1	2	3	4	5
$f(x)$	6	2	0	0	2	6

The above table tells us nothing about the behavior of the function between the points $x = 2$ and $x = 3$. It is necessary then to augment this table by computing the values of the function for values of x between $x = 2$ and $x = 3$.

x	$\dfrac{9}{4}$	$\dfrac{5}{2}$	$\dfrac{11}{4}$
$f(x)$	$\dfrac{-3}{16}$	$\dfrac{-1}{4}$	$\dfrac{-3}{16}$

The augmented table shows that $f(x)$ is negative for those values of x that we selected between $x = 2$ and $x = 3$. As a matter of fact, the function is always negative when $2 < x < 3$, since in this interval the factor $x - 2$ is positive while the factor $x - 3$ is negative.

The above nine points may now be plotted and then connected by a smooth curve. The result (Fig. 5) pictures the function at its more interesting points.

It should be noted that there is no limit to the number of corresponding values which we may compute and plot in a given interval along the X-axis. Hence any portion of a given graph may be plotted as accurately as desired by taking

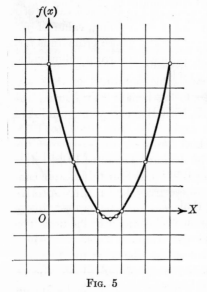

Fig. 5

a sufficiently large number of values of x.

In the above two examples, to small changes in the values of x

there correspond small changes in the values of $f(x)$. This fact suggests the idea of a **continuous** curve to represent $f(x)$. It must not be assumed, however, that all functions give continuous graphs; Article **24,** below, considers a graph made up of isolated points. The important fact for this course in algebra is that we may assume a continuous curve for all functions which are **polynomials** in x, although the proof of continuity is beyond the scope of this book. That is to say, it is proved in higher analysis that a function of the type

$$a_0x^n + a_1x^{n-1} + a_2x^{n-2} + \cdots + a_{n-1}x + a_n,$$

where n is a positive integer, has a continuous graph.

Hence, in finding the graph of a polynomial, when a sufficient number of points are located to suggest the general shape of the curve through them, draw a smooth curve through the points. In particular, it is proved in analytic geometry that when $n = 1$, *the graph of a function of this type is a straight line.*

24. Function Defined by a Table of Values

Much use is made of systems of coordinates in presenting statistical results when one set of data is to be compared with another set.

The following table shows the expectation of life in years for ages 20 to 75 at five-year intervals according to different mortality tables.   The American Experience table published in 1868 was based on the mortality experience in the United States during the years 1843–1858.   The American Men Ultimate table published in 1918 covered the mortality experience from 1900 to 1915. The Commissioners 1941 Standard Ordinary table covered the experience from 1930 to 1940. The Annuity Table for 1949—Male covered experience from 1939 to 1949. These four tables were constructed from data concerning insured lives during the respective periods. It is not to be inferred that they may be applied to any life, but only to an individual eligible for insurance at the time. The higher figures in the column for the Annuity Table for 1949— Male might very well be explained on the basis that the data pertain to an even more highly selected group of individuals. Hence, from these tables, one learns that a person aged 25 eligible for insurance a century ago might have expected on the average to live 38.81 years according to the American Experience table, whereas today such an individual would have a life expectancy of 49.41 years according to the Annuity Table for 1949—Male.

The figures in the last column of the table were made by the United States Government from data collected at the time of the 1950 census. These figures pertain to the mortality experienced by the whole population at that time.

EXPECTATION OF LIFE IN YEARS*

Age	American Experience	American Men Ultimate	Commissioners 1941 Standard Ordinary	Annuity Table for 1949 Male	United States Total Population
	(1843–1858)	(1900–1915)	(1930–1940)	(1939–1949)	(1949–1951)
20	42.20	45.93	46.54	54.23	51.20
25	38.81	41.83	42.12	49.41	46.56
30	35.33	37.70	37.74	44.61	41.91
35	31.78	33.51	33.44	39.85	37.31
40	28.18	29.32	29.25	35.15	32.81
45	24.54	25.22	25.21	30.57	28.49
50	20.91	21.29	21.37	26.23	24.40
55	17.40	17.62	17.78	22.20	20.57
60	14.10	14.29	14.50	18.48	17.04
65	11.10	11.34	11.55	15.01	13.83
70	8.48	8.81	8.99	11.86	10.92
75	6.27	6.69	6.82	9.09	8.40

Using the ages as abscissas and the corresponding expected years of life in the column headed American Men Ultimate as ordinates, we locate the upper set of points in Figure 6. The vertical unit is 5. The lower set of points is given by the column headed American Experience. In Figure 6 we thus present to the eye the relative expectation of life years according to these two tables covering two distinct periods of time.

The graph in this case is made up of 12 points. If we look upon the number of years a person may expect to live as a function of his age, this function is defined at only these 12 points in the given tables. The lines connecting the points in the figure are not necessary, but aid the eye to take in the whole situation. Where two

* From the *Life Insurance Fact Book* 1955, published by the Institute of Life Insurance, New York.

sets of data are exhibited in the same diagram as in Figure 6, the connecting lines prevent confusion of the two sets of points.

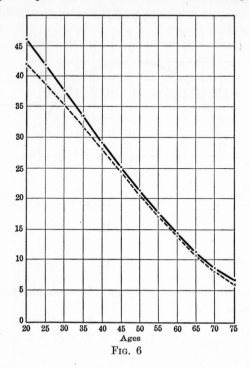

Ages

FIG. 6

EXERCISES

Plot the graphs of the following functions:

1. $2x + 5$.
2. $3x - 4$.
3. $4 - 3x$.
4. $f(x) = 3$.
5. $f(x) = -5$.

6. $16 - x^2$.
7. $x^2 - 5x - 14$.
8. $14 + 5x - x^2$.
9. $x^2 + 5x - 14$.
10. $x^2 + 5x + 14$.

11. $+ \sqrt{25 - x^2}$.

Solution: We find the following table:

$x = 0$	1	2	3	4	4.5	5	Greater than 5
$\sqrt{25 - x^2} = 5$	4.9	4.6	4	3	2.18	0	Imaginary

$x = -1$	-2	-3	-4	-4.5	-5	Less than -5
$\sqrt{25 - x^2} = 4.9$	4.6	4	3	2.18	0	Imaginary

Plotting these points and drawing a smooth curve through them, we have Figure 7.

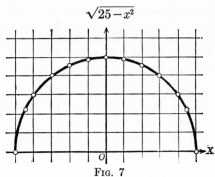

$$\sqrt{25 - x^2}$$

Fig. 7

12. $-\sqrt{25 - x^2}$.

13. $\pm \sqrt{4 - x}$.

14. $(x - 1)^2(x - 2)$.

15. $(x - 1)^3(x - 2)$.

16. $\dfrac{1}{x}$.

17. $\dfrac{1}{x^2}$.

Suggestion: In the exercises 16 and 17 above, plot points for the following values of x:

$$\pm \frac{1}{4},\ \pm \frac{1}{2},\ \pm \frac{3}{4},\ \pm 1,\ \pm \frac{3}{2},\ \pm 2,\ \pm 3,\ \pm 5,\ \pm 10.$$

18. $\dfrac{3 - x}{x - 2}$.

19. $\dfrac{x - 3}{x + 2}$.

20. From the table on page 42, show graphically on the same diagram the expectancy of life in years, at five-year intervals from ages 20 to 75 inclusive, according to the American Experience table and the Commissioners 1941 Standard Ordinary table.

21. Exhibit graphically on the same diagram the expectancy of life in years, according to the Commissioners 1941 Standard Ordinary table and the Annuity table for 1949—Male.

22. Exhibit graphically on the same diagram the expectancy of life in years, according to the Commissioners 1941 Standard Ordinary table and the United States Total Population table.

23. The breaking strength of ordinary manila rope is given by the formula $B = 7100D^2$ where B is the breaking weight in pounds and D is the diameter of the rope. Exhibit this formula graphically, plotting the breaking strength for diameters from $\frac{1}{4}$-inch

to 2 inches at $\frac{1}{8}$-inch intervals.

24. According to a chart issued by a company selling shoes by mail, if F represents the length of a man's foot in inches and s is the size of the shoe, then

$$3F = s + 22.$$

Represent graphically the relation between the length of the foot and the size of the shoe for the sizes 1 to 12.

25. The monthly rates for residential electric service in a certain city are:

Minimum charge including
     first 17 kw-hrs . . . . 75¢
Next 38 kw-hrs . . . . 4.25¢ per kw-hr.
Next 145 kw-hrs . . . . 2.6¢ per kw-hr.
Over 200 kw-hrs . . . . 2.0¢ per kw-hr.

Show graphically the cost of electricity per month as the number of kilowatt hours used varies from 0 to 300.

5 EQUATIONS AND THEIR SOLUTIONS

25. Equations and Identities

A statement that one expression is equal to another expression is called an **equality**. The two expressions are called **members** of the equality. There are two classes of equalities, **identical equalities** or **identities,** and **conditional equalities** or **equations.** An identity is defined in Article **10.** It is there stated that the two members of an identity are equal for all values of the symbols for which the expressions are defined. Thus,

$$x^2 - a^2 \equiv (x - a)(x + a) \quad \text{and} \quad 5a \equiv 10a - 5a$$

are identities. But in the equality $x - 5 = 4 - 2x$, the two expressions $x - 5$ and $4 - 2x$ are equal only when x has the value 3. An equality of this kind, in which the members can be equal only for particular values of the variables, is called a conditional equality. In this book we shall use the term "equation" to mean conditional equality.

26. Solution of an Equation

One of the important problems of algebra is to determine the values of the variable x that will make the left side of the equation $f(x) = 0$ equal to the right side. Any such value of x is said to satisfy the equation and is called a **solution** or **root** of the equation. Such a value of x is also called a **zero** of the function $f(x)$. Thus we say that the equation $x^2 + x - 6 = 0$ has solutions or roots 2 and $- 3$; or that 2 and $- 3$ are the zeros of the function x^2+x-6.

Throughout this book we shall frequently be concerned with the development of methods for finding the solutions of equations, or with the equivalent problem of finding the zeros of functions.

One method of attack on this problem is immediately obvious. The function $f(x)$ may be carefully plotted on coordinate paper and then we may attempt to read the values of x at which the graph of the function crosses the X-axis. The accuracy of the solutions will depend on the care with which the graph is plotted and how closely the abscissas of the points of intersection of the curve and the X-axis can be estimated.

EXERCISES

Plot the following functions, find their zeros, and check your results by substitution in the given function:

1. $4x - 5$.
2. $3x + 2$.
3. $3x - x^2 - 2$.

4. $3x + 5x^2$.
5. $4x^3 - 25x$.
6. $3x^3 - 2x^2$.

Use graphical methods to find the roots of the following equations correct to the nearest tenth and check your results by substitution in the given equation:

7. $6x^2 + x - 2 = 0$.
8. $x^3 - 1 = 0$.
9. $x^3 + x - 2 = 0$.
10. $x^3 + 2x^2 - x - 2 = 0$.

11. $x^2 - 3.4x + 2.53 = 0$.
12. $x^2 - 1.3x - 0.68 = 0$.
13. $x^2 + 2x - 5 = 0$.
14. $x^2 - 2x + 5 = 0$.

27. Equivalent Equations

Two equations are said to be **equivalent** when they have the same solutions; that is, when each equation is satisfied by the solutions of the other. Thus, the equations $x - 2 = 0$ and $3x - 6 = 0$ are equivalent, since $x = 2$ satisfies both of them and neither equation is satisfied by any other value of x. It should be noted that the second equation is obtained by multiplying both members of the first equation by 3. Again, the equations $x^2 - 5x + 6 = 0$ and $-10x^2 = -50x + 60$ are equivalent, for $x = 2$ and $x = 3$ satisfy both equations and neither equation is satisfied by any other value of x. The second of these equations may be obtained from the first by performing the following operations on both members.

(1) Multiply both members by -10,
(2) Add $-50x + 60$ to both members.

Graphs would show that these equations can be satisfied for no values of x other than $x = 2$ and $x = 3$.

It must not be inferred, when the same operation is performed on the two members of an equation, that there necessarily results an equivalent equation. The following examples will show that this is an unwarranted inference.

EXAMPLES

1. Consider the equation $3x = x + 4$. $\qquad\qquad$ (a)

Square both members, $9x^2 = x^2 + 8x + 16$. $\qquad\qquad$ (b)

The equation (b) is satisfied by 2 and -1, while (a) is satisfied by 2 and not by -1. Hence (a) and (b) are not equivalent.

2. Consider the equation $3x + 2 = 5x - 8$. $\qquad\qquad$ (c)

Multiply both members by $(x - 1)$,

$$(x - 1)(3x + 2) = (x - 1)(5x - 8).\qquad\qquad (d)$$

Equation (d) is satisfied by 1 and 5, while (c) is satisfied only by 5. Hence (c) and (d) are not equivalent.

3. Consider the equation $x^2 = 4x$. $\qquad\qquad$ (e)

Divide both members by x, $x = 4$. $\qquad\qquad$ (f)

Equation (e) is satisfied by 0 and 4, while (f) is satisfied only by 4. Hence (e) and (f) are not equivalent.

4. Consider the equation $\sqrt{1 - x} - x = -1$. $\qquad\qquad$ (g)

First add x to each member, then square both members. There results

$$1 - x = 1 - 2x + x^2.\qquad\qquad (h)$$

Equation (h) is satisfied by 0 and 1; but 0 does not satisfy (g). Hence (g) and (h) are not equivalent.

These simple examples show that the same operation performed on the two members of an equation does not necessarily lead to an equation equivalent to the original one.

It is manifestly important to know whether an equation is equivalent to that from which it is derived; and if non-equivalent, whether it contains at least all the solutions of the original equation.

The following operations which the student has often performed in elementary algebra lead to equivalent equations:

(a) *Adding the same quantity to or subtracting the same quantity from both members.*

(b) *Multiplying or dividing both members by the same constant provided that constant is not equal to zero.*

(c) *Changing the signs of all the terms.*

If a derived equation contains all the roots of the original equation and some others, we shall call it **redundant.** If the derived equation lacks some roots of the original equation, we shall call it **defective.** The student should always be on his guard against treating two equations as necessarily equivalent simply because the one has been derived from the other.

28. Operations That Lead to Redundant Equations

The following operations on the two members of an equation lead, in general, to redundant equations:

(a) Multiplying both members of the given equation by a function that has a zero (Art. **26**).

Example 1. Consider the equation $7x + 3 = 9x - 4.$ (a)

The root or solution is $x = \dfrac{7}{2}.$

Multiply each member by $(2x - 3)$. We have

$$(2x - 3)(7x + 3) = (2x - 3)(9x - 4). \tag{b}$$

Equation (b) has roots $\dfrac{7}{2}$ and $\dfrac{3}{2}$, but $\dfrac{3}{2}$ is not a root of equation (a).

Example 2. Consider the equation $x - 1 = 0.$ (c)

The solution is $x = 1.$

Multiplying each member by x, we have

$$x^2 - x = 0. \tag{d}$$

Equation (d) has roots 0 and 1, but 0 is not a root of (c).

(b) Raising both members to the same integral power.

Example 1. Take the equation $3x = x + 4.$ (e)

Squaring each member, we have

$$9x^2 = x^2 + 8x + 16. \tag{f}$$

Equation (f) has roots 2 and -1, but -1 is not a root of equation (e).

Example 2. Take the equation $-\sqrt{x} = 1.$ (g)

There is no value of x that satisfies (g).

Squaring both members, we have

$$x = 1. \tag{h}$$

While 1 thus satisfies equation (h), it does not satisfy (g).

NOTE: It is common practice to consider $\sqrt{x}$ as representing the positive square root of x. When both roots are meant we write $\pm \sqrt{x}$. Thus $\sqrt{4} = 2$, $\pm \sqrt{4} = \pm 2$.

29. An Operation That Leads to Defective Equations

The following operation leads, in general, to defective equations:

Dividing both members of an equation by a function, when such function has a zero (Art. **26**) and is a factor of each member.

Example 1.   Consider the equation

$$(x^2 - 6)(x - 2) = 3x - 6.$$

The roots are 2, 3, and -3.

Divide both members by $(x - 2)$ and we have

$$x^2 - 6 = 3,$$

the roots of which are 3, and -3.

That is, the root 2 is lost in dividing the members by $(x - 2)$.

Example 2.   Take the equation $x^3 - 5x^2 + 6x = 0$.

The roots are 0, 2, and 3.

Dividing the members by x, we have

$$x^2 - 5x + 6 = 0,$$

the roots of which are 2, and 3.

The root 0 is lost in dividing by x.

In concluding this review of equivalent equations, it need hardly be said that we have by no means exhausted all the types of operations which it may be necessary to perform on the members of an equation, but enough has been said about a few simple operations to warn the student against proceeding blindly in deriving equations from a given equation. Unless the operations on the members of an equation are known to lead to equivalent equations, the student should never regard the solution as complete until the **test of substitution** has been applied.

EXERCISES

Which of the following pairs of equations are equivalent? If a pair is not equivalent, is the second equation redundant or defective with respect to the first?

1. $2x^2 + 40 = 18x,$
$x^2 - 9x + 20 = 0.$

3. $4x^3 = 16x,$
$x = \pm 2.$

2. $4x^3 = 16x,$
$x = 2.$

4. $x^2 - 2x = 15,$
$(x - 1)(x + 3)(x - 5) = 0.$

5. $\sqrt{x} = (2 - x),$
$x = (2 - x)^2.$

Hint: The second equation is equivalent to $x^2 - 5x + 4 = 0$ or $(x - 4)(x - 1) = 0.$

6. Is the equation $(x - 1)^2 = 9x^2$ equivalent to the pair of equations $x - 1 = 3x$ and $x - 1 = -3x$?

7. Multiply both members of $\dfrac{4}{x - 3} - \dfrac{2}{x - 2} = 0$ by the least common denominator of the fractions. Is the given equation equivalent to $2x - 2 = 0$?

8. Are the equations $\dfrac{1 - x}{(x + 1)(x - 2)} + \dfrac{x + 1}{(x - 2)(x + 7)} = 0$ and $8 - 4x = 0$ equivalent?

30. Rational Integral Expressions — Polynomials

Any expression * in the form

$$a_0x^n + a_1x^{n-1} + \cdots + a_{n-1}x + a_n,$$

where n is a positive integer, and $a_0, a_1, a_2, \ldots, a_{n-1}, a_n$ represent any given numbers except that $a_0 \neq 0$, is called a **rational integral expression of degree n** in x, or also a **polynomial of degree n** in x (Art. **9**). In other words, a rational integral expression in x is the algebraic sum of terms of the type kx^m, where m is restricted to take positive integral values. For example,

$$2x^2 - 5x \quad \text{and} \quad \frac{3}{2}x^2 + 7x - \frac{2}{3}$$

are rational integral expressions in x.

* By substituting the word "function" for "expression" throughout this article, we obtain the definition of an important class of functions.

As an extension of this definition, we define a rational integral expression in $x, y, z, \ldots$ as the algebraic sum of terms of the type

$$kx^m y^p z^q \ldots,$$

where $m, p, q, \ldots$ are positive integers and k (called a coefficient) does not involve $x, y, z, \ldots$. For example,

$$5x^2 y + 3xz + 3x^2 - 1$$

is a rational integral expression in x, y, z.

By the **degree** of a term $kx^m y^p z^q \ldots$ in any letters $x, y, z, \ldots$ is meant the sum $m + p + q + \cdots$ of the exponents of the letters in question. The **degree of a rational integral expression** is defined as that of a term whose degree is equal to or greater than that of any other term in the expression. Thus,

$$5x^2 y + 3xz + 3x^2 - 1$$

is of degree two in x, one in y, one in z, one in y and z, two in x and z, three in x and y, three in $x, y,$ and z.

31. Rational Integral Equations

An equation, in one variable x, of the form

$$a_0 x^n + a_1 x^{n-1} + \cdots + a_{n-1}x + a_n = 0, \quad a_0 \neq 0,$$

in which the left-hand side is a rational integral expression of degree n in x (a polynominal of degree n in x) is called a **rational integral equation of degree n** in x. Thus,

$$2x^2 - 5x = 0,$$

and
$$\frac{3}{2} x^2 + 7x - \frac{2}{3} = 0$$

are rational integral equations of degree 2 in x.

As an extension of this definition, a rational integral equation in variables $x, y, z, \ldots$ is a statement that two rational integral expressions involving $x, y, z, \ldots$ are equal. For example,

$$3x^2 - 5xy - y^3 = 2xz^2 - 4xyz \tag{1}$$

is a rational integral equation in $x, y,$ and z.

The degree of a rational integral equation in certain variables is defined as the degree of a term whose degree is equal to or greater than that of any other term in the equation. Thus, equation (1) is of degree two in x, three in y, three in x and z, three in $x, y,$ and z.

In this course, the term degree is applied to equations only when they are in the rational integral form.

We sometimes speak of the degree of an equation without mentioning to what letters we refer. In this case, it is to be understood that we mean the degree in all the variables.

Equations of the first, second, third, fourth, and fifth degrees are called **linear, quadratic, cubic, quartic,** and **quintic** equations respectively.

ORAL EXERCISES

Give the degree of each of the following equations.

1. $ax + by + c = 0.$

2. $ax^2 + bxy + cy^2 = 0.$

3. $5x^2 + x^2y^2 - y = 0.$

4. $y^4 + 2x^2y^3 - 3x^3y - x^3 = 0.$

5. Give the degree of the expression $ax^5 - 4mx^2y^2 - 3nxy + y^3$ in x. In y. In x and y.

6. Give the degree of the equation

$$10x^5 - 4ax^2yz - 3xyz + by^2 = 5x^4 - 2x^2y^2$$

in x. In y. In z. In y and z. In x and z. In x and y. In x, y, and z.

7. Given an equation whose members are rational integral functions of x. If you multiply the members by $x - a$ where a is not a root of the given equation, what root is introduced into the derived equation? Illustrate with the given equation $x = b$.

8. If $x - a$ is a factor of each member of a given equation, what root of the given equation is, in general, lacking in the equation obtained by dividing the members of the given equation by $x - a$? Illustrate with the given equation $x(x - a) = b(x - a)$.

9. Give examples of rational integral equations in one variable, x, which are (1) linear, (2) quadratic, (3) cubic, (4) quartic, (5) quintic.

32. Linear Equations in One Variable

Every rational integral equation of the first degree in x can be reduced to the form

$$a_0x + a_1 = 0, \quad a_0 \neq 0. \tag{1}$$

If a_1 be subtracted from both members of (1) and if both members of the resulting equation be divided by a_0, we have the solution

$$x = -\frac{a_1}{a_0}. \tag{2}$$

That (2) actually is the solution of (1) may be verified by direct substitution of (2) in (1).

Example. Solve for x: $9x - 3 - 4(x - 5) = 7 - 5x$.

Solution: This equation is equivalent to

$$10x + 10 = 0,$$

and hence
$$x = -1.$$

Check: Substituting -1 for x in the given equation, we have

$$-9 - 3 - 4(-1 - 5) = 7 + 5,$$

or
$$-12 + 24 = 12.$$

33. Fractional Equations Reducible to Linear Equations

In this article we are considering equations containing fractions, such that, when both members of the given equation are multiplied by the least common denominator of the fractions involved, the derived equation is a rational integral equation of the first degree. The derived equation may or may not be equivalent to the given equation, but if the derived equation is not equivalent it will always be redundant with respect to the given equation. Hence the solution of the derived equation must always be checked in the given equation.

Example 1. Solve $\dfrac{5}{x - 2} - \dfrac{3}{x - 6} = 0$.

Solution: Multiply both members of the given equation by $(x - 2)(x - 6)$ and reduce the derived equation to

$$2x = 24.$$

Hence
$$x = 12.$$

Check: Substituting $x = 12$ in the given equation, we have

$$\frac{5}{10} - \frac{3}{6} = 0.$$

This is a true statement. Thus $x = 12$ is a solution of the given equation.

Example 2. Solve $\dfrac{x - 1}{x + 12} - \dfrac{2x^2}{(x + 12)(x - 4)} + \dfrac{x - 2}{x - 4} = 0$.

Solution: Multiply both members of the given equation by $(x + 12)(x - 4)$ and reduce the derived equation to

$$5x = 20.$$

Hence
$$x = 4.$$

Check: Upon substituting $x = 4$ in the given equation, it is found that the denominators of the second and third fractions are zero. Since division by zero has been excluded in mathematics (Art. **5**), the given equation does not have $x = 4$ as a solution. The original equation has no solution, since if it does have a solution, the work shows that that solution must be $x = 4$.

EXERCISES

Solve the following equations and check your results by substitution.

1. $7x - 3 = 9 + 2x$.

2. $(x - 2)(3 + x) = 4 - 2x + x^2$.

3. $(x - 2)(3 + x) = x + x^2 - 6$.

4. $\dfrac{x}{18} - \dfrac{4(x + 1)}{9} = \dfrac{3 + 2x}{2}$.

5. $\dfrac{2 + x}{4} + \dfrac{2 - 5x}{12} = \dfrac{8 - 2x}{5}$.

6. $\dfrac{5}{3(x - 2)} - \dfrac{1}{2(x - 3)} + \dfrac{2}{4 - 2x} = 0$.

7. $\dfrac{3}{3x - 1} + \dfrac{1}{x + 1} - \dfrac{4}{2x - 1} = 0$.

8. $\dfrac{1}{x^2 - x - 6} + \dfrac{2}{3x^2 + 5x - 2} + \dfrac{4}{10x - 3x^2 - 3} = 0$.

9. $\dfrac{4}{6x^2 - x - 1} + \dfrac{2}{2x^2 + 3x - 2} + \dfrac{5}{3 + 8x - 3x^2} = 0$.

10. $\dfrac{x - 2}{x - 3} + \dfrac{x - 3}{x - 2} = \dfrac{2x^2}{x^2 - 5x + 6}$.

11. $\dfrac{x + 3}{x - 3} + \dfrac{x + 2}{x - 2} = \dfrac{2x^2}{x^2 - 5x + 6}$.

12. $\dfrac{x + 3}{x - 3} + \dfrac{x - 10}{x - 2} = \dfrac{2x^2}{x^2 - 5x + 6}$.

34. Applied Problems

The person working in the physical, natural, or social sciences, or in engineering, agriculture, or wherever mathematics is applied, finds that in order to solve his problems he must first state them in terms of mathematical symbols. Having expressed his ideas in terms of mathematical symbols, he may then apply his knowledge of mathematics and perform the manipulations necessary to find the answers to his problems.

Expressing the ideas of the particular problem in terms of the mathematical symbols is in a sense equivalent to translating from English to a foreign language. The following steps are involved in the process.

(1) The student must completely understand all the ideas expressed in the English statement of the problem. Frequently this involves an intimate knowledge of the jargon peculiar to the field in question. While English is the common mode of communication between scientists in this country, the scientist restricts the meanings of words to such an extent that a statement might be totally incomprehensible to someone uninitiated in that field, even though the statement contains only ordinary English words. From the very beginning of this book, we have carried out a similar process. For example, consider the first two articles of this text and the use of the words "real," "rational," "irrational," "greater than," and "less than."

As a further example, consider this statement concerning a property of mercury: "The height of a column of mercury in a thermometer varies as the temperature." Here the key word is "varies." The physicist does not use the word in the sense of mere change, but he wishes to imply that the height changes with the temperature in a very special way, namely, that the height is equal to a constant times the temperature.

(2) The student must define his symbols clearly and completely. In other words, he must build his vocabulary giving the mathematical equivalents of the physical entities entering the problem.

Consider again the example of the thermometer above. The vocabulary may be stated thus:

Let T be the temperature of the medium surrounding the thermometer at any instant, and let h be the height of the column of mercury in the thermometer at the same instant.

(3) The last step is to write the mathematical statement of the problems in terms of the symbols defined in step (2).

Again referring to the problem of the thermometer, we have

$$h = kT,$$

where k is a constant that must be determined by some experimental means.

In the following exercises and also throughout the rest of the text, the student will encounter problems in which he will be expected to set up the mathematical equations to be solved. It is hoped that through these simple examples, he will gain some insight into the problem, so that he can carry over the process of restating given data in mathematical symbolism to other fields in which he may eventually work.

EXERCISES

1. The difference of the squares of two consecutive integers is 79. Find the integers.

2. The difference of the squares of two consecutive even integers is 92. Find the integers.

Hint: If n represents any integer, how may any even integer be represented?

3. The difference of the squares of two consecutive odd integers is 80. Find the integers.

4. A manufacturing plant has two pieces of apparatus, one of which produces 1,000 units of a commodity per hour, while the other produces 750 units per hour. How long should both machines be operated in order to produce 40,000 units?

5. In problem 4, the faster machine broke down at the end of three hours. After spending 20 minutes making repairs, the operator was able to continue producing at half speed. How long did it take to produce the 40,000 units?

6. Two cars start at the same instant from P. Car A travels at the constant speed of 60 miles per hour. Car B travels in the same direction at a constant speed of 50 miles per hour for two hours and then travels at a speed of 70 miles per hour until it overtakes A. At what time does B overtake A? How far have the cars moved from P?

7. Two towns 12 miles apart are located on the same bank of a river. A motorboat capable of traveling 8 miles per hour in still water leaves A and travels downstream toward B. At the same instant, another craft capable of traveling 10 miles per hour in still water leaves B and travels upstream toward A. Each boat completes its trip in the same time. Find the rate of the current. How long did it take each boat to make the trip? At what time did the boats pass? Where did they pass relative to A?

8. In 8 hours, two boys are able to row 18 miles downstream on a river and back to their starting place. Their rate in still water is twice the rate of the stream. Find how long it takes them to row upstream.

9. A man travels to a city 150 miles distant at the average rate of 30 miles per hour and returns at an average rate of 25 miles per hour. Find his average rate for the round trip.

10. Refer to the situation of problem 9 and derive a general formula for the average rate on the round trip, when d is the distance between the cities, r_1 is the average rate going, and r_2 is the average rate returning.

11. A chemist has 6 ounces of a 2% solution of hydrochloric acid. How many ounces of a 3% solution should be added to the given solution in order to obtain a $2\frac{1}{2}$% solution?

12. A grocer has two grades of coffee that sell for 80¢ and 95¢ a pound respectively. He wishes to make a mixture that can be sold for 90¢ a pound. How many pounds of each grade must be used to give 10 pounds of the mixture?

13. A chemist has 12 ounces of an 8% acid solution. What should be the strength of a second solution so that when 10 ounces of the second solution are added to the first a 10% solution results?

14. A chemist has a ounces of a solution that is x% pure alcohol and b ounces of a solution that is y% pure alcohol. If he mixes the two solutions, what will be the strength of the mixture?

15. At what time between three and four o'clock will the hands of a clock be pointing in the same direction? In opposite directions? At right angles?

Hint: At three o'clock, the minute hand points directly toward 12 and the hour hand directly toward 3. If the hour hand moves through x spaces, through how many spaces will the minute hand move?

16. A man can do a piece of work in 10 days and his son can do the same job alone in 15 days. How long would it take them to do the work together?

Hint: If a job can be done in x days, then the part of the work done in one day is $\dfrac{1}{x}$.

17. A tank can be filled in 6 hours by liquid flowing from a pipe. If full, the tank can be drained in 10 hours through another pipe. Suppose the tank were half full and both pipes were open, how long would it take to fill the tank?

18. Two ungraduated mercury thermometers of equal uniform capillary bore are placed with their bulbs in a bath of small pieces of melting ice and distilled water. When the mercury in each thermometer has reached a steady state, the thermometers are scratched with a file to show the position of the mercury. The file mark on one thermometer is to be designated by the number 32° Fahrenheit and the mark on the other thermometer is to be designated by 0° Centigrade. The thermometers are then immersed in a steam bath and after the mercury has again reached a steady state, its position is marked on the thermometers. This new mark on the Fahrenheit thermometer is to be designated 212°F. and the new mark on the Centigrade thermometer is to be designated 100°C. All these operations are supposed to be carried out under standard atmospheric conditions, that is, under atmospheric pressure of 760 mm. On the Fahrenheit thermometer, the interval between the markings for the melting point of ice and the boiling point of water is divided into 180 equal parts, and on the Centigrade thermometer the interval is divided into 100 equal parts. If the thermometers are now placed in air, and if the reading on the Fahrenheit thermometer is F and on the Centigrade thermometer is C, derive an equation showing the relationship that exists between F and C. Use this equation to solve the following problems:

(*a*) Ordinary room temperature is assumed to be 70°F. Find the equivalent Centigrade temperature.

(*b*) Normal temperature of the human body is 98.6°F. Find the equivalent Centigrade temperature.

(*c*) Change − 273°C. to the Fahrenheit scale.

(*d*) Change − 15°C. to the Fahrenheit scale.

(*e*) Change 27°C. to the Fahrenheit scale.

19. A metal rod of length l_1 is initially at temperature t_1 degrees Centigrade. The rod is heated to temperature t_2 degrees Centigrade, and its length is then found to be l_2. It can then be stated that to within a fair degree of accuracy the quotient of the change in length of the rod by the change in the temperature of the rod is a constant times the original length. The constant is designated by α and is called the coefficient of linear expansion. Write the equation which shows the relationship between l_1, l_2, t_1, t_2, and α.

(*a*) A steel rod of 50 cms. in length at 25°C. is heated to 60°C. If the coefficient of linear expansion for steel is 0.0000110, find the length of the heated rod.

(b) A copper rod measured at 0°C. is found to be exactly 20 inches long. When the temperature of the wire is increased to 80°C., the wire is found to be 20.0012720 inches in length. Find the coefficient of linear expansion for copper.

(c) Five miles of steel railroad track were laid when the average temperature was 50°F. If temperature increases of 60°F. may be anticipated and if the coefficient of linear expansion for steel is 0.00001145 feet per foot per degree C., how much must be allowed for expansion of the track?

6 SYSTEMS OF LINEAR EQUATIONS

35. Type Form

An equation of the form

$$ax + by + c = 0, \tag{1}$$

is called a linear equation in two variables.

When $b \neq 0$, it can be put into the form $y = -\dfrac{ax}{b} - \dfrac{c}{b}$. (2)

Since in (2) we may assign to x any value and compute a corresponding value for y, the equation defines y as a function of x in accordance with our definition of a mathematical function (Art. **20**).

The graph of the linear function is a straight line (Art. **23**). The straight line representing the function $-\dfrac{ax}{b} - \dfrac{c}{b}$ is also the locus of all points whose coordinates satisfy the equation $y = -\dfrac{ax}{b} - \dfrac{c}{b}$. Hence, the graphical representation of the equation $ax + by + c = 0$ is a straight line.

EXERCISES

Graph each of the following equations.

1. $x - y = 1$.

Solution: This equation may be written in the form

$$y = x - 1.$$

The graph of the linear function $x - 1$ is the line shown in Figure 8, and is by definition the graph of the equation $x - y = 1$.

Since we know the graph to be a straight line, it is necessary to plot two points only, and to draw a straight line through them. The farther apart the two points are, the more accurate the graph is likely to be.

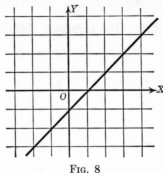

Fig. 8

2. $y - 4x = 6.$

3. $2x + 5y + 20 = 0.$

4. $7x - 4y = 11.$

5. $2x - 3y = 0.$

6. $2x - 7 = 0.$

7. $3y + 8 = 0.$

8. $3x + 4y = 8.$

9. $3x - 4y = 8.$

10. $4x + 3y = 8.$

11. $4x - 3y = 8.$

12. $\dfrac{x + y}{4} + \dfrac{x - y}{3} = 2.$

36. Graphical Solution of a Set of Linear Equations

As stated in Article **35,** the graph of any linear equation in x and y is a straight line. Any such equation is satisfied by an indefinitely large number of pairs of values of x and y, that is, by the coordinates of all points on its graph. In the graphical solution of the system of two equations, we seek the coordinates of points common to the graphs of the two equations.

As the graphs are two straight lines, three cases arise:

(1) In general, two lines intersect in one and only one point.

(2) Two lines may be parallel, and thus have no point in common.

(3) Two lines may be coincident, and thus have an indefinitely large number of points in common.

Corresponding to these three cases, a set of two linear equations has, in general, one and only one solution, but it may have no solution or an indefinitely large number of solutions. When the graphs are two parallel lines, there is no pair of numbers which satisfies both equations, and the equations are said to be **incompatible** or **inconsistent**.   When the graphs are two coincident straight lines, the two equations of the system are equivalent (Art. **27**).   Examples of each case are given in the following exercises.

EXERCISES

Find the solutions of the following equations by plotting the graphs.

1. $x - y + 1 = 0$,
$4x + y - 16 = 0$.
See Figure 9.

2. $2x - 3y + 12 = 0$,
$3x + 4y + 1 = 0$.

3. $4x - 5y + 4 = 0$,
$2x - 3 = 0$.

4. $7x - 10y = 26$,
$2x - y = 0$.

5. $2x + 3y = 6$,
$4x + 3y = 24$.

6. $3x - 4y = 18$,
$12y - 9x + 54 = 0$.

7. $3x - 4y = 18$,
$4x + 3y = -1$.

8. $3x - 4y = 18$,
$3x - 4y = 12$.

9. $3x + 2y = 1$,
$x + y = 0$.

10. $2x + 3y = 6$,
$2x - y = 4$.

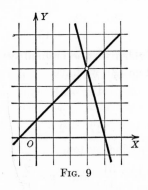

Fig. 9

11. Graph $3x - 2y = 1$.   Multiply both sides of this equation by 2 and graph the resulting equation.   Compare the graphs.

12. Graph $3x - 2y = c$ for two different values of c.   Compare the graphs.

13. On the same coordinate axes used in problem 12, graph $2x + 3y = c$ for two different values of c.   Compare these lines with those of problem 12.

37. Solution by Elimination

The process of solving two linear equations in two variables consists of deriving an equivalent but simpler system of two equations. We seek to have in the equivalent system at least one equation in which only one of the variables appears. The process of deriving such a system is called the process of **elimination**.

Elimination by **addition or subtraction** is illustrated in the following example.

Example. Solve $2x + 3y = 4,$
$$3x - 4y = 5.$$

Solution. To eliminate x we first multiply the members of the first equation by 3 and those of the second by 2, obtaining

$$6x + 9y = 12,$$
$$6x - 8y = 10. \tag{1}$$

Note that the new system is equivalent to the original system. Subtracting corresponding members of system (1), we obtain

$$17y = 2.$$

Next eliminate y from the original system by multiplying the first equation by 4 and the second by 3, obtaining

$$8x + 12y = 16,$$
$$9x - 12y = 15. \tag{2}$$

System (2) is equivalent to the original system, and on adding the equations in system (2), we have

$$17x = 31.$$

The system $17x = 31,$
$$17y = 2 \tag{3}$$

is equivalent to the original system.

Hence $x = \dfrac{31}{17}$ and $y = \dfrac{2}{17}.$

Check: Substituting $\dfrac{31}{17}$ for x and $\dfrac{2}{17}$ for y in the original system, we have

$$2 \cdot \frac{31}{17} + 3 \cdot \frac{2}{17} = \frac{62}{17} + \frac{6}{17} = \frac{68}{17} = 4,$$

$$3 \cdot \frac{31}{17} - 4 \cdot \frac{2}{17} = \frac{93}{17} - \frac{8}{17} = \frac{85}{17} = 5.$$

Another method of arriving at the solution would be to obtain the system (1) and then the equation $17y = 2$ as before. This latter equation and either of the equations of the original system will form a system equivalent to the given system. Thus

$$3x - 4y = 5,$$
$$17y = 2 \tag{4}$$

is equivalent to the given system. The second equation of system (4) yields $y = \dfrac{2}{17}$. On substituting this value in the first equation of system (4), we have

$$3x - \frac{8}{17} = 5 \quad \text{or} \quad x = \frac{31}{17}.$$

The same example will be used to illustrate the method of elimination by **substitution.**

Solution. From the second equation of the given system, we obtain x in terms of y,

$$3x = 5 + 4y,$$
or
$$x = \frac{5 + 4y}{3}. \tag{5}$$

Substituting $\dfrac{5 + 4y}{3}$ for x in the first equation of the system yields

$$2 \cdot \frac{5 + 4y}{3} + 3y = 4,$$
or
$$10 + 8y + 9y = 12,$$
whence
$$17y = 2. \tag{6}$$

Equations (5) and (6) form a system equivalent to the given system. From (6), we have

$$y = \frac{2}{17}.$$

Substituting this value in (5), we find

$$x = \frac{5 + \dfrac{8}{17}}{3} = \frac{31}{17}.$$

These values for x and y check with those obtained by the method of elimination by addition and subtraction.

EXERCISES

Solve for x and y by any of the methods of elimination.

1. $2x - y = 11,$
$x + 3y = 23.$

2. $3x + 2y = 5,$
$5y - 2x = -16.$

3. $7x - 2y = 12,$
$3x + 5y = 8.$

4. $30x - 15y - 32 = 0,$
$75x + 60y - 2 = 0.$

5. $12x + 4y = 3,$
$3y - 10x = 7.$

6. $.2x + .3y + .1 = 0,$
$.4y - .5x - .02 = 0.$

7. $.03x + .05y = .75,$
$2x - 3y = 12.$

8. $5(x - 1) + 2(y - 3) = 8,$
$3(x - 1) - 7(y - 3) = 13.$

9. $mx - ny - 2mn = 0,$
$nx - my = n^2 + m^2.$

10. $\dfrac{x}{a} - \dfrac{y}{b} = 1,$

$\dfrac{x}{b} - \dfrac{y}{a} = 1.$

38. Solution by Determinants

Let
$$a_1x + b_1y = c_1,$$
$$a_2x + b_2y = c_2,$$

be two linear equations in two variables. Multiply the members of the first by b_2, and those of the second by $-b_1$. Adding the members of the two resulting equations, we obtain

$$(a_1b_2 - a_2b_1)x = (b_2c_1 - b_1c_2),$$

or
$$x = \frac{b_2c_1 - b_1c_2}{a_1b_2 - a_2b_1}, \text{ provided } a_1b_2 - a_2b_1 \neq 0.$$

In a similar manner, by multiplying the first and second equations by $-a_2$ and a_1 respectively, we obtain

$$y = \frac{a_1c_2 - a_2c_1}{a_1b_2 - a_2b_1}, \text{ provided } a_1b_2 - a_2b_1 \neq 0.$$

We note that the denominators of the above fractions are alike. The denominator may be denoted by the symbol

$$\begin{vmatrix} a_1 & b_1 \\ a_2 & b_2 \end{vmatrix}$$

which is called a **determinant**. Since it has two rows and two columns, it is said to be of the second order. The letters a_1, b_1,

a_2, b_2, are called the **elements** of the determinant, and a_1, b_2, constitute the **principal diagonal**. A determinant of the second order then represents the number which is obtained by subtracting from the product of the terms in the principal diagonal, the product of the other two terms. Thus,

$$\begin{vmatrix} x & y \\ z & w \end{vmatrix} = xw - yz, \qquad \begin{vmatrix} 1 & 2 \\ 3 & 4 \end{vmatrix} = 4 - 6 = -2.$$

Using the determinant notation, we may now write the solutions of our equations in the form

$$x = \frac{\begin{vmatrix} c_1 & b_1 \\ c_2 & b_2 \end{vmatrix}}{\begin{vmatrix} a_1 & b_1 \\ a_2 & b_2 \end{vmatrix}}, \qquad y = \frac{\begin{vmatrix} a_1 & c_1 \\ a_2 & c_2 \end{vmatrix}}{\begin{vmatrix} a_1 & b_1 \\ a_2 & b_2 \end{vmatrix}}.$$

We note that the numerator of the solution for x is obtained from the denominator by substituting in place of a_1, a_2, which are the coefficients of x in the equations to be solved, the constant terms c_1, c_2. In a similar manner, in the numerator of the solution for y we replace b_1, b_2 by c_1, c_2 respectively.

EXERCISES

Solve the following equations by the use of determinants.

1. $2x + 3y = 4$,
$3x - 4y = 5$.

Solution: The equations must first be arranged so that the terms containing the variables are on the left-hand side and the constant terms are on the right-hand side. The values of x and y are then each given by the quotient of two determinants. The determinant in each denominator is the determinant of the coefficients of x and y in the given equations. In this case it is

$$\begin{vmatrix} 2 & 3 \\ 3 & -4 \end{vmatrix}.$$

The determinant in the numerator of the value of x is the same as the above determinant except that the column of coefficients of x is replaced by the constant terms in the given equations. Hence

$$x = \frac{\begin{vmatrix} 4 & 3 \\ 5 & -4 \end{vmatrix}}{\begin{vmatrix} 2 & 3 \\ 3 & -4 \end{vmatrix}} = \frac{-16 - 15}{-8 - 9} = \frac{31}{17}.$$

The determinant in the numerator of the value of y is the same as the determinant in the denominator except that the column of coefficients of y is replaced by the constant terms in the given equations. Thus

$$y = \frac{\begin{vmatrix} 2 & 4 \\ 3 & 5 \end{vmatrix}}{\begin{vmatrix} 2 & 3 \\ 3 & -4 \end{vmatrix}} = \frac{10 - 12}{-8 - 9} = \frac{2}{17}.$$

These results may be checked with the example of Article **37**.

2. $3x + 2y = 8,$
$\quad\, 2x - 3y = 27.$

3. $\quad\ 4x - 9y = 2,$
$\quad\ 8x - 15y - 3 = 0.$

4. $5x + 7y - 4 = 0,$
$\quad\ 3x + 5y = 0.$

5. $4y - 7x = 36,$
$\quad\ 9y + 4x = 2.$

6. $\dfrac{y}{2} - \dfrac{x}{5} = \dfrac{1}{15},$

$\quad \dfrac{3x}{10} + \dfrac{8y}{3} = \dfrac{7}{12}.$

7. $.8x - .3y = 1.20,$
$\quad\ .4y - .3x = \ .47.$

8. $\dfrac{2}{x} - \dfrac{3}{y} - 18 = 0,$

$\quad \dfrac{4}{y} + \dfrac{5}{x} + 1 = 0.$

Hint: Solve for $\dfrac{1}{x}$ and $\dfrac{1}{y}$.

9. $\dfrac{3}{x - 2} + \dfrac{5}{y + 1} = 19,$

$\quad \dfrac{7}{x - 2} - \dfrac{4}{y + 1} = 13.$

10. $3x - 4y = 12,$
$\quad\ 8y - 6x = 5.$

11. The equations $ax + by = c$ and $kax + kby = kc$ are equivalent, where k is a constant not equal to zero. Show that if we attempt to solve these equations for x and y by determinants, all the determinants are zero.

12. In solving a system of equations

$$a_1x + b_1y = c_1,$$
$$a_2x + b_2y = c_2$$

by determinants, show that if the determinant in the denominator and the determinants in the numerators are all zero, then the two equations are equivalent.

39. Systems of Three Linear Equations in Three Variables. Method of Elimination

A system of three linear equations in three variables may be solved by the methods of elimination. There are special systems in which there are no solutions or infinitely many solutions. Such systems are not considered in this chapter. The method of solution illustrated by the following example may be carried over to four equations in four variables, and eventually to n equations in n variables.

Example. Solve
$$x - 2y - z = -7,$$
$$2x + y + z = 0,$$
$$3x - 5y + 8z = 13.$$

Solution: Add together the first two equations to eliminate z.

$$\begin{array}{l} x - 2y - z = -7, \\ 2x + y + z = 0 \\ \hline 3x - y = -7. \end{array} \qquad (1)$$

Multiply the second of the given equations by 8 and from this result subtract the third equation:

$$\begin{array}{l} 16x + 8y + 8z = 0, \\ 3x - 5y + 8z = 13, \\ \hline 13x + 13y = -13, \end{array}$$

or
$$x + y = -1. \qquad (2)$$

The equations (1) and (2) together with any one of the given equations form a system equivalent to the given system.

Hence
$$\begin{array}{l} 3x - y = -7, \\ x + y = -1, \\ 2x + y + z = 0 \end{array} \qquad (3)$$

is a system equivalent to the given system.

Add the first two equations of the system (3) and form the system

$$\begin{array}{l} 4x = -8, \\ x + y = -1, \\ 2x + y + z = 0. \end{array} \qquad (4)$$

From the first equation of system (4), it is evident that $x = -2$. Using this value for x in the second equation, we find that $y = 1$.

Using these values for x and y in the third equation, we find that $z = 3$.

Check:
$$(-2) - 2(1) - (3) = -7,$$
$$2(-2) + (1) + (3) = 0,$$
$$3(-2) - 5(1) + 8(3) = 13.$$

EXERCISES

Solve the following systems of equations.

1. $2x + 3y + z = 0,$
$5x + y - 2z = 9,$
$10x - 5y + 3z = 4.$

2. $5x - 4y + z = 17,$
$x + y + z = 4,$
$3x - 5y - 2z = 5.$

3. $2x - 3y - z = -4,$
$2y + z - x = 6,$
$x + 2z - y = 14.$

4. $9x + 10y = 2,$
$3x + 6z = 4,$
$3z - 3y = 1.$

5. $3x + 2y - 2z = -1,$
$x - 3y - 3z = -16,$
$2x + y + 4z = 9.$

9. $A - 2B + 3C = 4,$
$B - 2C + 3D = 8,$
$3A + C - 2D = -12,$
$-2A + 3B + D = 8.$

6. $x - y = 5,$
$y - 2z = 6,$
$z - 3x = 7.$

7. $\dfrac{2}{x} + \dfrac{3}{y} + \dfrac{5}{z} = 3,$

$\dfrac{2}{x} - \dfrac{9}{y} + \dfrac{20}{z} = 2,$

$\dfrac{6}{x} + \dfrac{6}{y} - \dfrac{10}{z} = 3.$

8. $\dfrac{x+y}{2} = \dfrac{15-z}{3},$

$\dfrac{x+z}{2} = \dfrac{16-y}{3},$

$\dfrac{y+z}{2} = \dfrac{17-x}{3}.$

10. $x - 2y + 3z + 4w = 4,$
$3x - 4y + 5z + 6w = 1,$
$2x + 3y - 4z - 3w = 1,$
$x + y + z + w = 0.$

40. Determinants

The square array of nine numbers with bars on the sides

$$\begin{vmatrix} a_1 & b_1 & c_1 \\ a_2 & b_2 & c_2 \\ a_3 & b_3 & c_3 \end{vmatrix}$$

is called a determinant of the third order. As in the case of the determinant of the second order, the numbers a_1, b_1, c_1, etc. are called the elements, and the numbers a_1, b_2, c_3 form the principal diagonal. The value of the determinant is defined to be

$$a_1 \cdot \begin{vmatrix} b_2 & c_2 \\ b_3 & c_3 \end{vmatrix} - b_1 \cdot \begin{vmatrix} a_2 & c_2 \\ a_3 & c_3 \end{vmatrix} + c_1 \cdot \begin{vmatrix} a_2 & b_2 \\ a_3 & b_3 \end{vmatrix},$$

or $\qquad a_1(b_2c_3 - b_3c_2) - b_1(a_2c_3 - a_3c_2) + c_1(a_2b_3 - a_3b_2).$

The value of the symbol or the expansion of the determinant is thus found according to the following rule:

Start with the element in the upper left-hand corner and multiply it by the two-rowed determinant that is left when the first row and first column are stricken out; add to this result the negative of the element in the first row and second column multiplied by the determinant that remains when the first row and second column are stricken out; to this result add the element in the first row and third column multiplied by the determinant that remains when the first row and third column are stricken out.

This rule may be extended to determinants containing n rows and n columns. The work may be tedious, but he who perseveres will attain the expansion.

Example 1. Obtain the expansion of the determinant

$$\begin{vmatrix} 1 & 3 & 4 \\ 2 & 7 & 3 \\ 1 & 3 & 5 \end{vmatrix}.$$

Solution: By the rule for expanding determinants, we have

$$1 \begin{vmatrix} 7 & 3 \\ 3 & 5 \end{vmatrix} - 3 \begin{vmatrix} 2 & 3 \\ 1 & 5 \end{vmatrix} + 4 \begin{vmatrix} 2 & 7 \\ 1 & 3 \end{vmatrix}$$

or $\qquad (35 - 9) - 3(10 - 3) + 4(6 - 7) = 26 - 21 - 4 = 1.$

Example 2. Obtain the expansion of the determinant

$$\begin{vmatrix} 3 & -2 & 0 & 4 \\ 1 & 0 & -1 & 2 \\ -2 & 3 & 5 & -7 \\ 6 & -3 & 4 & 1 \end{vmatrix}$$

Solution: By the rule for expanding determinants, we have

$$3 \begin{vmatrix} 0 & -1 & 2 \\ 3 & 5 & -7 \\ -3 & 4 & 1 \end{vmatrix} + 2 \begin{vmatrix} 1 & -1 & 2 \\ -2 & 5 & -7 \\ 6 & 4 & 1 \end{vmatrix} - 4 \begin{vmatrix} 1 & 0 & -1 \\ -2 & 3 & 5 \\ 6 & -3 & 4 \end{vmatrix}.$$

On expanding these three-rowed determinants, we have
$$3(36) + 2(-3) - 4(39) = -54.$$

EXERCISES

Expand the following determinants.

1.
$$\begin{vmatrix} 3 & 2 & 4 \\ 0 & -3 & 1 \\ -1 & 5 & 2 \end{vmatrix}.$$

4.
$$\begin{vmatrix} 3 & -2 & 5 \\ x & 4 & 7 \\ x & 4 & 7 \end{vmatrix}.$$

2.
$$\begin{vmatrix} 5 & -6 & 0 \\ 3 & 1 & 3 \\ -2 & 8 & 4 \end{vmatrix}.$$

5.
$$\begin{vmatrix} 2 & -4 & 6 \\ 3 & 7 & 9 \\ -1 & 2 & -3 \end{vmatrix}.$$

3.
$$\begin{vmatrix} 1 & 5 & -2 & -3 \\ 0 & -3 & 4 & 0 \\ 2 & -1 & 5 & 1 \\ 3 & 2 & -1 & 6 \end{vmatrix}.$$

6.
$$\begin{vmatrix} 1 & 0 & -1 & 2 \\ 0 & 1 & 2 & -1 \\ -1 & 2 & 1 & 0 \\ 2 & -1 & 0 & 1 \end{vmatrix}.$$

7. Show that
$$\begin{vmatrix} a_1 & b_1 & c_1 \\ a_2 & b_2 & c_2 \\ a_3 & b_3 & c_3 \end{vmatrix} = a_1 \begin{vmatrix} b_2 & c_2 \\ b_3 & c_3 \end{vmatrix} - a_2 \begin{vmatrix} b_1 & c_1 \\ b_3 & c_3 \end{vmatrix} + a_3 \begin{vmatrix} b_1 & c_1 \\ b_2 & c_2 \end{vmatrix}.$$

In other words, we may expand a determinant by going across the first row or going down the first column.

8. Given a determinant of the third order, rewrite the first and second columns to the right as below:

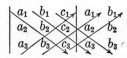

The products of the numbers in the three diagonals going down from left to right give three terms in the expansion. The negatives of the products of the numbers in the three diagonals going up from left to right give the remaining three terms. Verify these statements. This method of expansion is valid only for a three-rowed determinant.

9. Work problems 1, 2, 3, 4 by the method of exercise 7.

10. Work problems 1, 2, 4, 5 by the method of exercise 8.

11. Show that
$$\begin{vmatrix} a_1 & b_1 & ka_1 \\ a_2 & b_2 & ka_2 \\ a_3 & b_3 & ka_3 \end{vmatrix} = 0.$$

12. Show that
$$\begin{vmatrix} a_1 + b_1 & c_1 & d_1 \\ a_2 + b_2 & c_2 & d_2 \\ a_3 + b_3 & c_3 & d_3 \end{vmatrix} = \begin{vmatrix} a_1 & c_1 & d_1 \\ a_2 & c_2 & d_2 \\ a_3 & c_3 & d_3 \end{vmatrix} + \begin{vmatrix} b_1 & c_1 & d_1 \\ b_2 & c_2 & d_2 \\ b_3 & c_3 & d_3 \end{vmatrix}.$$

13. Show that
$$\begin{vmatrix} a_1 + kb_1 & b_1 & c_1 \\ a_2 + kb_2 & b_2 & c_2 \\ a_3 + kb_3 & b_3 & c_3 \end{vmatrix} = \begin{vmatrix} a_1 & b_1 & c_1 \\ a_2 & b_2 & c_2 \\ a_3 & b_3 & c_3 \end{vmatrix}.$$

14. Use exercise 13 to expand
$$\begin{vmatrix} 1 & -1 & 0 \\ 5 & -4 & 2 \\ -2 & 3 & 3 \end{vmatrix}.$$

15. Solve for x:
$$\begin{vmatrix} 1 & x & x \\ 3 & -2 & 1 \\ -1 & 3 & 2 \end{vmatrix} = 0.$$

16. Solve the system for x and y:
$$\begin{vmatrix} x & y & -3 \\ 2 & -3 & 1 \\ -1 & 2 & 0 \end{vmatrix} = 0, \qquad \begin{vmatrix} x & 0 & 1 \\ y & 1 & 1 \\ -3 & -1 & 0 \end{vmatrix} = 0.$$

41. Solution of a System of Linear Equations by Determinants

Consider the system of three linear equations in three variables

$$a_1x + b_1y + c_1z = d_1, \qquad (1)$$
$$a_2x + b_2y + c_2z = d_2, \qquad (2)$$
$$a_3x + b_3y + c_3z = d_3. \qquad (3)$$

Multiplying (1) and (2) by b_2 and $-b_1$ respectively and adding, we get

$$(a_1b_2 - a_2b_1)x + (b_2c_1 - b_1c_2)z = d_1b_2 - d_2b_1. \qquad (4)$$

Eliminating y in a similar manner from (1) and (3), we find

$$(a_3b_1 - a_1b_3)x + (b_1c_3 - b_3c_1)z = d_3b_1 - d_1b_3. \tag{5}$$

Eliminating z from (4) and (5), we find

$$[(a_1b_2 - a_2b_1)(b_1c_3 - b_3c_1) - (a_3b_1 - a_1b_3)(b_2c_1 - b_1c_2)]x$$
$$= (d_1b_2 - d_2b_1)(b_1c_3 - b_3c_1) - (d_3b_1 - d_1b_3)(b_2c_1 - b_1c_2),$$

which after some simplification gives us

$$x = \frac{d_1(b_2c_3 - b_3c_2) - d_2(b_1c_3 - b_3c_1) + d_3(b_1c_2 - b_2c_1)}{a_1(b_2c_3 - b_3c_2) - a_2(b_1c_3 - b_3c_1) + a_3(b_1c_2 - b_2c_1)}.$$

The form of this result suggests that the numerator and the denominator may each be expressed as a three-rowed determinant. Hence we can write the solution for x in the form

$$x = \frac{\begin{vmatrix} d_1 & b_1 & c_1 \\ d_2 & b_2 & c_2 \\ d_3 & b_3 & c_3 \end{vmatrix}}{\begin{vmatrix} a_1 & b_1 & c_1 \\ a_2 & b_2 & c_2 \\ a_3 & b_3 & c_3 \end{vmatrix}},$$

provided the denominator is not zero.

In a similar way, we can find the values for y and z;

$$y = \frac{\begin{vmatrix} a_1 & d_1 & c_1 \\ a_2 & d_2 & c_2 \\ a_3 & d_3 & c_3 \end{vmatrix}}{\begin{vmatrix} a_1 & b_1 & c_1 \\ a_2 & b_2 & c_2 \\ a_3 & b_3 & c_3 \end{vmatrix}}, \qquad z = \frac{\begin{vmatrix} a_1 & b_1 & d_1 \\ a_2 & b_2 & d_2 \\ a_3 & b_3 & d_3 \end{vmatrix}}{\begin{vmatrix} a_1 & b_1 & c_1 \\ a_2 & b_2 & c_2 \\ a_3 & b_3 & c_3 \end{vmatrix}}.$$

The denominators in the expressions for x, y, and z are the same, each denominator being the determinant by the coefficients of the variables in the given system of equations. The numerators are obtained from the denominators by replacing the coefficients of the variable in question by the constant terms. For example, in the numerator of y, the constants d_1, d_2, d_3 replace the coefficients of y, namely, b_1, b_2, b_3 respectively.

This method of solution by determinants may be extended to n equations in n variables. Each variable is then the quotient of two determinants of the n-th order. The determinant in the denominator is the determinant formed by the coefficients of the variables in the given system of equations. The determinant in the numerator is obtained from the one in the denominator by replacing the coefficients of the variable in question by the constant terms.

Example. Solve
$$x - 2y - z = -7,$$
$$2x + y + z = 0,$$
$$3x - 5y + 8z = 13.$$

Solution:

$$x = \frac{\begin{vmatrix} -7 & -2 & -1 \\ 0 & 1 & 1 \\ 13 & -5 & 8 \end{vmatrix}}{\begin{vmatrix} 1 & -2 & -1 \\ 2 & 1 & 1 \\ 3 & -5 & 8 \end{vmatrix}} = \frac{-104}{52} = -2.$$

$$y = \frac{\begin{vmatrix} 1 & -7 & -1 \\ 2 & 0 & 1 \\ 3 & 13 & 8 \end{vmatrix}}{\begin{vmatrix} 1 & -2 & -1 \\ 2 & 1 & 1 \\ 3 & -5 & 8 \end{vmatrix}} = \frac{52}{52} = 1.$$

$$z = \frac{\begin{vmatrix} 1 & -2 & -7 \\ 2 & 1 & 0 \\ 3 & -5 & 13 \end{vmatrix}}{\begin{vmatrix} 1 & -2 & -1 \\ 2 & 1 & 1 \\ 3 & -5 & 8 \end{vmatrix}} = \frac{156}{52} = 3.$$

EXERCISES

Use determinants to solve the following.

1. $2x - 3y - z = 4,$
$\quad x - 2y - z = 1,$
$\quad x - y + 2z = 9.$

2. $5x - 4y + z = 3,$
$\quad x + y + z = -1,$
$\quad 3x - 5y - 2z = 7.$

3. $x + y + z = 0,$
$\quad 3y - x - 2z = 10,$
$\quad 3z + 2y - 2x = 22.$

4. $2x + 3y + 4z = 2,$
$\quad 3x + 4y - 2z = -4,$
$\quad 4x - 2y - 3z = 9.$

5.
$$x + y + z + w = 0,$$
$$2x + y \quad\ - 3w = 4,$$
$$y - 2z - 5w = 2,$$
$$3x - y - 4z \quad\ = 0.$$

7.
$$x + y + z + w = 0,$$
$$3x - 4y + 5z + 6w = 1,$$
$$x - 2y + 3z + 4w = -3,$$
$$2x + 3y - 4z - 3w = 1.$$

6.
$$\frac{3}{x} + \frac{1}{y} - \frac{1}{z} = 15,$$
$$\frac{1}{x} + \frac{3}{y} - \frac{1}{z} = 17,$$
$$\frac{1}{x} + \frac{1}{y} - \frac{3}{z} = -7.$$

8.
$$\frac{1}{x-1} + \frac{1}{y+1} + \frac{2}{2z-3} = 7,$$
$$\frac{1}{x-1} + \frac{1}{y+1} + \frac{1}{2z-3} = 5,$$
$$\frac{3}{x-1} - \frac{2}{y+1} + \frac{1}{2z-3} = 1.$$

MISCELLANEOUS PROBLEMS

1. A number consists of three digits whose sum is 7. Twice the ten's digit is equal to three times the unit's digit. If the digits are reversed the number remains the same. What is the number?

Hint: The number 356 means $3 \cdot (100) + 5 \cdot (10) + 6 \cdot (1)$. A number having x as the hundred's digit, y as the ten's digit, and z as the unit's digit is represented by $x \cdot (100) + y \cdot (10) + z \cdot (1)$.

2. If a two digit number is divided by the digit in the unit's place, the result is 21. Subtracting 27 from the number reverses the digits. Find the number.

3. A was m times as old as B a years ago, and will be n times as old as B in b years from now. Find the ages of A and B, first when $a = 4$, $m = 3$, $b = 5$, $n = 2$; and then in terms of a, b, m, n.

4. A linear function of x takes the value 2 when $x = 3$, and 10 when $x = 7$. What is the function?

5. A quadratic function of x of the form $ax^2 + bx + c$ takes the value 7 when $x = 2$, 60 when $x = 5$, and 82 when $x = 7$. Find the function.

6. A quadratic function of x takes the value y_0 when $x = -h$, y_1 when $x = 0$, and y_2 when $x = h$. Find the coefficients a, b, c of the quadratic function in terms of h, y_0, y_1, y_2, and then write the function.

7. A certain individual's diet should consist of 4.6 ounces protein, 2.1 ounces fat, and 18.1 ounces carbohydrate and be made of cereal, milk, and eggs. If cereal contains 14% protein, 2% fat, 72% carbohydrate; milk 3% protein, 4% fat, 5% carbohydrate; eggs 15% protein, 10% fat; how many ounces of each are needed?

8. The sum of the three angles of a triangle is 180°. The largest angle is four times the smallest one and is equal to the sum of the two smaller angles. Find the angles.

9. The sum of the four interior angles of a quadrangle is 360°. The largest angle is equal to the sum of its two adjacent angles. The smallest angle is opposite the largest and is equal to one fourth of the largest angle. The smallest angle is equal to the difference of its adjacent angles. Find the angles.

10. The perimeter of a rectangular field is 160 rods. The length is 20 rods less than three times the width. Find the dimensions of the field.

11. The sum of the reciprocals of three numbers is $-\dfrac{1}{6}$. The reciprocal of the first number exceeds that of the second by $\dfrac{1}{6}$. The reciprocal of the first exceeds twice that of the third by $\dfrac{5}{2}$. Find the numbers.

12. A man and his two sons can do a piece of work in five days. Working alone, the man could do the job in the same time that it would take his sons working together. The man works twice as rapidly as one of his sons. How long would it take each to do the job alone?

13. A man has $30,000, part invested at $2\frac{1}{2}\%$ and the rest at 3%. His yearly income is $810. How is the capital divided?

14. A man distributes $130 annually among 15 different organizations. To one group of these organizations he gives $5 each, to a second group $10 each, and to the rest $20 each. The first group receives the same total amount as the third. Find the number of organizations in each group.

15. A man distributes P dollars among n persons of three classes, the first class receiving a dollars each, the second b dollars each, and the third class c dollars each. The first class receives the same total amount as the other two classes. Find in terms of P, n, a, b, and c the number that received a, b, and c dollars.

16. Four numbers have the property, that when successively the arithmetic average of three of them is added to the fourth, the numbers 29, 33, 41, 47 result. What are the numbers?

17. A chemist has a 4% and a 10% acid solution. What amounts of each solution should be used to give 8 ounces of a 6% solution?

18. A bar of metal is 85% pure silver and another bar is 63% pure silver. How many ounces of each bar should be used so that when the parts are melted together a bar weighing 30 ounces is obtained which is 70% pure silver?

19. An alloy contains 35% pure silver and 40% pure gold. How much pure silver and pure gold should be added to 100 ounces of the alloy to give a new alloy which is 45% pure silver and 45% pure gold?

20. A bar of metal is composed of silver and gold. It weighs 50 ounces in air and loses 3.2 ounces when weighed in water. How much gold and how much silver did the bar contain if the specific gravity of gold is 19.3 and that of silver is 10.5?

Explanation of specific gravity. A body like a piece of gold or silver when weighed in water loses an amount of weight equal to the weight of the water displaced. The specific gravity of a substance is defined to be the quotient of the weight of the body in air by the loss of weight in water. (See problem 5, p. 30.) To say that the specific gravity of gold is 19.3 means that 19.3 ounces of gold lose one ounce when weighed in water. Hence one ounce of gold loses $\frac{1}{19.3}$ ounces when weighed in water and x ounces of gold lose $\frac{x}{19.3}$ ounces when weighed in water.

21. A mixture of copper and aluminum weighs 20 ounces in air and 14.14 ounces in water. If the specific gravity of copper is 8.9 and that of aluminum is 2.7, find how much copper and how much aluminum is in the mixture.

22. Two runners are practicing on a circular track 150 yards in circumference. When running in opposite directions they pass each other every 15 seconds. When they run in the same direction, the faster passes the slower every 105 seconds. Find the speed of each. How long does it take each man to run a mile?

23. If h represents the height in meters above sea level, and b represents the reading of a barometer in millimeters, it is known that b is a linear function of h. On a certain day at a height of 120 meters above sea level the barometer read 751.0 mm., at a height of 540 meters it read 714.8 mm. What is the functional relationship between b and h?

In gunnery, a rough rule that is frequently used is that the atmospheric pressure diminishes 9 mm. for each increase of 100 meters in altitude. Use the result of the first part of this problem to test the accuracy of this rule.

24. The boiling point of water in degrees Centigrade is a linear function of the height, h, in feet above sea level. It is observed that at the height of 2200 feet above sea level water boils at 97.8°C. At sea level, the boiling point is 100°C. What is the formula showing the relationship between w and h? By how much is the boiling point of water changed when the elevation is increased by 100 feet?

EXPONENTS AND RADICALS

42. Positive Integral Exponents

In Article **8**, the symbol a^r was defined for positive integral values of r. Thus a^r is the product of the number a by itself r times, or

$$a^r = aaa \cdots \text{to } r \text{ factors.}$$

As a consequence of this definition, we have the following five laws of exponents.

I. $$a^r a^s = a^{r+s}.$$

Illustrations: $5^3 \cdot 5^4 = 5^7$, $3 \cdot 3^2 \cdot 3^3 \cdot 3^5 = 3^{11}$.

II. $$\frac{a^r}{a^s} = a^{r-s}, \ (r > s);$$

and $$\frac{a^r}{a^s} = \frac{1}{a^{s-r}}, \ (r < s).$$

Illustrations: $\dfrac{5^6}{5^4} = 5^2$, $\dfrac{5^4}{5^6} = \dfrac{1}{5^2}$.

III. $$(a^r)^s = a^{rs}.$$

Illustration: $(3^4)^5 = 3^{20}$.

IV. $$(abc \cdots)^r = a^r b^r c^r \cdots.$$

Illustration: $(3 \cdot 5 \cdot 7 \cdot 4)^2 = 3^2 \cdot 5^2 \cdot 7^2 \cdot 4^2$.

V. $$\left(\frac{a}{b}\right)^r = \frac{a^r}{b^r}.$$

Illustration: $$\left(\frac{3}{7}\right)^3 = \frac{3^3}{7^3}.$$

ORAL EXERCISES

What number should be written in each of the parentheses in the following?

1. $3^4 \cdot 3^5 = 3^{(\ )}$.

2. $(4^2)^3 = 4^{(\ )} = 2^{(\ )}$.

3. $\dfrac{2^3 \cdot 3^2}{2^2 \cdot 3^4} = \dfrac{2^{(1)}}{3^{(2)}}$.

4. $\left(\dfrac{3^5}{3^3}\right)^4 = 3^{(\ )}$.

5. $\left(\dfrac{9}{8}\right)^3 \cdot \left(\dfrac{4}{3}\right)^4 = 2^{(\ )} \cdot 3^{(\ )}$.

Perform the indicated operations and simplify the results when possible. Fractions should be reduced to lowest terms.

6. $(a^3b^2)(a^2b^7)$.

7. $(4a^3b^5)^3$.

8. $\dfrac{a^3b^2}{a^2b^7}$.

9. $\dfrac{8h^{n+4}}{4h^3}$.

10. $x^{a+3} \cdot x^{a-2}$.

11. $\dfrac{x^{a+3}}{x^{a-2}}$.

12. $\dfrac{x^{2a+3}}{x^{a+1}}$.

13. $\dfrac{18x^2z^5}{6xyz^3}$.

14. $\dfrac{4a^3b^2c^4}{14a^2b^5}$.

15. $(-2x^3y^5)^2$.

16. $(-3x^2y)^3$.

17. $(-x^3y^2)^{2k+1}$.

18. $\dfrac{(-10x^2y^5)^3}{(-5x^3y^2)^5}$.

19. $\dfrac{(-6x^4y^7)^2}{(4xy^3)^3}$.

20. $(3a^n)^3$.

21. $(2a^2b^2)^n$.

22. $(2a^nb^{3n})^2$.

23. $(2a^nb^{2n})^n$.

24. $\dfrac{a^nb^{3n}}{a^{4n}b^{2n}}$.

25. $\dfrac{a^{2n}b^n}{a^{3n}b^3c^2}$.

WRITTEN EXERCISES

Simplify the following:

1. $\left(\dfrac{10x^2}{y}\right)^3\left(\dfrac{y^3}{5x}\right)^2$

2. $\left(\dfrac{10x^2}{y}\right)^3 \div \left(\dfrac{2x^2}{y}\right)^2$.

3. $\dfrac{1}{(2a)^2} - \dfrac{1}{a^2}\left(\dfrac{b}{a}\right) + \left(\dfrac{b}{a^2}\right)^2$.

4. $\left(\dfrac{a^2}{x^3}\right)^n\left(\dfrac{b^2}{y^3}\right)^n\left(\dfrac{x^ny^n}{ab^n}\right)^3$.

5. $\dfrac{x^{r+s}y^r - x^sy^{r+2s}}{x^r - y^s}$.

6. $\dfrac{(b-a)^2}{(a^2-b^2)}$.

7. $\dfrac{a^3-b^3}{(b-a)^3}$.

8. $\dfrac{(2a-b)^{5n}}{(b-2a)^{2n}}$.

9. $\dfrac{(2a-b)^{5n}}{(b-2a)^{3n}}$.

10. $\dfrac{18x^{3a-2b}y^{6a+5}}{9x^{2a-6b}y^{4a+2}}$.

11. $\dfrac{x^6 - y^6}{(x^3 + y^3)^2} \div \dfrac{(y - x)^3}{x^3 + y^3}$.

12. Find the value of $\dfrac{2}{x} + \dfrac{3}{x^2} + \dfrac{4}{x^3} + \dfrac{5}{x^4}$ when $x = 10$.

13. Establish the laws of exponents II, III, IV, V, stating at each step the principle used.

14. State the five laws of exponents in words.

43. Meaning of $a^{\frac{1}{q}}$

The proofs of the above five laws of exponents assume that the exponents are positive integers. According to the definition of a^r (Art. **42**), such an expression as $a^{\frac{1}{3}}$ has no meaning whatever. If we use such expressions, we must first give them a meaning. It is convenient to define them in such a way that the laws for positive integral exponents hold also for fractional exponents.

Assuming Law I, Article **42,** to hold, we shall have

$$a^{\frac{1}{3}} \cdot a^{\frac{1}{3}} \cdot a^{\frac{1}{3}} = a^{\frac{1}{3}+\frac{1}{3}+\frac{1}{3}} = a.$$

Assuming that some number exists whose third power is a, we shall denote it by $a^{\frac{1}{3}}$. Another way of writing $a^{\frac{1}{3}}$ is $\sqrt[3]{a}$, which is read "the cube root of a." In general, if q is a positive integer,

$$a^{\frac{1}{q}} \cdot a^{\frac{1}{q}} \cdot a^{\frac{1}{q}} \cdots \text{to } q \text{ factors} = a^{\frac{1}{q}+\frac{1}{q}+\frac{1}{q}+ \cdots \text{ to } q \text{ terms}} = a,$$

and $a^{\frac{1}{q}}$ means a number whose qth power is a. Another way of writing $a^{\frac{1}{q}}$ is $\sqrt[q]{a}$, which is read "the qth root of a."

Thus, the fractional exponent $\dfrac{1}{q}$ serves the same purpose as the radical sign $\sqrt[q]{\ }$.

44. Meaning of $a^{\frac{p}{q}}$

According to Law I, Article **42**, if p and q are positive integers,

$$a^{\frac{1}{q}} \cdot a^{\frac{1}{q}} \cdot a^{\frac{1}{q}} \cdots \text{to } p \text{ factors} = a^{\frac{1}{q}+\frac{1}{q}+\frac{1}{q}+ \cdots \text{ to } p \text{ terms}} = a^{\frac{p}{q}},$$

and $a^{\frac{p}{q}}$ means **the pth power of the qth root of a.**

That is,
$$a^{\frac{p}{q}} = (\sqrt[q]{a})^p.$$

45. Principal Roots

It will be seen later (Art. **110**) that any number a has q distinct qth roots. Thus, the number 4 has the two square roots ± 2. The number -27 has three cube roots, one of which is -3. We shall define the **principal qth root of a real number a** as follows:

1. If $a > 0$, the one positive real number b which is such that $b^q = a$, is called the principal qth root of a.

2. If $a < 0$ and q is an odd integer, the single negative real number $-c$, which is such that $(-c)^q = a$, is called the principal qth root of a.

3. If $a < 0$ and q is an even integer, the qth root of a shall remain undefined, and this case will be excluded in the following discussion.

The symbols $a^{\frac{1}{q}}$ and $\sqrt[q]{a}$ shall represent the principal qth root of a as defined above.

Assuming the first law of exponents to hold, we have

$$a^{\frac{p}{q}} \cdot a^{\frac{p}{q}} \cdot a^{\frac{p}{q}} \cdots \text{ to } q \text{ factors} = a^{\frac{pq}{q}} = a^p.$$

Hence
$$\left(a^{\frac{p}{q}}\right)^q = a^p \quad \text{and} \quad a^{\frac{p}{q}} = \sqrt[q]{a^p}.$$

Thus so long as we consider only principal roots, we have

$$a^{\frac{p}{q}} = \sqrt[q]{a^p} = (\sqrt[q]{a})^p.$$

Without this restriction to principal roots, it will be seen from the following illustration that the pth power of a qth root of a number is not necessarily equal to the qth root of the pth power:

$(4^{\frac{1}{2}})^4 = 16$, while the square root of 4^4 may be either $+16$ or -16.

46. Meaning of the Zero Exponent

In order that the first law of exponents hold for an exponent zero, it is necessary that

$$a^0 \cdot a^m = a^{0+m},$$

or
$$a^0 \cdot a^m = a^m \tag{1}$$

But by equation (3) of Article **4**, we have

$$1 \cdot a^m = a^m. \tag{2}$$

In order that equations (1) and (2) be consistent, we must define

$$a^0 = 1, \ a \neq 0.$$

That is, any number a with the exponent 0 is equal to 1, provided a itself is not 0.

Query: Why must $a = 0$ be excluded from the above discussion?

47. Meaning of a Negative Exponent

Let $n = -m$, where m is a positive number. If the first law of exponents is to hold, then

$$a^m \cdot a^{-m} = a^{m-m} = a^0,$$

or
$$a^m \cdot a^{-m} = 1, \ a \neq 0. \tag{1}$$

But by equation (4) of Article **4**, we have

$$a^m \cdot \frac{1}{a^m} = 1, \ a \neq 0. \tag{2}$$

If equations (1) and (2) are to be consistent, we must define

$$a^{-m} = \frac{1}{a^m}, \ a \neq 0;$$

and
$$a^n = \frac{1}{a^{-n}}, \ a \neq 0.$$

That is, an expression containing negative exponents may be reduced to one containing only positive exponents.

Illustration 1. $\quad \dfrac{2^2 \cdot 3^{-4}}{7 \cdot 5^{-2}} = \dfrac{2^2 \cdot 3^{-4}}{7 \cdot 5^{-2}} \cdot \dfrac{3^4 \cdot 5^2}{3^4 \cdot 5^2} = \dfrac{2^2 \cdot 5^2}{7 \cdot 3^4}.$

Illustration 2. $\quad \dfrac{x^{-4} - y^{-2}}{x^{-2} + y^{-1}} = \dfrac{x^{-4} - y^{-2}}{x^{-2} + y^{-1}} \cdot \dfrac{x^4 \cdot y^2}{x^4 \cdot y^2}$

$$= \frac{y^2 - x^4}{x^2 y^2 + x^4 y} = \frac{y - x^2}{x^2 y}.$$

We have now found meanings for fractional, zero, and negative exponents consistent with the first law of exponents. To give logical completeness, it is necessary to show that the meanings are consistent * with all the laws of exponents, but we shall assume this.

* See Chrystal's *Algebra*, Fifth Edition, Part I, p. 182.

ORAL EXERCISES

Simplify the following expressions.

1. $(36)^{\frac{1}{2}}$.
2. $(0.36)^{\frac{1}{2}}$.
3. $(0.36)^{-\frac{1}{2}}$.
4. $(2^{-12})^{\frac{1}{4}}$.
5. $[(16)^{\frac{1}{4}}]^{-3}$.
6. $[(16)^{-\frac{1}{4}}]^{3}$.
7. $3x^0$.
8. $(3x)^0$.
9. $6 \cdot 3^{-1}$.
10. $(20)^{\frac{1}{2}}(4)^{-\frac{1}{2}}$.
11. $\left(\dfrac{1}{5}\right)^{-2}$.
12. $\left(\dfrac{3}{2}\right)^{-3}$.

13. $\left(\dfrac{16}{25}\right)^{-\frac{1}{2}}$.
14. $\left(\dfrac{8}{125}\right)^{-\frac{1}{3}}$.
15. $\left(-\dfrac{32}{x^{10}}\right)^{\frac{1}{5}}$.
16. $\left(-\dfrac{32}{x^{10}}\right)^{-\frac{1}{5}}$.
17. $2^{-1} \cdot x^3 \cdot x^{-3}$.
18. $x^{\frac{2}{3}} \cdot x^{\frac{4}{3}} \cdot x^{-2}$.
19. $(x+y)^{-1} \cdot (x+y)^2$.
20. $(x^2 + 2y^2 + 8)^0$.

WRITTEN EXERCISES

Perform the indicated operations and simplify.

1. $(x^{\frac{1}{3}})^6$.
2. $(a^{\frac{2}{5}}b^{\frac{3}{5}}c^{\frac{1}{2}})^{10}$.
3. $(27a^{12}b^6c^9)^{\frac{1}{3}}$.
4. $(x^{0.3}y^{0.5})^{0.2}$.
5. $(-a^3y^9z^{-6})^{\frac{5}{3}}$.
6. $(a^0x^{\frac{2}{3}}y^{-\frac{5}{6}})^{-6}$.
7. $\left(\dfrac{p^{1.42}}{p}\right)^{\frac{1}{3}}$.

8. $\left(\dfrac{a^{2n+1}}{a^{n+1}}\right)^{\frac{1}{n}}$.
9. $\left(\dfrac{1}{a^{n-1}} \cdot \dfrac{1}{a^{n+1}}\right)^{\frac{1}{n}}$.
10. $\dfrac{2^{n+1}}{(2^n)^{n-1}} \div \dfrac{4^{n+1}}{(2^{n-1})^{n+1}}$.
11. $\left[x \cdot (x \cdot x^{\frac{1}{3}})^{\frac{1}{3}}\right]^{\frac{1}{3}}$.
12. $(x^{\frac{1}{2}} + y^{\frac{1}{2}})(x^{\frac{1}{2}} - y^{\frac{1}{2}})$.

13. $(x^{-\frac{1}{2}} + y^{-\frac{1}{2}})(x^{-\frac{1}{2}} - y^{-\frac{1}{2}})$.
14. $(a^{\frac{2}{3}} + 2a^{\frac{1}{3}} + 4)(a^{\frac{1}{3}} - 2)$.
15. $(x^{\frac{1}{4}} - 1)(x^{\frac{1}{4}} + 1)(x^{\frac{1}{2}} + 1)$.
16. $(x + 27) \div (x^{\frac{1}{3}} + 3)$.
17. $(x^{-5} - 32) \div (x^{-1} - 2)$.
18. $(x^4 + 4y^{-4}) \div (x^2 - 2xy^{-1} + 2y^{-2})$.
19. $(x^{\frac{5}{2}} + x^2 + x^{\frac{3}{2}} + x + x^{\frac{1}{2}} + x^0) \div (x^{\frac{3}{2}} + x^{\frac{1}{2}} + x^{-\frac{1}{2}})$.

Change the following expressions into equal expressions having as small a positive integer as possible with a fractional exponent.

20. $(16)^{\frac{1}{3}} = (8 \cdot 2)^{\frac{1}{3}} = (2^3 \cdot 2)^{\frac{1}{3}} = 2 \cdot 2^{\frac{1}{3}}$.

21. $(32)^{\frac{1}{4}}$.   **24.** $(27,000)^{\frac{1}{2}}$.

22. $(72)^{\frac{1}{2}}$.   **25.** $(20,000)^{\frac{2}{3}}$.

23. $(250)^{\frac{1}{3}}$.   **26.** $(2,187)^{\frac{1}{6}}$.

Introduce the coefficients of the following parentheses into the parentheses.

27. $2(3)^{\frac{1}{2}} = 4^{\frac{1}{2}} \cdot 3^{\frac{1}{2}} = (12)^{\frac{1}{2}}$.

28. $2(5)^{\frac{1}{3}}$.   **30.** $2(7^2)^{\frac{1}{5}}$.

29. $9(6)^{\frac{2}{3}}$.   **31.** $4(3)^{\frac{2}{3}}$.

Calculate the value of the following.

32. $\left(\dfrac{1}{2}\right)^{-2} - (2)^{-2}$.   **37.** $\left[4^{-1} - \left(\dfrac{1}{4}\right)^{-1}\right]$.

33. $-(2)^{-2} - (-2)^{-2}$.

38. $\left[4^{-1} - \left(\dfrac{1}{4}\right)^{-1}\right]^{-1}$

34. $\left(\dfrac{1}{2}\right)^{-2} - 2^2$.

39. $\left[4^{-1} - \dfrac{1}{4}\right]^{-1}$.

35. $\left(\dfrac{1}{2}\right)^{-2} - (-2)^{-2}$.

36. $\left[4 - \dfrac{1}{4}\right]^{-1}$.

Express in terms of positive exponents and simplify.

40. $(2x)^{-1} - 3x^{-2}$.

41. $(x + y)^{-1}$.

42. $(x^{-1} + y^{-1})^{-1}$.

44. $\left(\dfrac{x^{-3}y^{-3}}{x^{-3} + y^{-2}}\right)^{-1}$.

43. $\dfrac{2x^{-2}y^3}{3^{-1}xy^{-2}}$.

45. $\left(\dfrac{x^{-2} - y^{-2}}{x^{-1} - y^{-1}}\right)^{-3}$.

46. $\dfrac{(x + y)^{-1} + (x - y)^{-1}}{(x + y)^{-1} - (x - y)^{-1}}$.

47. $(3 + 2x)^{\frac{1}{2}} + x(3 + 2x)^{-\frac{1}{2}}$.

48. $\dfrac{(2 - 3t)^{\frac{1}{3}}(2 + 3t)^{-\frac{2}{3}} + (2 + 3t)^{\frac{1}{3}}(2 - 3t)^{-\frac{2}{3}}}{(2 - 3t)^{\frac{2}{3}}}$.

49. Find the value of $y = x^3 + 2x^2 + 4x - 11 \cdot 7^{\frac{1}{2}}$ when $x = 7^{\frac{1}{2}}$.

50. If $2^{\frac{1}{2}}$ and $5^{\frac{1}{2}}$ are substituted for x in the expression

$$x^5 - x^4 - 7x^3 + 7x^2 + 10x,$$

show that the results reduce to the same number.

51. If $pv^{\frac{3}{2}} = 10,000$, calculate p when $v = 25$.

52. If $t = \dfrac{(2s)^{\frac{1}{2}}}{g^{\frac{1}{2}}}$, find t when $s = 400$ and $g = 32$.

53. The horsepower, H, generated by a water wheel is given by the formula

$$H^{\frac{1}{2}} = 53.25 \frac{F^{\frac{5}{4}}}{n},$$

where F is the fall of the water in feet and n is the number of revolutions of the wheel per minute. Calculate H when $F = 16$ and $n = 160$.

Scientific notation. A number is said to be written in scientific notation if it is expressed as the product of a number between 1 and 10 and the appropriate power of 10. For example, 125,000,000 $= 1.25 \times 10^8$ and 0.000,003,502 $= 3.502 \times 10^{-6}$.

54. Write the following numbers in scientific notation: 0.000,02; 1,500,000,000; 0.000,000,027; 2,005,000,000.

55. The number of molecules in a pint of air under standard atmospheric conditions at 0°C is about 14,000,000,000,000,000,-000,000. Write this number in scientific notation.

56. The velocity of light is 29,986,000,000 centimeters per second. Write the velocity in scientific notation.

57. Two spherical particles, each one gram in mass, whose centers are one centimeter apart, attract each other with a force of 0.000,000,066,6 dyne. Express this number in scientific notation.

58. Some authorities say that the mass of a hydrogen atom is 1.663×10^{-24} grams. How would this number be written in ordinary decimal notation?

59. The radius of the first Bohr ring of hydrogen is given as 0.5305×10^{-8} centimeters. Write this number in ordinary decimal notation. Write the number in scientific notation.

60. First estimate and then evaluate the product of 3.40×10^{10} and 2.10×10^{-5}. Try the problem if the numbers are expressed in ordinary decimal notation.

61. First estimate and then evaluate the quotient of 1.012×10^6 by 1.296×10^{-3}. Try the problem if the numbers are expressed in ordinary decimal notation.

62. Show that $\dfrac{\frac{1}{3}y^{-\frac{1}{3}}+\frac{1}{3}y^{\frac{1}{3}}x^{-\frac{2}{3}}}{x^{\frac{1}{3}}}$ reduces to $\dfrac{a^{\frac{2}{3}}}{3x^{\frac{4}{3}}y^{\frac{1}{3}}}$, when $x^{\frac{2}{3}}+y^{\frac{2}{3}}=a^{\frac{2}{3}}$.

63. Show that $\dfrac{\dfrac{1}{2}+\dfrac{1}{2}y^{\frac{1}{2}}x^{-\frac{1}{2}}}{x}$ reduces to $\dfrac{a^{\frac{1}{2}}}{2x^{\frac{3}{2}}}$, if $x^{\frac{1}{2}}+y^{\frac{1}{2}}=a^{\frac{1}{2}}$.

48. Radicals

The symbol $\sqrt[n]{a}$ is called a **radical**. The number a is called the **radicand** and n is called the **index** of the root. The radical is said to be of the nth **order**. In accordance with Article **45**, the symbols $\sqrt[n]{a}$ and $a^{\frac{1}{n}}$ are equivalent and represent the principal nth root of a.

Illustration 1. $\sqrt{3}$ is a radical of the second order. The radicand is 3 and the index of the root is 2.

Illustration 2. $\sqrt[3]{64}$ is a radical of the third order. The radicand is 64 and the index of the root is 3.

Illustration 3. $\sqrt[11]{a+b}$ is a radical of order eleven. The radicand is $a+b$ and the index of the root is 11.

ORAL EXERCISES

1. Give the index of each of the radicals $\sqrt{6}$, $\sqrt[3]{a}$, $\sqrt[7]{a+b}$.

2. Give the order of each of the radicals $\sqrt{6}$, $\sqrt[3]{a}$, $\sqrt[7]{a+b}$.

3. What is the radicand in each of the radicals $\sqrt{6}$, $\sqrt[3]{a}$, $\sqrt[7]{a+b}$.

4. Fill the blanks in $(\sqrt{3})^2 = $ ——, $(\sqrt[5]{7})^5 = $ ——, $(\sqrt[8]{27})^8 = $ ——.

5. Express $\sqrt[3]{a^2}$ by means of fractional exponents.

49. Changes in the Form of a Radical

Changes in the form of a radical may often be made by use of the definition of the nth root of a number, say of a, which implies that $(\sqrt[n]{a})^n = a$, and by the use of the following equalities:

$$\text{I.} \quad \sqrt[n]{a} \cdot \sqrt[n]{b} = \sqrt[n]{ab}.$$

$$\text{II.} \quad \frac{\sqrt[n]{a}}{\sqrt[n]{b}} = \sqrt[n]{\frac{a}{b}}.$$

$$\text{III.} \quad \sqrt[m]{\sqrt[n]{a}} = \sqrt[mn]{a}.$$

The truth of these equalities is apparent from the laws of exponents. Thus,

$$\sqrt[n]{a} \cdot \sqrt[n]{b} = a^{\frac{1}{n}} \cdot b^{\frac{1}{n}} = (ab)^{\frac{1}{n}} = \sqrt[n]{ab},$$

$$\frac{\sqrt[n]{a}}{\sqrt[n]{b}} = \frac{a^{\frac{1}{n}}}{b^{\frac{1}{n}}} = \left(\frac{a}{b}\right)^{\frac{1}{n}} = \sqrt[n]{\frac{a}{b}},$$

$$\sqrt[m]{\sqrt[n]{a}} = \left(a^{\frac{1}{n}}\right)^{\frac{1}{m}} = a^{\frac{1}{mn}} = \sqrt[mn]{a}.$$

Oral Exercise. In so far as possible, state I, II, and III in words.

Radicals are frequently changed to advantage in one or more of the following ways:

(1) By removing factors from the radicand.

Illustration 1. $\sqrt{75} = \sqrt{5^2 \cdot 3} = \sqrt{5^2} \cdot \sqrt{3} = 5\sqrt{3}.$

Illustration 2. $\sqrt[3]{24a^4b^3} = \sqrt[3]{2^3 \cdot 3a^4b^3} = \sqrt[3]{2^3a^3b^3} \cdot \sqrt[3]{3a} = 2ab\sqrt[3]{3a}.$

(2) By introducing a coefficient under the radical sign.

Illustration 1. $7\sqrt{2} = \sqrt{7^2} \cdot \sqrt{2} = \sqrt{7^2 \cdot 2} = \sqrt{98}.$

Illustration 2. $2a^2b\sqrt[3]{abx} = \sqrt[3]{8a^6b^3} \cdot \sqrt[3]{abx} = \sqrt[3]{8a^7b^4x}.$

(3) By reducing a radical with a fractional radicand to one whose radicand is integral.

Illustration 1. $\sqrt{\dfrac{2}{5}} = \sqrt{\dfrac{2}{5} \cdot \dfrac{5}{5}} = \dfrac{\sqrt{10}}{\sqrt{25}} = \dfrac{\sqrt{10}}{5} = \dfrac{1}{5}\sqrt{10}.$

Illustration 2. $\sqrt{\dfrac{a}{b}} = \sqrt{\dfrac{a}{b} \cdot \dfrac{b}{b}} = \dfrac{\sqrt{ab}}{\sqrt{b^2}} = \dfrac{\sqrt{ab}}{b}.$

This process is called **rationalizing the denominator** as no radical remains in the denominator.

(4) By reducing a radical to lower order.

Illustration 1. $\sqrt[4]{100} = \sqrt[4]{2^2 \cdot 5^2} = \sqrt{\sqrt{2^2 \cdot 5^2}} = \sqrt{2 \cdot 5} = \sqrt{10}.$

Exercise. Carry out an equivalent process in fractional exponents for $(100)^{\frac{1}{4}}$.

Illustration 2. $\sqrt[6]{8a^3b^{3n}} = (2^3 \cdot a^3b^{3n})^{\frac{1}{6}} = 2^{\frac{1}{2}}a^{\frac{1}{2}}b^{\frac{n}{2}} = \sqrt{2ab^n}.$

A radical is said to be in its **simplest form:** (1) when the radicand contains no factor to a power whose exponent equals the order of the radical, (2) when the radicand is integral, (3) when the order of the radical is as small as possible.

EXERCISES

Change each of the following to a radical form:

1. $a^{\frac{3}{4}}.$

2. $2a^{\frac{3}{2}}.$

3. $(3a)^{\frac{2}{3}}.$

4. $a^{\frac{3}{2}}b^{\frac{5}{2}}c^{\frac{2}{3}}.$

5. $(a+b)^{\frac{1}{4}}.$

6. $a^{\frac{1}{4}} + b^{\frac{1}{4}}.$

7. $x^{\frac{2}{3}}y^{\frac{5}{6}}.$

8. $x^{\frac{2}{3}}y^{\frac{1}{2}}.$

9. $(a^{\frac{1}{2}} + b^{\frac{1}{2}})^{\frac{1}{2}}.$

10. $(a^{\frac{5}{2}})^{\frac{1}{4}}.$

Change each of the following to a form involving exponents instead of radicals:

11. $\sqrt[3]{a^2}$.

12. $\sqrt{a^3b^2c^4}$.

13. $\sqrt[6]{a^2b^3}$.

14. $\sqrt[3]{-27x^{-5}y^7z^2}$.

15. $\sqrt[3]{\dfrac{x^9y^6}{a^{12}b^3}}$.

16. $\sqrt[5]{\dfrac{32x^8}{y^{12}z^9}}$.

17. $\sqrt[3]{\sqrt{a^4}}$.

18. $\sqrt{\sqrt[3]{a^4}}$.

19. $\sqrt{a^3b} \cdot \sqrt[3]{ab^2}$.

20. $\sqrt[4]{8x^3y^2} \cdot \sqrt{2xy^3}$.

Introduce the coefficient under the radical sign:

21. $3\sqrt[3]{3}$.

22. $5\sqrt{3}$.

23. $x\sqrt[4]{y}$.

24. $10\sqrt[3]{0.01}$.

25. $0.01\sqrt[3]{10,000}$.

26. $2\sqrt{a+b}$.

27. $(2+x)\sqrt[3]{2+x}$.

28. $-2a\sqrt[3]{ab}$.

29. $-(x-5)\sqrt[5]{5-x}$.

30. $\dfrac{\sqrt{a-b}}{b-a}$.

Change each of the following to radicals of lower order:

31. $\sqrt[6]{81}$.

Solution: $\sqrt[6]{81} = \sqrt[3]{\sqrt{81}} = \sqrt[3]{9}$.

32. $\sqrt[4]{169}$.

33. $\sqrt[6]{27}$.

34. $\sqrt[8]{16}$.

35. $\sqrt[6]{0.001}$.

Change the following to radicals of the same order:

36. $\sqrt{a}$, $\sqrt[3]{a}$.

Solution: $\sqrt{a} = a^{\frac{1}{2}} = a^{\frac{3}{6}} = \sqrt[6]{a^3}$.

$\sqrt[3]{a} = a^{\frac{1}{3}} = a^{\frac{2}{6}} = \sqrt[6]{a^2}$.

37. $2\sqrt{xy}$, $5\sqrt[3]{xy^2z^3}$.

Solution: $2\sqrt{xy} = 2x^{\frac{1}{2}}y^{\frac{1}{2}} = 2x^{\frac{3}{6}}y^{\frac{3}{6}} = 2\sqrt[6]{x^3y^3}$.

$5\sqrt[3]{xy^2z^3} = 5x^{\frac{1}{3}}y^{\frac{2}{3}}z = 5x^{\frac{2}{6}}y^{\frac{4}{6}}z^{\frac{6}{6}} = 5\sqrt[6]{x^2y^4z^6}$.

38. $\sqrt{2}$, $\sqrt[3]{2}$.

39. $\sqrt{x}$, $\sqrt[5]{y}$.

40. $3\sqrt{2}$, $5\sqrt[3]{3}$, $2\sqrt[6]{5}$.

41. $\sqrt[3]{x^2}$, $\sqrt{x^3}$.

42. $\sqrt{a^3b^5}$, $\sqrt[4]{ab^3}$.

43. $2\sqrt[3]{x^4y^2z^5}$, $3\sqrt[4]{x^2y^3z^5}$.

In each of the following pairs, show which radical is the larger.

44. $\sqrt[3]{3}$, $\sqrt{2}$.

45. $\sqrt[4]{72}$, $\sqrt[4]{18}$.

46. $\sqrt[3]{-3}$, $\sqrt[5]{-7}$.

47. $\sqrt[3]{-2}$, $\sqrt[7]{-5}$.

Reduce each radical to simplest form:

48. $\sqrt[3]{16}$.

49. $\sqrt{54}$.

50. $\sqrt{\dfrac{1}{3}}$.

51. $\sqrt[3]{\dfrac{-1}{25}}$.

52. $\sqrt[3]{0.125}$.

53. $\sqrt[3]{1.25}$.

54. $\sqrt[3]{3\sqrt{3}}$.

55. $\sqrt{5\sqrt[3]{5}}$.

56. $\sqrt[4]{4x^2 - 4xy + y^2}$.

57. $\sqrt[6]{(a + b)^2}$.

58. $\sqrt[6]{x^3 - 6x^2 + 12x - 8}$.

59. $\sqrt{x^4 - 2x^3y + 2x^2y^2 - 2xy^3 + y^4}$.

60. $\sqrt[3]{-\dfrac{54}{32}}$.

61. $\sqrt[5]{\dfrac{a^3}{16c^{10}}}$.

62. $\sqrt{20a^3b^2}$.

63. $\sqrt[3]{216x^5y^7}$.

64. $\sqrt{64a^{4n}b^{2n^2}c^6}$.

65. $\sqrt[n]{a^{4n}b^{2n^2}c^{6n^2-2n}}$.

50. Rational and Irrational Numbers

A **rational number** is defined as one that can be expressed as the quotient of two integers. A real number which cannot be thus expressed is called an **irrational number**. (See Articles **1** and **2**.)

Thus, 16, $\dfrac{1}{2}$, and $\dfrac{19}{23}$ are rational numbers; $\sqrt{2}$,* $\sqrt[3]{2}$, $\sqrt{3}$, $\sqrt{5}$, $1 + \sqrt{5}$, and $9^{\frac{1}{3}}$ are irrational numbers.

Any irrational number can be enclosed between two rational numbers that differ from one another by as small a number as we please.

* To show that $\sqrt{2}$ cannot be expressed as the quotient of two integers, suppose it is possible that

$$\sqrt{2} = \frac{m}{n},$$

where $\dfrac{m}{n}$ is a rational fraction in its lowest terms. At least one of the numbers m or n is odd. Clearing of fractions and squaring both sides, we get

$$2n^2 = m^2.$$

From this equation, we see that m^2 is an even number. Hence m is an even number. If m is even, m^2 contains the factor 4. Hence n^2 is an even number, and n is itself even. This is contrary to the hypothesis that $\dfrac{m}{n}$ is a fraction in its lowest terms.

This proof is found in Euclid (about 300 B.C.), and is supposed to be due to a much earlier mathematician than Euclid.

Thus, we may write,

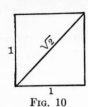

FIG. 10

$$1 \quad < \sqrt{2} < 2.$$
$$1.4 \quad < \sqrt{2} < 1.5.$$
$$1.41 < \sqrt{2} < 1.42.$$

Either of the two sequences of numbers in the two outer columns determines $\sqrt{2}$ in much the same way that .3, .33, .333, $\cdots$, determine $\frac{1}{3}$.

As a geometrical illustration of an irrational number we may take the diagonal of a square whose side is 1.

ORAL EXERCISES

1. Tell which of the following numbers are rational: 5, $\frac{6}{0.3}$, $\sqrt{64}$, 0.5, $\sqrt{10}$, 0.444, $\sqrt{2} + 1$.

2. Give an example of a rational number that is not an integer.

3. Can every integer be expressed as the quotient of two integers? Explain.

4. Figure 10 illustrates how a line $\sqrt{2}$ units long may be constructed. Using this result, construct a line $\sqrt{3}$ units long.

51. Addition and Subtraction of Radicals

Two radicals which have the same order and the same radicand are said to be **similar.**

Thus, $5\sqrt{2}$ and $-2\sqrt{2}$ are similar; so also are $\sqrt[3]{81}$ and $2b\sqrt[3]{3a^3}$ since $\sqrt[3]{81} = 3\sqrt[3]{3}$ and $2b\sqrt[3]{3a^3} = 2ab\sqrt[3]{3}$.

On the other hand, $\sqrt{2}$ and $\sqrt{3}$ are dissimilar; so are $\sqrt{2}$ and $\sqrt[3]{2}$.

The algebraic sum of similar radicals equals the common radical factor multiplied by the sum of its coefficients.

Illustration 1. $8\sqrt{2} + 3\sqrt{2} - 4\sqrt{2} = (8 + 3 - 4)\sqrt{2} = 7\sqrt{2}.$

Illustration 2. $\sqrt{75} + 3\sqrt{12} - 5\sqrt{27}$
$$= \sqrt{25 \cdot 3} + 3\sqrt{4 \cdot 3} - 5\sqrt{9 \cdot 3}$$
$$= 5\sqrt{3} + 6\sqrt{3} - 15\sqrt{3}$$
$$= -4\sqrt{3}.$$

Illustration 3. $\dfrac{1}{2}\sqrt{a^3} + 2b\sqrt{\dfrac{b^2}{a}} - 3b\sqrt{25a^5b^2}$

$$= \frac{1}{2}\sqrt{a^2 \cdot a} + 2b\sqrt{\frac{ab^2}{a^2}} - 3b\sqrt{25a^4b^2a}$$

$$= \frac{a}{2}\sqrt{a} + \frac{2b^2}{a}\sqrt{a} - 15a^2b^2\sqrt{a}$$

$$= \left(\frac{a}{2} + \frac{2b^2}{a} - 15a^2b^2\right)\sqrt{a}.$$

EXERCISES

Perform the indicated operations and simplify.

1. $3\sqrt{2} + 5\sqrt{2}.$

2. $4\sqrt{3} - 7\sqrt{3} + 9\sqrt{3}.$

3. $2\sqrt{18} + \sqrt{8} - 3\sqrt{50}.$

4. $2\sqrt{125} - \sqrt{63} + 4\sqrt{175} - 3\sqrt{45}.$

5. $5\sqrt[3]{32} - 3\sqrt[3]{108}.$

6. $4\sqrt[3]{81} - 5\sqrt[3]{48} - 5\sqrt[3]{24}.$

7. $2\sqrt{\dfrac{2}{3}} - \sqrt{54} - 2\sqrt{\dfrac{27}{8}} + 5\sqrt{6}.$

8. $\sqrt{8x} - \sqrt{2x} + \sqrt{50x}.$

9. $\sqrt[4]{81y^5} - 2\sqrt[4]{x^8y^9} + \sqrt[4]{yz^{12}}.$

10. $\sqrt[3]{ab^2} - 5\sqrt[3]{a^4b^5c^6} + \sqrt[3]{64b^{11}c^3}.$

11. $\sqrt[5]{64a^6b^7c^{12}} + abc\sqrt[5]{486ab^2c^2} - \sqrt[5]{a^{11}b^2c^7}.$

12. $\sqrt[3]{\dfrac{x^2}{y}} + \sqrt[3]{\dfrac{y^2}{x}} - \sqrt[3]{x^2y^2}.$

13. $\sqrt{(a-b)^3} - \sqrt{a^3 - a^2b} + \sqrt{ab^2 - b^3}.$

14. $\sqrt{a} + \dfrac{1}{\sqrt{a}} + \sqrt{a^3 + 2a^2 + a}.$

15. $a\sqrt{\dfrac{a}{b}} - 2\sqrt{ab} + b\sqrt{\dfrac{b}{a}}.$

16. $\sqrt{x^4y^2 + x^2y^4} - 2\sqrt{x^4 + x^2y^2} + 3\sqrt{x^2y^2 + y^4}$
$- \sqrt{(x+y)^2(x^2+y^2)}.$

17. $\sqrt[3]{(x+y)^4} - \sqrt[3]{x^4 + x^3y} - \sqrt[3]{8xy^3 + 8y^4}.$

18. $2x^{\frac{1}{2}}y^{\frac{1}{2}} - 5x^{\frac{3}{2}}y^{\frac{5}{2}} + 2x^{\frac{1}{2}}y^{\frac{3}{2}}.$

Solution: $2x^{\frac{1}{2}}y^{\frac{1}{2}} - 5x^{\frac{3}{2}}y^{\frac{5}{2}} + 2x^{\frac{1}{2}}y^{\frac{3}{2}} = (2 - 5xy^2 + 2y)x^{\frac{1}{2}}y^{\frac{1}{2}}.$

19. $x^{\frac{4}{3}}y^{\frac{5}{3}} - 3x^{\frac{4}{3}}y^{\frac{2}{3}} + 2x^{\frac{1}{3}}y^{\frac{5}{3}}.$

20. $2a^{\frac{7}{3}}y^{\frac{2}{5}} - 3a^{\frac{1}{3}}y^{\frac{7}{5}}.$

21. $2^{\frac{1}{2}}a^{\frac{3}{2}}b^{\frac{1}{3}} - 50^{\frac{1}{2}}ab^{\frac{5}{6}} + 6\sqrt{2}a^{\frac{1}{2}}b^{\frac{4}{3}}.$

22. $a + 2a^{\frac{1}{2}}b^{\frac{1}{2}} + b.$

23. $a - 3a^{\frac{2}{3}}b^{\frac{1}{3}} + 3a^{\frac{1}{3}}b^{\frac{2}{3}} - b.$

24. $a^{\frac{1}{3}}b^{\frac{1}{4}} - 2a^{\frac{7}{6}}b^{\frac{5}{4}} + a^{\frac{5}{6}}b^{\frac{1}{2}}.$

52. Multiplication of Radicals

The product of two radicals is obtained either by the use of the principle $\sqrt[n]{a} \cdot \sqrt[n]{b} = \sqrt[n]{ab}$ (Art. **49**), or by the use of fractional exponents (Arts. **43, 44, 45**). The following examples will illustrate both of these methods.

Illustration 1. Multiply $\sqrt{3}$ by $\sqrt{5}$.

Solution 1.	$\sqrt{3} \cdot \sqrt{5} = \sqrt{15}.$	(Law I, Art. **49**)
Solution 2.	$\sqrt{3} \cdot \sqrt{5} = 3^{\frac{1}{2}} \cdot 5^{\frac{1}{2}},$	(Art. **43**)
	$= 15^{\frac{1}{2}},$	(Law IV, Art. **42**)
	$= \sqrt{15}.$	

Illustration 2. Multiply $2\sqrt{ab}$ by $5\sqrt[3]{a^2b}$.

Solution 1.
$$2\sqrt{ab} = 2\sqrt[6]{a^3b^3},$$
$$5\sqrt[3]{a^2b} = 5\sqrt[6]{a^4b^2},$$
$$2\sqrt[6]{a^3b^3} \cdot 5\sqrt[6]{a^4b^2} = 10\sqrt[6]{a^7b^5} = 10a\sqrt[6]{ab^5}.$$

Solution 2.
$$2\sqrt{ab} \cdot 5\sqrt[3]{a^2b} = 2a^{\frac{1}{2}}b^{\frac{1}{2}} \cdot 5a^{\frac{2}{3}}b^{\frac{1}{3}},$$
$$= 10a^{\frac{7}{6}}b^{\frac{5}{6}},$$
$$= 10a\sqrt[6]{ab^5}.$$

EXERCISES

Perform the indicated multiplications and simplify as far as possible.

1. $3\sqrt{5} \cdot 2\sqrt{7}.$

2. $5\sqrt{2} \cdot \sqrt{10} \cdot 7\sqrt{15}.$

3. $2\sqrt{a} \cdot 8\sqrt{bc}.$

4. $5\sqrt{ab} \cdot 3\sqrt{bc}.$

5. $\sqrt{x} \cdot \sqrt[3]{x^2}.$

6. $\sqrt{10} \cdot \sqrt[4]{3}.$

7. $\sqrt[5]{9} \cdot \sqrt[5]{27}.$

8. $\sqrt[3]{2} \cdot \sqrt[3]{12} \cdot \sqrt[3]{9}.$

9. $\sqrt{ab} \cdot \sqrt[3]{ab^2}.$

10. $2\sqrt{b} \cdot 3\sqrt[3]{ab^2} \cdot 4\sqrt[4]{a^3b^3}.$

11. $\sqrt[5]{72} \cdot \sqrt[5]{108}.$

12. $\sqrt[3]{128} \cdot \sqrt{1000}.$

13. $xy^{\frac{2}{3}}z^{\frac{1}{4}} \cdot x^{\frac{5}{6}}y^{\frac{3}{4}}z^{\frac{1}{2}} \cdot x^{\frac{3}{2}}y^{\frac{1}{6}}z^{\frac{2}{3}}.$

14. $3x^{-\frac{1}{3}}y^{\frac{1}{2}} \cdot 2x^{\frac{1}{12}}y^{\frac{1}{6}} \cdot x^{\frac{1}{4}}y^{\frac{2}{3}}.$

15. $(-8a^{\frac{2}{3}}b^{\frac{1}{5}})(-5a^{\frac{3}{2}}b^{\frac{3}{10}}).$

16. $(7r^{\frac{5}{8}}s^{\frac{7}{6}})(-3r^{\frac{1}{8}}s^{\frac{1}{3}}).$

17. $x^{-\frac{1}{3}}y^{-\frac{1}{3}}(x^{\frac{2}{3}}y^{\frac{1}{3}} + x^{\frac{1}{3}}y^{\frac{2}{3}}).$

18. $a^{-\frac{3}{2}}b^{-\frac{1}{2}}(2a^{\frac{5}{2}}b^{\frac{3}{2}} + 3a^{\frac{3}{2}}b^{\frac{7}{2}}).$

19. $2\sqrt{3}(\sqrt{3} + \sqrt{2} - 4\sqrt{6}).$

20. $a\sqrt{b}(b\sqrt{a} + \sqrt{ab} - 2a\sqrt{b}).$

21. $(\sqrt{7} - \sqrt{5})(\sqrt{7} + \sqrt{5}).$

22. $(2\sqrt{5} - 3\sqrt{2})(2\sqrt{5} + 3\sqrt{2}).$

23. $(5\sqrt{3} - \sqrt{5})(2\sqrt{3} + 3\sqrt{5}).$

24. $(3\sqrt{5} - 4\sqrt{3})^2.$

25. $(2\sqrt{7} + 8\sqrt{28} - \sqrt{63})^2$

26. $(\sqrt{6} - 2\sqrt{3} + \sqrt{2})^2.$

27. $(2a^{\frac{1}{4}} - 3a^{\frac{1}{6}})^2.$

28. $(a^{\frac{1}{2}} - b^{\frac{1}{4}})^2.$

29. $(a^{\frac{1}{4}} - b^{\frac{1}{4}})(a^{\frac{1}{4}} + b^{\frac{1}{4}})(a^{\frac{1}{2}} + b^{\frac{1}{2}}).$

30. $(a^{\frac{1}{3}} - 2b^{\frac{2}{3}})(a^{\frac{2}{3}} + 2a^{\frac{1}{3}}b^{\frac{2}{3}} + 4b^{\frac{4}{3}}).$

31. $(x^{\frac{3}{2}} - y^{\frac{3}{2}})(x^{\frac{3}{2}} + y^{\frac{3}{2}}).$

32. $(3b\sqrt{a} - 4a\sqrt{b})(2\sqrt{a} + 3\sqrt{b}).$

33. $(a^{\frac{1}{3}} + b^{\frac{1}{3}})^3.$

34. Find the value of $x^2 - 6x - 11$ when $x = 3 - 2\sqrt{5}.$

35. Find the value of $9x^2 + 12x - 5$ when $x = \dfrac{-2 - \sqrt{7}}{3}.$

36. Find the value of $ax^2 + bx + c$ when $x = \dfrac{-b + \sqrt{b^2 - 4ac}}{2a}.$

53. Division of Radicals — Rationalization of Denominators

Division of radicals of the same order may be performed by use of the principle

$$\frac{\sqrt[n]{a}}{\sqrt[n]{b}} = \sqrt[n]{\frac{a}{b}}. \qquad \text{(Art. 49)}$$

If the radicals are not of the same order, they must first be reduced to the same order before the above principle is applied.

Illustration 1. $\dfrac{6\sqrt{6}}{2\sqrt{3}} = 3\sqrt{\dfrac{6}{3}} = 3\sqrt{2}.$

Illustration 2. $\dfrac{3\sqrt{6}}{2\sqrt[3]{3}} = \dfrac{3\sqrt[6]{6^3}}{2\sqrt[6]{3^2}} = \dfrac{3}{2}\sqrt[6]{\dfrac{2^3 \cdot 3^3}{3^2}} = \dfrac{3\sqrt[6]{24}}{2}.$

For purposes of computation it is usually desirable that the denominator of the quotient be made rational. In fact, division of radicals usually becomes a process called **rationalizing the denominator.** The process of rationalizing the denominator is based on the principle

$$\sqrt[q]{a^r} \cdot \sqrt[q]{a^{q-r}} = a$$

and the type products of Article **12.**

Illustration 3. $\dfrac{\sqrt{10}}{\sqrt{7}} = \dfrac{\sqrt{10}\sqrt{7}}{\sqrt{7}\sqrt{7}} = \dfrac{\sqrt{70}}{7}$.

Illustration 4. $\dfrac{\sqrt[3]{14}}{\sqrt[3]{36}} = \dfrac{\sqrt[3]{14} \cdot \sqrt[3]{6}}{\sqrt[3]{36}\sqrt[3]{6}} = \dfrac{\sqrt[3]{84}}{\sqrt[3]{216}} = \dfrac{\sqrt[3]{84}}{6}$.

Illustration 5. $\dfrac{3\sqrt{5} + \sqrt{2}}{2\sqrt{5} - 3\sqrt{2}} = \dfrac{(3\sqrt{5} + \sqrt{2}) \cdot (2\sqrt{5} + 3\sqrt{2})}{(2\sqrt{5} - 3\sqrt{2}) \cdot (2\sqrt{5} + 3\sqrt{2})}$

$= \dfrac{30 + 2\sqrt{10} + 9\sqrt{10} + 6}{20 - 18} = \dfrac{36 + 11\sqrt{10}}{2}$.

EXERCISES

Perform the following divisions, obtaining results with rational denominators.

1. $\sqrt{10} \div \sqrt{2}$.

2. $\sqrt{48} \div \sqrt{3}$.

3. $\sqrt{45} \div \sqrt{5}$.

4. $\sqrt{52} \div \sqrt{8}$.

5. $\sqrt[3]{20} \div \sqrt[3]{4}$.

6. $\sqrt[3]{a^2b^2c} \div \sqrt[3]{ac}$.

7. $9\sqrt{7} \div 3$.

8. $9\sqrt{7} \div 3\sqrt{7}$.

9. $\sqrt{\dfrac{1}{3}} \div \sqrt{\dfrac{3}{2}}$.

10. $\sqrt[3]{\dfrac{20}{49}} \div \sqrt[3]{\dfrac{35}{2}}$.

11. $\sqrt{ab} \div \sqrt[3]{a}$.

12. $\sqrt[3]{x^2y} \div \sqrt{xy^2}$.

13. $\sqrt[5]{8ab^3c^2} \div \sqrt[3]{4a^2bc^2}$.

14. $(\sqrt{15} - 3\sqrt{6}) \div \sqrt{3}$.

15. $(\sqrt{x} - \sqrt[3]{x}) \div \sqrt[4]{x}$.

16. $(3\sqrt{10} + 2\sqrt{15} - 12\sqrt{35}) \div 6\sqrt{5}$.

17. $(2\sqrt{a} - 3\sqrt{b}) \div \sqrt{ab}$.

18. $(2 - 3\sqrt{5}) \div (3 - 2\sqrt{5})$.

19. $1 \div (4\sqrt{3} - 5\sqrt{2})$.

20. $(9\sqrt{5} - 10\sqrt{3}) \div (2\sqrt{5} - 3\sqrt{3})$.

21. $(\sqrt{3} + \sqrt{2}) \div (\sqrt{3} - \sqrt{2})$.

22. $6\sqrt{3} \div (5\sqrt{3} - 3\sqrt{2})$.

23. $\dfrac{\sqrt[3]{2}}{\sqrt[3]{4} - \sqrt[3]{6} + \sqrt[3]{9}}$.

24. $\dfrac{\sqrt[3]{2}}{\sqrt[3]{3} - \sqrt[3]{2}}$.

25. $\dfrac{\sqrt{2}}{\sqrt{2} + \sqrt{3} - \sqrt{5}}$.

26. $\dfrac{5}{\sqrt[4]{3} - \sqrt[4]{2}}$.

27. $\dfrac{3}{\sqrt[4]{3} - \sqrt[4]{2}}$.

Use Table 1 (p. 349) to evaluate the following to four significant figures * both before and after rationalizing the denominator.

28. $\dfrac{2}{\sqrt{3}}$.

29. $\dfrac{5}{\sqrt{7} - \sqrt{3}}$.

30. $\dfrac{2}{2 - \sqrt{2}}$.

31. $\dfrac{2}{2^{\frac{1}{2}} + 3^{\frac{1}{2}}}$.

32. $\dfrac{4}{\sqrt{5} - \sqrt{3}}$.

33. $\dfrac{\sqrt{5} + \sqrt{3}}{\sqrt{15}}$.

34. $\dfrac{\sqrt{5} + \sqrt{3}}{\sqrt{8}}$.

35. $\dfrac{\sqrt{5} - \sqrt{3}}{\sqrt{5} + \sqrt{3}}$.

36. $\dfrac{3\sqrt{7} + 4\sqrt{6}}{8\sqrt{7} + 7\sqrt{6}}$.

37. $\dfrac{1}{4 - \sqrt{15}}$.

54. Solution of Equations Containing Radicals

Certain equations in which the variable is involved under the radical sign can be reduced to equations of the first degree. In solving such equations, it is usually convenient to proceed as follows:

(1) *Isolate the radical, that is, place it by itself on one side of the equation. If more than one radical occurs, isolate the most complicated one.*

(2) *Raise both sides of the equation to a suitable power.*

(3) *If a radical remains, isolate it and again raise to a suitable power.*

(4) *Solve the resulting equation.*

(5) *Check the result.*

Checking the result is of the utmost importance in these problems (Art. **27**). The following examples illustrate the method of solving some typical equations in which the above reductions can be made.

---

* In giving a result such as 2.2361 to four significant figures, we write 2.236. In giving the same result to three significant figures, we write 2.24 rather than 2.23, for 2.24 differs less from 2.236 than 2.23 differs from 2.236. In fact, it is usually desirable in giving any number of figures of an approximate result, to find whether the next figure beyond those to be retained in the result is less or greater than 5; for, if we should obtain a result 2.23 and know that the next figure is greater than 5, the result should be given to three significant figures as 2.24 (Art. **63**).

EXAMPLES

1. Solve the equation $\sqrt{3x+1} = 5$.

Solution: Squaring both members,
$$3x + 1 = 25.$$
Solving for x, $\qquad x = 8.$

Check: $\qquad\qquad \sqrt{25} = 5.$

It should be recalled that $\sqrt{25} = +5$, and does not equal ± 5; that is, when no sign precedes the radical the positive value of the root is to be taken. If both positive and negative roots are meant, we shall write both signs before the radical.

2. Solve $\sqrt{4x+5} + 2\sqrt{x-3} = 17$.

Solution: Transposing,
$$\sqrt{4x+5} - 17 = -2\sqrt{x-3}.$$
Squaring, $\qquad 4x + 5 - 34\sqrt{4x+5} + 289 = 4x - 12.$

Transposing and simplifying, $\qquad \sqrt{4x+5} = 9.$

Squaring, $\qquad\qquad\qquad 4x + 5 = 81.$

Solving for x, $\qquad\qquad\qquad x = 19.$

Check: $\qquad\qquad \sqrt{81} + 2\sqrt{16} = 17$

or, $\qquad\qquad\qquad\qquad 17 = 17.$

3. Solve $(x-2)^{\frac{1}{2}} - (x+3)^{\frac{1}{2}} = 1$.

Solution: Transposing $(x+3)^{\frac{1}{2}}$ and squaring,
$$x - 2 = x + 3 + 2(x+3)^{\frac{1}{2}} + 1.$$
This reduces to $\qquad\qquad (x+3)^{\frac{1}{2}} = -3.$

Squaring both sides and solving, $\qquad x = 6.$

Check: $\qquad\qquad (4)^{\frac{1}{2}} - (9)^{\frac{1}{2}} \neq 1,$

or $\qquad\qquad\qquad\qquad 2 - 3 \neq 1.$

Hence 6 is not a solution of the given equation. In fact, the given equation has no solution.

Example 3 illustrates the fact that results obtained by squaring the sides of an equation containing radicals must be checked by substitution in the original equation to determine whether or not a result is a solution of that equation.

EXERCISES

Solve and check by substitution.

1. $\sqrt{x+5} = 3.$ $\qquad\qquad$ **3.** $\sqrt{3x+7} = 2.$

2. $5 + \sqrt{x} = 8.$ $\qquad\qquad$ **4.** $\sqrt{3x+1} + 4 = 0.$

notice that the point representing $i \cdot i \cdot 2$ should coincide with the point representing -2. Hence the angle θ must be 90°. Consequently we conclude that it will be consistent with our previous ideas to represent the pure imaginary numbers by points on a line through O and perpendicular to the real number line. This new line is called the **axis of imaginaries.**

If the real number line and the axis of imaginaries are regarded as a set of coordinate axes, then to any point with coordinates (a, b), where a and b are real numbers, will correspond a number of the form $a + ib$, and to every number of the form $a + ib$ there will correspond a point with the coordinates (a, b). The totality of the numbers $a + ib$ is called the system of **complex numbers.** If $b = 0$, the number is real; if $a = 0$, it is a pure imaginary number; if $b \neq 0$, the number is called imaginary. Numbers of the form $a + ib$ and $a - ib$ are called **conjugate complex numbers.**

In order to perform operations with imaginary numbers we use the following device. If a is a positive real number, always replace $\sqrt{-a}$ with $i\sqrt{a}$ and operate with i as with any other letter, but replace i^2 in any expression by -1. Thus if a and b are positive real numbers,

$$\sqrt{-a} \cdot \sqrt{-b} \neq \sqrt{ab},$$

but $\quad \sqrt{-a} \cdot \sqrt{-b} = i\sqrt{a} \cdot i\sqrt{b} = i^2\sqrt{ab} = -\sqrt{ab}.$

We define addition, subtraction, multiplication, and division of imaginary numbers as follows.

Addition: $\quad (a + ib) + (c + id) = (a + c) + i(b + d).$

Subtraction: $\quad (a + ib) - (c + id) = (a - c) + i(b - d).$

Multiplication: $\quad (a + ib)(c + id) = ac + ibc + iad + i^2bd,$
$$= (ac - bd) + i(ad + bc)$$

Division: $\quad \dfrac{a + ib}{c + id} = \dfrac{a + ib}{c + id} \cdot \dfrac{c - id}{c - id}$
$$= \dfrac{(ac + bd) + i(bc - ad)}{c^2 + d^2}$$

In Chapter 13, the student will find a more complete discussion of imaginary numbers. These numbers play a very important role in advanced mathematics and in the application of mathematics to some other fields. For instance, they are used extensively in physics, electrical engineering, and aeronautical engineering.

EXERCISES

Express in terms of i.

1. $\sqrt{-36}$.   **2.** $-\sqrt{-81}$.   **3.** $-\sqrt{-12a^2}$.

4. $\sqrt{-\dfrac{25}{64}}$.   **5.** $\sqrt{\dfrac{-16x^2}{121y^2}}$.   **6.** $\sqrt{4ab - a^2 - 4b^2}$.

Perform the indicated operations and simplify when possible by replacing i^2 by -1.

7. $(1 + i) \div (2 - i)$.

Solution:
$$\frac{1+i}{2-i} = \frac{(1+i)(2+i)}{(2-i)(2+i)}$$
$$= \frac{2 + 2i + i + i^2}{4 - i^2}$$
$$= \frac{1 + 3i}{5}$$

8. $(3 + 2i) + (2 - 5i)$.

9. $(7 + 4i) - (3 - 2i)$.

10. $(5 + 2i) + (7 - 2i)$.

11. $(9 - 2i) - (9 + 2i)$.

12. $\sqrt{-3} \cdot \sqrt{-4}$.

13. $\sqrt{3} \cdot \sqrt{-4}$.

14. $(4 + i)(4 - i)$.

15. $(3 - \sqrt{-7})^2$.

16. $\left(-\dfrac{1}{2} + \dfrac{i\sqrt{3}}{2}\right)\left(-\dfrac{1}{2} - \dfrac{i\sqrt{3}}{2}\right)$.

17. $\left(-\dfrac{1}{2} + \dfrac{i\sqrt{3}}{2}\right) \div \left(-\dfrac{1}{2} - \dfrac{i\sqrt{3}}{2}\right)$

18. $(8 - i^3) \div (2 - i)$.

19. $(\sqrt{2} - \sqrt{-3})(\sqrt{2} + \sqrt{-3})$.

20. $(1 + i) \div (1 - i)$.

21. $(2 - 3i) \div (2 + 3i)$.

22. $(3 - 2i)^2 + (3 + 2i)^2$.

23. $(\sqrt{-2} - 2\sqrt{-3})(3\sqrt{-2} + \sqrt{-3})$.

24. $\dfrac{3\sqrt{-2} + \sqrt{-3}}{\sqrt{-2} - 2\sqrt{-3}}$.

25. $(2 - 3i)^3$.

26. $(-1 + i\sqrt{3})^3$.

27. $(x - 1 + 2i)(x - 1 - 2i)$.

28. $(2x + 3 + 4i)(2x + 3 - 4i)$.

29. Evaluate $x^2 + 2x + 4$ when $x = -1 - i\sqrt{3}$.

8 LOGARITHMS

56. Generalization of Exponents

In Article **42,** a^x is defined when x is a positive integer. Thus, $4^5 = 4 \cdot 4 \cdot 4 \cdot 4 \cdot 4$. Also a meaning is obtained (Arts. **43–47**) from the laws of exponents for a^x when x is any rational number. Thus, $8^{\frac{2}{3}}$ is the square of the cube root of 8. But no meaning has been obtained for a^x when x is an irrational number. For example, $4^{\sqrt{2}}$ is thus far undefined. But approximations to $\sqrt{2}$ are given by the sequence of rational numbers

$$1, \; 1.4, \; 1.41, \; 1.414, \; 1.4142, \cdots.$$

If these successive decimal approximations to $\sqrt{2}$ are used as exponents, closer and closer approximations to $4^{\sqrt{2}}$ are obtained. If we write the sequence

$$4^1, \; 4^{1.4}, \; 4^{1.41}, \; 4^{1.414}, \; 4^{1.4142}, \cdots,$$

we can have as close an approximation to $4^{\sqrt{2}}$ as we please.*

In this chapter we shall assume that a^x (a positive) has a meaning when x is irrational and that the laws of exponents may be used for all *real* values of the exponents, *rational* or *irrational.*

57. Definition of a Logarithm

If $a^x = y(a > 0, \; a \neq 1)$, *then x is said to be the* **logarithm** *of y to the base a,* and this is written $x = \log_a y$.

* If x is an irrational number and a variable z takes on a sequence of rational values approaching x as a limit, it may be proved in more advanced mathematics that a^z ($a > 0$) has a limit equal to a^x.

The two equations $\qquad a^x = y$ $\hfill (1)$
and $\qquad\qquad\qquad x = \log_a y$ $\hfill (2)$

are two ways of expressing the same thing, i.e., the exponent applied to a to give y is equal to x. The number a is called the **base** of the system of logarithms.

We shall assume in what follows:

Corresponding to any two positive numbers y and a ($a \neq 1$) there exists one and only one real number x such that $a^x = y$.

This assumption is sometimes expressed by saying that any positive number has one and only one logarithm, whatever positive number is the base (unity excepted).

EXERCISES

1. $\log_7 49 = ?$ $\log_3 81 = ?$ $\log_5 1 = ?$ $\log_{10} .01 = ?$ $\log_{15} 15 = ?$

2. Find x in the following: $\log_x 16 = 4$, $\log_{81} 9 = x$, $\log_4 x = \dfrac{1}{2}$, $\log_{\frac{1}{2}} x = 4$, $\log_x 32 = -5$.

3. Fill out the following table:

Base	Number	Logarithm
	27	3
$\dfrac{1}{9}$	3	
16		$-\dfrac{1}{2}$
a	a	
	1	0

58. Derived Properties of Logarithms

1. *The logarithm of a product equals the sum of the logarithms of its factors.*

Let $\qquad\qquad \log_a u = x$ and $\log_a v = y,$ $\hfill (1)$

then, $\qquad\qquad a^x = u,\ a^y = v,$ (Definition of logarithm)

and $\qquad\qquad uv = a^{x+y}.$ $\hfill$ (Arts. **42** and **56**)

Hence, $\qquad \log_a uv = x + y,$ $\hfill$ (Art. **57**)

that is, $\qquad \mathbf{\log_a uv = \log_a u + \log_a v.}$

Similarly, $\log_a (uvw) = \log_a u + \log_a v + \log_a w,$

and so on for any number of factors.

Example: $\log_{10} 255 = \log_{10} 3 + \log_{10} 5 + \log_{10} 17.$

2. *The logarithm of a quotient is equal to the logarithm of the dividend minus the logarithm of the divisor.*

As above, let $\quad \log_a u = x$ and $\log_a v = y,$

then, $\qquad\qquad a^x = u,\ a^y = v,$

and $\qquad\qquad \dfrac{u}{v} = a^{x-y}.$

Hence, $\qquad\qquad \log_a \dfrac{u}{v} = x - y,$

that is, $\qquad\qquad \log_a \dfrac{u}{v} = \log_a u - \log_a v.$

Example: $\qquad \log_{10} \dfrac{625}{133} = \log_{10} 625 - \log_{10} 133.$

3. *The logarithm of u^v is equal to v multiplied by the logarithm of u.*

To prove this, let $\qquad x = \log_a u$ or $a^x = u.$ $\qquad\qquad$ (1)

Then, from (1), $\qquad u^v = a^{vx}.$

Hence, $\qquad\qquad \log_a u^v = vx = v \log_a u.$ $\qquad\qquad$ (2)

Example: $\qquad \log_{10} (257)^{\frac{1}{2}} = \dfrac{1}{2} \log_{10} 257.$

Making $v = n$ and $v = \dfrac{1}{n}$ respectively, we have

(a) *The logarithm of the nth power of a number is the logarithm of the number multiplied by n.*

(b) *The logarithm of the real positive nth root of a number is the logarithm of the number divided by n.*

It should be noted that these three laws of logarithms are merely restatements of the first three laws of exponents in Article **42.**

EXERCISES

1. From a consideration of the three laws of logarithms, for what types of computational problems may logarithms be useful?

2. Could other devices like a slide rule or a computing machine be used to carry out all the processes mentioned in the answer to problem 1? List the advantages and disadvantages of logarithms and these computing devices in carrying out these processes.

Express the logarithms of the following expressions in terms of the logarithms of integers.

3. * $\log \dfrac{\sqrt[4]{8}}{9^{\frac{1}{5}}6^{\frac{2}{3}}}$.

Solution:

$$\log \frac{\sqrt[4]{8}}{9^{\frac{1}{5}}6^{\frac{2}{3}}} = \log \sqrt[4]{8} - \log 9^{\frac{1}{5}} - \log 6^{\frac{2}{3}} \qquad \text{(1 and 2, Art. 58)}$$

$$= \frac{1}{4} \log 8 - \frac{1}{5} \log 9 - \frac{2}{3} \log 6. \qquad \text{(3, Art. 58)}$$

4. $\log \dfrac{3^2}{5^3}$.

5. $\log \dfrac{3^2 \cdot \sqrt{5}}{2^3 \cdot \sqrt{7}}$.

6. $\log \dfrac{6^2 \cdot \sqrt{7}}{2 \cdot 3^{\frac{1}{2}}}$.

7. $\log \sqrt{\dfrac{7}{3^3}}$.

Express the logarithms of the following in terms of the logarithms of prime integers.

8. $\log \dfrac{(50)^{\frac{1}{3}}}{(30)^{\frac{2}{3}}}$.

9. $\log \dfrac{(12)^3 \cdot 7}{(14) \cdot \sqrt{6}}$.

10. $\log \dfrac{\sqrt{2} \cdot \sqrt[3]{3}}{\sqrt[4]{4}}$.

11. $\log \left[\dfrac{2}{13} \sqrt{(5)^2 + (12)^2} \right]^{\frac{1}{2}}$.

Given $\log_{10} 2 = 0.3010$, $\log_{10} 3 = 0.4771$, $\log_{10} 7 = 0.8451$, find the logarithms of the following numbers to the base 10.

12. 5.

13. 63.

14. 35.

15. $\dfrac{28}{15}$.

16. $\dfrac{9}{25}$.

17. $\sqrt[3]{5}$.

18. 90.

19. $3^{-\frac{1}{2}}$.

20. $\sqrt[3]{\dfrac{2}{5}}$.

21. $\dfrac{\sqrt[3]{14}}{\sqrt[5]{35}}$.

22. $\sqrt[3]{800}$.

23. $\sqrt{504}$.

24. 13,720.

25. 137.2.

26. 0.01372.

27. 1.372×10^k .

* When in a problem the same base is used throughout, it is customary not to write the base.

59. Common Logarithms

While any positive number different from 1 can be used as the base of some system of logarithms, there are two systems in general use. These are the **common** or **Briggsian** system and the **natural** or **Napierian** system. In the common system the base is 10, while in the natural system the base is a certain irrational number $e = 2.71828 \cdots$. It may be stated that the common system is adapted to numerical computation, while the natural system is adapted to analytical work.*

In the following discussion of common logarithms, $\log x$ is written as an abbreviation of $\log_{10} x$.

Since,
$$10^0 = 1 \qquad\qquad 10^{-1} = 0.1$$
$$10^1 = 10 \qquad\qquad 10^{-2} = 0.01$$
$$10^2 = 100 \qquad\qquad 10^{-3} = 0.001$$
$$10^3 = 1000 \qquad\qquad 10^{-4} = 0.0001$$

it follows that
$$\log 1 \quad = 0 \qquad\qquad \log 0.1 \quad = -1$$
$$\log 10 \quad = 1 \qquad\qquad \log 0.01 \quad = -2$$
$$\log 100 \quad = 2 \qquad\qquad \log 0.001 \quad = -3$$
$$\log 1000 = 3 \qquad\qquad \log 0.0001 = -4$$

So far as these powers of 10 are concerned, it may be observed that the logarithm of the number becomes greater as the number increases. In accordance with this observation, we may assume, if $a < x < b$, that
$$\log a < \log x < \log b.$$
For example, $\qquad \log 100 < \log 765 < \log 1000,$
or $\qquad\qquad\qquad 2 < \log 765 < 3.$

When the logarithm of a number is not an integer, it may be represented at least approximately by the sum of an integer and a positive decimal fraction. Thus, $\log 765 = 2.8837$ correct to four decimal places.

The integral part of a logarithm is called the **characteristic** and the decimal part is called the **mantissa**. In log 765, the characteristic is 2 and the mantissa is 0.8837. For convenience in

* The notation $\ln x$ for $\log_e x$ and $\log x$ for $\log_{10} x$ is frequently used when both kinds of logarithms appear in the same problem.

constructing tables, it is desirable to select the mantissa as positive even if the logarithm is a negative number. For example, $\log \frac{1}{2} = -0.3010$; but since $-0.3010 = 9.6990 - 10$, this may be written $\log \frac{1}{2} = 9.6990 - 10$ with a positive mantissa. The following illustration shows the method of writing the characteristic and mantissa:

$$\log 7185 \quad = 3.8564$$
$$\log 718.5 \quad = 2.8564$$
$$\log 71.85 \quad = 1.8564$$
$$\log 7.185 \quad = 0.8564$$
$$\log 0.7185 \quad = 9.8564 - 10$$
$$\log 0.07185 = 8.8564 - 10$$

60. Characteristic

With our decimal system of notation, the characteristic in the case of the base 10 is very easy to determine by a simple rule. Herein lies the advantage of this base.

If n is a number such that $1 \leq n < 10$, that is, there is exactly *one* digit to the left of the decimal point, then by Article 59, $\log n$ satisfies the inequality $0 \leq \log n < 1$. Hence if $1 \leq n < 10$, then $\log n$ has the characteristic 0. The value of $\log n$ will be read from a table as explained in Article 66.

If x is a number greater than 1, having $k + 1$ digits to the left of the decimal point, then in scientific notation (Page 87) $x = n \times 10^k$, where $1 \leq n < 10$. By the laws of logarithms

$$\log x = \log n + k.$$

Since $1 \leq n < 10$, we know from above that $0 \leq \log n < 1$. Hence the characteristic of $\log x$ is k, the mantissa is $\log n$, and we have the rule:

The characteristic of the common logarithm of a number greater than 1 is 1 less than the number of digits to the left of the decimal point.

If y is a positive number less than 1, having k zeros between the decimal point and the first significant digit, then in scientific notation $y = n \times 10^{-(k+1)}$, where $1 \leq n < 10$. By the laws of logarithms

$$\log y = \log n - (k + 1).$$

Again $0 \leq \log n < 1$ and consequently the characteristic of $\log y$ is $-(k + 1)$, while the mantissa is $\log n$.

Hence, *the characteristic of the common logarithm of any positive number less than 1 is negative and numerically 1 greater than the number of zeros between the decimal point and the first significant digit.*

When y is a positive number less than 1, and k is less than 10, it is common practice to write the characteristic of log y as

$$10 - (k + 1) - 10$$

or
$$(9 - k) - 10.$$

This method of writing the characteristic leads to the alternate rule:

To find the characteristic of the common logarithm of a decimal fraction, subtract from 9 the number of zeros between the decimal point and the first significant figure. From the number so obtained subtract 10.

Example 1. If log 7.185 = 0.8564, find log 718.5.

$$718.5 = 7.185 \times 10^2,$$
$$\log 718.5 = \log 7.185 + 2,$$
$$\log 718.5 = 0.8564 + 2,$$
$$\log 718.5 = 2.8564.$$

Example 2. Find log 0.0007185.

$$0.0007185 = 7.185 \times 10^{-4},$$
$$\log 0.0007185 = \log 7.185 - 4,$$
$$\log 0.0007185 = \log 7.185 + (10 - 4) - 10,$$
$$\log 0.0007185 = 0.8564 + 6 - 10,$$
$$\log 0.0007185 = 6.8564 - 10.$$

61. Approximate Numbers

Most of the numbers used in this chapter are approximations. For example, when we read log 7.185 = 0.8564, it does not mean that log 7.185 is exactly 0.8564, but that 0.8564 gives the value of log 7.185 as nearly as can be done with four figures. The approximate number 0.8564 would be written in a four-place table for any number between the exact numbers 0.85635 and 0.85645, and is "correct to four significant figures," while log 7.185 = 0.85642677 is "correct to eight significant figures." (See footnote, page 97.)

62. Significant Figures

In counting the number of significant figures, we usually consider the digits 1, 2, 3, 4, 5, 6, 7, 8, 9, but under certain circumstances 0 may be significant. It is always so if it occurs between two other significant figures. For example, in the following logarithms, the zeros are significant, 2.5011, 1.9009. On the other hand, the zeros in 0.00379 are not significant but are used simply to locate the decimal point. Zeros at the end of a number may or may not be significant. If we say that the population of the United States is 170,000,000, the last zeros are not significant for we do not know just what numbers should be there, since we cannot count the population correct to a single person. Again, if measurements are taken to the nearest tenth of an inch and the length of a desk is put down as 60.0 inches, then both zeros are significant.

The position of the decimal point has no influence on the number of significant figures, for example, the numbers 576.35, 57.635, 0.057635, considered as approximate numbers, are all correct to five significant figures.

63. Rejecting Figures

It is often necessary to reject figures at the end of an approximate number. This rejection of figures is often called "rounding off" the number. For example, if we are working with four-place data, the last two figures in the number 0.376741 are unnecessary and we write simply 0.3767. However, if the first rejected figure is greater than 5 or 5 followed by figures not all zeros, the last unrejected figure should be increased by 1. Thus, it is clear that 0.7686 is a closer approximation to 0.768583 than is 0.7685. If the rejected figure is 5 or 5 followed by zeros, it is often customary among computers to increase the last unrejected number by 1 if it is an odd number, but to leave it unchanged if it is an even number. For example, 1.4865 becomes 1.486, but 0.839350 becomes 0.8394 when these numbers are cut down to four significant figures. If this rule is followed in a long piece of computation, the errors tend to compensate one another. This rule has been followed in working the problems in this book.*

---

* Business and government agencies frequently use the rule: If the rejected figure is 5 or greater, the last unrejected figure is increased by 1, otherwise the last unrejected figure remains unchanged.

64. Computation with Approximate Numbers

The results of calculations based upon approximate numbers are ordinarily approximate numbers.

While it is beyond the scope of a college algebra to go far into the propagation of errors in computing with approximate numbers, we shall give, without proof, two rules that are rather generally adopted by computers and that are likely to put us on our guard against retaining useless figures in computing with approximate numbers.

Rule for addition. *In the sum of a given set of numbers of which at least one is an approximate number, it is seldom useful to retain more decimal places than are found in one of the approximate numbers with the least number of decimal places.*

Thus, in adding

$$3.1416$$
$$6.28$$
$$2.412$$
$$\underline{7.9}$$
$$19.7$$

in which 7.9 is an approximate number, we report the sum 19.7.

A similar rule holds with regard to subtraction.

Rule for multiplication and division. *In a product or quotient, it is seldom useful to retain more significant figures than are found in one of the given approximate numbers with the least number of significant figures.*

Thus, if 8.3 is an approximate number, we write $(8.3)(3.1416)$ = 26, and report only two significant figures.

Although the above rules ordinarily give useful approximate results, it will be shown in some of the following exercises that the last figure is not the most accurate that could be given.

EXERCISES

1. Explain the difference between the approximate numbers 71.4, 71.40, 71.400 where the zeros are to be considered as significant.

2. Distinguish between the numbers 7, 7.0, 7.00, 7.000, assuming each digit a significant number.

3. To twelve significant figures $\pi = 3.14159265359$. Write π to eleven, to ten, to nine, $\cdots$, to two significant figures.

4. The value $\dfrac{22}{7}$ is often used for π. To what number of signif-icant figures is this value equivalent?

5. Add the following numbers which are to be considered as the results of measurements: 31.5, 3.126, 25.4301, 0.438.

6. The product of the approximate numbers 3.17 and 7.98 may take on any value between what two numbers? What is the product according to the above rules?

7. The product of the three approximate numbers 0.37, 7.3, and 2.1 may take on any value between what two numbers? What is the product according to our rules?

8. Suppose in the fraction $\dfrac{75}{0.389}$ that the numerator is an exact number, and the denominator is an approximate number, find the extreme values which the fraction may represent. What is the quotient in decimal notation according to our rules?

9. If both numerator and denominator of the fraction $\dfrac{75.0}{0.389}$ are approximate numbers, find in decimal notation the extreme values which the fraction may represent. What is the quotient according to our rules?

10. There are 2.540005 centimeters in one inch. A board measures 14.7 feet in length measured to the nearest tenth of an inch. Express the length in meters. Between what two numbers does the result lie?

65. Use of Tables

Table 2, page 350, is a "four-place" table of logarithms. In this table, the logarithms of all numbers consisting of three digits from 1.00 to 9.99 are recorded correct to four decimal places. By Article **60**, we may read from this table the mantissas of all num-bers consisting of at most three significant figures. "Five-place," "six-place," and "seven-place" tables of logarithms are in common use, but this four-place table will serve our present purpose. Methods by which such a table can be constructed will be discussed in Article **212**.

The table serves us in two ways. It enables us to find the logarithm of a given number and conversely it enables us to determine the number which has a given logarithm.

66. To Find from the Table the Logarithm of a Given Number

Example 1. Find the logarithm of 821.

From Article **60**, log 821 = log 8.21 + 2. To find log 8.21, turn to Table 2 and glance down the column headed *n* for the first two significant figures. Then move across the row 82 to the column headed 1 at the top of the table. In row 82 under column 1 is found 9143, and these digits prefixed with a decimal point give log 8.21. Hence log 821 = 0.9143 + 2 = 2.9143.

Example 2. Find the logarithm of 0.06842.

By Article **60**, log 0.06842 = log 6.842 − 2. Since 6.842 has more than three significant figures, its logarithm is not recorded in Table 2. The logarithm of 6.842 may however be approximated from use of the table by a process called **interpolation**. In this process, it is assumed that to a small change in the number, there corresponds a change in the logarithm which is proportional to the change in the number. This assumption is called the **principle of proportional parts**. Table 2 yields log 6.84 = 0.8351 and log 6.85 = 0.9357. Arrange this information in tabular form:

$$6.84 \qquad 0.8351$$
$$6.842 \qquad \log n$$
$$6.85 \qquad 0.8357$$

The number 6.842 is two-tenths of the interval from 6.84 to 6.85. Hence for log *n* we seek a number two-tenths of the interval from 0.8351 to 0.8357. Since the difference between the two logarithms is 0.0006, we must add 0.2 × 0.0006 = 0.0001 to 0.8351. Hence log *n* is 0.8352 and log 0.06842 = 0.8352 − 2 = 8.8352 − 10.

67. To Find from the Table the Number Which Corresponds to a Given Logarithm

Example 1. Find the number whose logarithm is 2.4675.

Let log *x* = 2.4675 and log *n* = 0.4675. Then log *x* = log *n* + 2. The logarithm 4675 is not recorded in the table, but lies between 4669 in row 29 column 3 and 4683 in row 29 column 4. In tabular form we have

$$2.93 \qquad 0.4669$$
$$n \qquad 0.4675$$
$$2.94 \qquad 0.4683$$

Since 0.4675 is $\dfrac{3}{7}$ of the interval from 0.4669 to 0.4683, we seek for

n a number $\dfrac{3}{7}$ of the interval from 2.93 to 2.94. Hence $n = 2.93 +$

$\dfrac{3}{7}(0.01) = 2.93 + 0.004 = 2.934$. Now $\log x = \log 2.934 + 2$ and

by Article **60**, $x = 2.934 \times 10^2 = 293.4$.

Example 2. Find the number whose logarithm is 9.3025 − 10.

Let $\log y = 9.3025 - 10 = 0.3025 - 1$, and let $\log n = 0.3025$. From Table 2, 0.3025 is a logarithm between 3010 in row 20 column 0 and 3032 in row 20 column 1. Thus in tabular form:

2.00	0.3010
n	0.3025
2.01	0.3032

By the principle of proportional parts, $n = 2.00 + \dfrac{15}{22}(0.01)$ or

$n = 2.007$. But $\log y = \log 2.007 - 1$ and by Article **60**,

$y = 2.007 \times 10^{-1} = 0.2007$.

EXERCISES

Obtain from the table the common logarithms of the following:

1. 37.
2. 0.037.
3. 684.5.
4. 8.903.
5. 0.9978.
6. 389.9.

7. 3.142.
8. 0.004725.
9. 531,400,000.
10. 7.306×10^5.
11. 5.263×10^{-10}.
12. 0.000,000,000,047,6.

Use the table to obtain the numbers whose common logarithms are the following:

13. 1.8633.
14. 0.0784.
15. 2.6870.
16. 8.6009 − 10.
17. 9.9994 − 10.
18. 6.3936 − 10.

19. 4.4972.
20. 7.7988.
21. 1.8144 − 10.
22. 1.8144 − 20.
23. 8.6776 − 20.
24. 14.7240.

68. Computation by Means of Logarithms

The application of logarithms to shorten calculations depends upon the properties of logarithms given in Article **58**. By means of logarithms laborious multiplications and divisions may be replaced by additions and subtractions; the problem of raising a number to a power may be replaced by a simpler problem in multiplication; and the problem of taking a root of a number may be replaced by a problem in simple division.

EXAMPLES

1. Find the value of $N = \dfrac{6.320 \times 8.674}{2.851}$ to four significant figures.

$$
\begin{aligned}
\log 6.320 &= 0.8007 \\
\log 8.674 &= 0.9382 \\
\log (6.320)(8.674) &= 1.7389 \\
\log 2.851 &= 0.4550 \\
\log N &= 1.2839 \\
N &= 19.23.
\end{aligned}
$$

In using logarithms, *much time is saved and the liability of error is decreased by making a so-called form for all the work before using the table at all.*

Thus, in Example 1, the "form" is*

$$
\begin{aligned}
\log 6.320 &= \\
\log 8.674 &= \\
\log (6.320)(8.674) &= \\
\log 2.851 &= \\
\log N &= \\
N &=
\end{aligned}
$$

* The logarithm of the reciprocal of x is called the **cologarithm** of x and is written colog x. Since log $1 = 0$,

$$
\operatorname{colog} x = \log \frac{1}{x} = - \log x.
$$

In a series of operations involving multiplications and divisions, we have both additions and subtractions if logarithms are used. These operations are all additions if cologarithms are introduced in the calculations. Example 1 could then be worked as follows:

$$
\begin{aligned}
\log 6.320 &= 0.8007 \\
\log 8.674 &= 0.9382 \\
\operatorname{colog} 2.851 &= 9.5450 - 10 \\
\log N &= 1.2839 \\
N &= 19.23
\end{aligned}
$$

2. Make a form for evaluating $N = \dfrac{(6.85)^{\frac{1}{2}} \sqrt[3]{8.642}}{\sqrt{65.27}}$.

$$\log 6.85 =$$
$$\log 8.542 =$$
$$\log 65.27 =$$
$$\log (6.85)^{\frac{1}{2}} =$$
$$\log (8.542)^{\frac{1}{3}} =$$
$$\log \left[(6.85)^{\frac{1}{2}}(8.542)^{\frac{1}{3}}\right] =$$
$$\underline{\log (65.27)^{\frac{1}{2}} =}$$
$$\log N =$$
$$N =$$

3. Evaluate $\sqrt[3]{-58.61}$.

Whenever negative numbers are involved, first find the sign of the result. Thus

$$\sqrt[3]{-58.61} = -\sqrt[3]{58.61} = -N,$$

where $N = \sqrt[3]{58.61}$. Then evaluate N by means of logarithms.

$$\log 58.61 = 1.7680$$
$$\log (58.61)^{\frac{1}{3}} = 0.5893$$
$$N = 3.885.$$

Hence $\qquad \sqrt[3]{-58.61} = -\sqrt[3]{58.61} = -3.885.$

4. Evaluate $(0.37)^{0.37}$.

$$\log 0.37 = 9.5682 - 10$$
$$\log (0.37)^{0.37} = 0.37(9.5682 - 10)$$
$$= 3.5402 - 3.7000$$
$$= -0.1598$$
$$= 9.8402 - 10$$
$$(0.37)^{0.37} \doteq 0.6922.$$

EXERCISES AND PROBLEMS

Compute to four significant figures by means of logarithms.

1. 76.23×538.6.

2. $829.1 \div 73.39$.

3. $79.35 \times 230.8 \times 0.09578$.

4. $\dfrac{18.27 \times 0.8157}{4.253 \times 0.008927}$.

5. $\dfrac{0.02953}{0.07128}$.

6. $(9.837)^4$.

7. $(0.07272)^5$.

8. $(0.08539)^{-3}$.

9. $\left(\dfrac{0.06379}{0.8724}\right)^2$.

10. $\left(\dfrac{-0.003758}{0.008675}\right)^3$.

11. $(39.75)^{\frac{3}{4}}$.

12. $(2.718)^{-\frac{3}{2}}$.

13. $(0.007685)^{\frac{1}{3}}$.

14. $(0.001572)^{-\frac{2}{5}}$.

15. $\sqrt[5]{\dfrac{-0.08912}{7.752}}$.

16. $\sqrt[4]{\dfrac{0.006275}{0.007184}}$.

17. $(10)^{0.1}$.

18. $(10)^{-0.01}$.

19. $(0.01)^{0.01}$.

20. $(0.95)^{0.45}$.

21. $\dfrac{(4.253)(-0.09678)}{(291.8)^{\frac{1}{2}}}$.

22. $(7.81)^2 \sqrt[3]{\dfrac{7.624}{9.258}}$.

23. $\sqrt{(297.6)^2 - (134.7)^2} = \sqrt{(297.6 + 134.7)(297.6 - 134.7)}$.

24. $\sqrt{(29.85)^2 - (14.70)^2}$.   **25.** $\sqrt[3]{(70.05)^2 - (51.06)^2}$.

26. $\left[\dfrac{9}{2} \times \dfrac{1.819 \times 10^{-4}}{0.920 \times 980} \times 2.39 \times 10^{-3} \right]^{\frac{1}{2}}$.

27. $\dfrac{3.89 \times 10^{-13} \times 980}{\dfrac{115}{300} \times \dfrac{1}{0.453} \times 2.39 \times 10^{-3}}$.

28. $(\log 18)(\log 5)$.

29. $(\log 0.3)(\log 0.2)$.

30. $\dfrac{\log 3}{\log 2}$.

31. $\dfrac{(\log 5)(\log 12)}{(\log 20)(\log 3)}$.

32. $\log 3^2 - (\log 3)^2$.

33. $\log \sqrt{81.09} - \sqrt{\log 81.09}$.

34. $\dfrac{\log 30.40}{\log 0.3591}$.

35. $\log \dfrac{2.36}{7.08} + \dfrac{\log 2.36}{\log 7.08}$.

In the following eight problems, find the value of N without using tables of logarithms.

36. $N = 10^{\log 2}$.

37. $N = 10^{2 \log 3}$.

38. $N = 10^{-1 + \log 5}$.

39. $N = 100^{6 - \log 7}$.

40. $\log N = 3 + \log 5$.

41. $\log N = 2 \log 125 - 4 \log 5$.

42. $\log N = 4 \log 81 \div 5 \log 27$.

43. $\log N = 10^{\log 3}$.

44. Find the area of a triangle if the base is 20.52 inches and the altitude is 13.74 inches.

45. If a, b, c are the lengths of the sides of a triangle, then the area is given by $\sqrt{s(s - a)(s - b)(s - c)}$, where s is one-half the perimeter of the triangle. Calculate the area of the triangle whose sides are $a = 303.7$ yards, $b = 291.5$ yards, $c = 169.3$ yards.

46. The length of the hypotenuse of a right triangle is 725.3 feet and the length of one leg is 392.9 feet. Find the length of the other leg.

47. The probable error in the coefficient of variability, C, of n measurements is given by

$$\frac{0.6745 \cdot C \cdot (1 + 2C^2)^{\frac{1}{2}}}{(2n)^{\frac{1}{2}}}.$$

Compute this probable error when $C = 0.3500$ and $n = 1000$.

48. The area in square feet of the top of a well-designed chimney is given by the formula

$$A = 0.03 \frac{Q}{\sqrt{h}},$$

where Q is the quantity of coal in pounds used per hour and h is the height of the chimney. What should be the area of the top of a chimney 170 feet high which is connected with a furnace using 12,500 pounds of coal per hour?

49. The volume of a sphere is 635.7 cubic inches. Find the radius. (The volume of a sphere is $\frac{4}{3}\pi r^3$.)

50. The lengths of the diagonals of a rhombus are 28.63 inches and 53.87 inches. Find the area. (A rhombus is a parallelogram whose sides are equal. A formula for its area in terms of the lengths of the diagonals should be developed by the student, using his knowledge of plane geometry.)

51. Estimate the weight of a cork ball 5 feet in diameter, then calculate its weight in pounds. A cork whose volume is 1 cubic inch weighs 0.139 ounces.

52. First estimate and then calculate the increase in weight of the ball in problem 42 if the radius is increased 1 inch.

53. The time t of oscillation of a simple pendulum of length l feet is given in seconds by the formula

$$t = \pi \sqrt{\frac{l}{32.16}}.$$

Find the time of oscillation of a pendulum 3.783 feet long. (Take $\pi = 3.142$.)

54. What is the weight in tons of a solid cast-iron sphere whose radius is 2.827 feet, if the weight of a cubic foot of cast-iron is 446.1 pounds?

55. Find the volume and the area of the surface of a sphere whose radius is 2.137 feet. (The area of the surface of a sphere is $4\pi r^2$.)

56. Express the volume of a sphere in terms of the area of its surface. If the area of the surface of a sphere is 90.14 square inches, use your formula to calculate the volume.

57. The stretch of a brass wire when a mass, m, is hung at its free end is given by the relation

$$S = k \frac{mgl}{\pi r^2},$$

where $g = 980$ centimeters per second per second, l is the length of the wire, r is its radius, and k is a constant. Find k for the following values: $m = 1083.9$ grams, $l = 198.9$ centimeters, $r = 0.24$ centimeters, and $S = 0.060$ centimeters.

58. Find the length, l, of a wire which stretches 4.3 centimeters when a mass of 1735 grams is hung at its free end, the diameter of the wire being 0.050 centimeters, and $k = 98 \times 10^{-12}$.

59. The weight P in pounds which will crush a solid cylindrical cast-iron column is given by the formula

$$P = 9.892 \times 10^4 \cdot \frac{d^{3.55}}{l^{1.7}},$$

where d is the diameter in inches and l is the length in feet. What weight will crush a cast-iron column 9.8 feet long and 3.9 inches in diameter?

60. For wrought-iron columns the crushing weight is given by

$$P = 2.996 \times 10^5 \cdot \frac{d^{3.55}}{l^2}.$$

What weight will crush a wrought-iron column of the same dimensions as that in problem 50?

61. The weight, W, of one cubic foot of saturated steam depends upon the pressure in the boiler according to the formula

$$W = \frac{P^{0.941}}{330.36},$$

where P is the pressure in pounds per square inch. What is W if the pressure is 425 pounds per square inch?

62. The diameter, d, in inches of a connecting rod depends upon the diameter, D, of the engine cylinder, l the length of the connecting rod, and P the maximum steam pressure in pounds per square inch. According to Mark's formula

$$d = 0.02758 \sqrt{D \cdot l \cdot \sqrt{P}}.$$

What is d when $D = 18$, $l = 60$, and $P = 300$?

63. The discharge of water from a triangular weir is given by

$$q = \frac{8c}{15} \cdot H^{\frac{5}{2}} \cdot \sqrt{2g},$$

where c is a constant 0.592, g is the acceleration due to gravity 32.2 feet per second per second, and H is the waterhead. Find q when $H = 0.4$ foot.

64. The number, n, of vibrations per second made by a stretched string is given by the relation

$$n = \frac{1}{2l}\sqrt{\frac{T}{\rho}},$$

where l is the length of the string, T the tension in the string, ρ the density of the string. Find n, when $l = 80.2$ centimeters, $T = 5{,}732 \times 10^3$ dynes, and $\rho = 0.00721$ grams per centimeter of length.

65. What is the density of a wire which is 72.4 centimeters long, if under a tension of $5{,}718 \times 10^3$ dynes it can be made to vibrate 256 times per second?

66. The formula $y = ks^x g^{cx}$, where $\log k = 5.03370116$, $\log s = -0.003296862$, $\log g = -0.00013205$, $\log c = 0.04579609$, gives the number of persons living at age x in Hunter's *Makehamized American Experience Table of Mortality*. Find, to such a degree of accuracy as you can secure with a four-place table of logarithms, the number (1) living at age 10, (2) living at age 30.

69. Change of Base

The logarithm of a number y to the base b is equal to the product of its logarithm to the base a and the logarithm of a to the base b.

That is, $\qquad \log_b y = \log_a y \cdot \log_b a.$ $\qquad\qquad$ (1)

Let $\qquad u = \log_a y$ and $v = \log_b y.$ $\qquad\qquad$ (2)

Then, $\qquad a^u = y,\ b^v = y,$ $\qquad\qquad\qquad\qquad$ (3)

and $\qquad a^u = b^v.$ $\qquad\qquad\qquad\qquad\qquad$ (4)

$$a = b^{\frac{v}{u}},$$ $\qquad\qquad\qquad\qquad\qquad$ (5)

$$\frac{v}{u} = \log_b a,$$

$$v = u \log_b a.$$ $\qquad\qquad\qquad\qquad\qquad$ (6)

From (2) and (6), $\qquad \log_b y = \log_a y \log_b a.$ $\qquad$ (7)

Example: $\qquad \log_{10} 128 = \log_2 128 \log_{10} 2.$

Since tables to the base 10 are usually available, by making $b = 10$ in (7) we may write

$$\log_a y = \frac{\log_{10} y}{\log_{10} a} \tag{8}$$

which is useful in finding the logarithm of y to any base.

Example: $\log_7 127 = \dfrac{\log_{10} 127}{\log_{10} 7} = \dfrac{2.1038}{0.8451} = 2.4894.$

By making $y = b$ in (7), we obtain

$$1 = \log_a b \log_b a.$$

That is,
$$\log_b a = \frac{1}{\log_a b}. \tag{9}$$

The number $\log_b a$ is often called the **modulus** of the system of base b with respect to the system of base a.

In Article **60**, attention is called to the advantages of 10 for the base of a system of logarithms to be used in numerical calculations. For analytical purposes, as will appear in the calculus, it is convenient to use **natural** logarithms. This system has for its base an irrational number $e = 2.71828\cdots$. In the chapter on Infinite Series, there will be given a series from which this approximation to e is obtained, and another series from which the logarithm of a number to the base e can be obtained to any number of decimal places. It turns out that

$$\log_e 10 = 2.3026,$$

and
$$\log_{10} e = \frac{1}{\log_e 10} = 0.4343.$$

By (1),
$$\log_{10} y = \log_e y \log_{10} e,$$
$$= 0.4343 \log_e y,$$

and
$$\log_e y = 2.3026 \log_{10} y.$$

The number $\log_{10} e = 0.4343$ is the **modulus** (to four significant figures) of common logarithms with respect to natural logarithms.

EXERCISES

Find the logarithms of the following numbers to the base e.

1. 2.
2. 3.
3. 5.
4. 7.
5. 9.

6. $\dfrac{1}{3}$.

7. $\dfrac{1}{2}$.

8. e.

9. $\sqrt{2}$.
10. 5,280.
11. 0.0789.
12. 1.356×10^{-4}.

Find the logarithms of the following numbers to the indicated base.

13. 10 to the base 5.

14. 10 to the base 4.

15. 4 to the base 5.

16. 5 to the base 4.

17. 4 to the base 12.

18. 12 to the base 4.

19. 300 to the base 3.

20. 7 to the base 2.

21. 0.03 to the base 2.

22. 0.03 to the base 0.2.

70. Graphs of Logarithmic Functions

A general notion of the value of the logarithm of any number can be easily fixed by reference to the graph of $y = \log_a x$. This graph is also the graph of $x = a^y$. In the graph (Fig. 12) we take

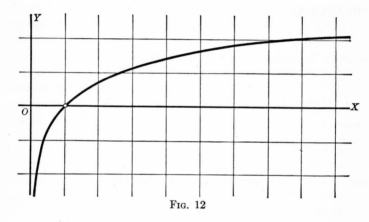

Fig. 12

$a = e = 2.718 \cdots$, but the general form of the curve is not changed if a be given any other positive value greater than 1. If the student retains this picture, he should find it easy to keep in mind the following facts when the base is greater than unity.

1. A negative number does not have a real number for its logarithm.

2. The logarithm of 1 is zero.

3. The logarithm of a positive number is positive or negative according as the number is greater than or less than 1.

4. If x approaches zero, $\log x$ decreases without limit.

5. If x increases indefinitely, $\log x$ increases without limit.

EXERCISES

1. Plot the graph of $y = \log_{10} x$ by using the tables to find $\log_{10} x$.

2. Plot the graph of $y = \log_6 x$.

Hint: $$\log_6 x = \frac{\log_{10} x}{\log_{10} 6}.$$

3. Plot the graph of $x = \log_6 y$.

4. Plot the graph of $x = \log_3 y$.

71. Exponential and Logarithmic Equations

An equation which involves the variable or variables in the exponents is often called an **exponential equation**. Thus, $2^x = 16$ is an exponential equation in x. In this simple example, the value of x can be obtained by inspection; but a table of logarithms is, in general, of value in solving exponential equations.

Such equations arise in a variety of problems. For example, the pressure of the atmosphere in pounds per square inch at a height of x feet is given approximately by the relation

$$P = P_0 e^{-kx}$$

where P_0 is the pressure at sea level and k is a constant.

Example: What is the pressure of the atmosphere per square inch at a height of one mile, given $k = 0.00003776$ and pressure at sea level, 14.72 pounds per square inch?

Solution: Let P be the pressure at 5280 feet, then

$$P = 14.72e^{-kx},$$
$$\log P = \log 14.72 - kx \log e,$$
$$= 1.1679 - 0.00003776 \cdot 5280 \cdot 0.4343,$$
$$= 1.0813,$$
$$P = 12.06 \text{ pounds per square inch.}$$

Equations of this type also occur in certain compound interest problems. Examples will be found in Chapter 17.

An equation which involves the logarithm of an expression that contains a variable is sometimes called a **logarithmic equation**. Thus,

$$\log_{10} 2x = 3$$

is a logarithmic equation. To solve this equation, we may write, from the definition of a logarithm,

$$2x = 10^3 = 1000.$$
Hence, $$x = 500.$$

EXERCISES AND PROBLEMS

Solve the following equations for x.

1. $5^x = 10$.

Solution: Since $5^x = 10$,
$$\log_{10} 5^x = \log_{10} 10 = 1.$$
$$x \log_{10} 5 = 1.$$
$$x = \frac{1}{\log_{10} 5}$$
$$= \frac{1}{.6990} = 1.431.$$

2. $2^{3x} \cdot 5^{2x-1} = 4^{5x} \cdot 3^{x+1}$.

Solution: $\log_{10} 2^{3x} \cdot 5^{2x-1} = \log_{10} 4^{5x} \cdot 3^{x+1}$,

$$3x \log_{10} 2 + (2x - 1) \log_{10} 5 = 5x \log_{10} 4 + (x + 1) \log_{10} 3$$
$$= 10x \log_{10} 2 + (x + 1) \log_{10} 3.$$

Transposing and collecting terms, we have
$$x(2 \log_{10} 5 - 7 \log_{10} 2 - \log_{10} 3) = \log_{10} 3 + \log_{10} 5.$$
$$x = \frac{\log_{10} 3 + \log_{10} 5}{2 \log_{10} 5 - 7 \log_{10} 2 - \log_{10} 3}$$
$$= \frac{0.4771 + 0.6990}{1.3980 - 2.1070 - 0.4771}$$
$$= -0.9916.$$

3. $16 = \log_{10} x^2$.

Solution: $\qquad 16 = \log_{10} x^2,$ $\qquad\qquad$ (1)

From (1), $\qquad\quad x^2 = 10^{16},$ $\qquad\qquad$ (2)

$\qquad\qquad\qquad x = \pm\, 10^8.$ $\qquad\qquad$ (3)

4. $3^x = 5$.

5. $(0.3)^x = 5$.

6. $(0.3)^x = 0.5$.

7. $(32)^x = 256$.

8. $(3.2)^x = 25.6$.

9. $5^{2x-3} = 10$.

10. $9^{x^2} = 100$.

11. $2^x = 3^{x-1}$.

12. $7^{2x+3} = 5^{x-2}$.

13. $3^{2x} \cdot 5^{x-1} = 4^{3x-2} \cdot 7^{x+1}$.

14. $5 \log_{10} x - 7 = 0$.

15. $5 \log_{10} x + 7 = 0$.

16. $\log_{10} x - \log_{10} (x + 1) = 2$.

17. $\log_{10} (x + 1) - \log_{10} x = \log_{10} 3$.

18. $\log_{10} x^5 - 2 \log_{10} x = 4$.

Solve the following systems of equations for x and y:

19.
$$5^{x+y} = 82, \tag{1}$$
$$3^{x-y} = 4. \tag{2}$$

Solution: From (1) and (2),

$$(x + y) \log 5 = \log 82, \tag{3}$$
$$(x - y) \log 3 = \log 4. \tag{4}$$

Solving the linear equations (3) and (4) for x and y, we get

$$x = \frac{\log 82}{2 \log 5} + \frac{\log 4}{2 \log 3} = \frac{1.9138}{1.398} + \frac{0.6021}{0.9542} = 2.000. \tag{5}$$

$$y = \frac{\log 82}{2 \log 5} - \frac{\log 4}{2 \log 3} = 0.7380. \tag{6}$$

20. $7^{2x+y} = 10$,
$3^{x-y} = 2^3$.

21. $7^{x-y} = 3^{5x}$,
$2x - 3y = 5$.

22.
$$5^{2x-y} = 3^{2x},$$
$\log_{10} x - \log_{10} (y + 2) = 1$.

23. A chemical substance decomposes according to the law

$$x = x_0 \cdot e^{-kt},$$

where x_0 is the amount of the substance initially, x the amount remaining at the end of t units of time, and k is a constant. If $x_0 = 16$ grams and there are 8 grams remaining at the end of 2 minutes, find k. How many grams remain at the end of 4 minutes? How much time has elapsed when only one gram remains?

24. Consider a chemical substance which decomposes according to the law of the preceding problem. If initially there are 7 grams of the substance and at the end of 3 hours there are 5 grams of the substance, find k. How much of the substance will remain at the end of 5 hours? How much time has elapsed when 2 grams of the substance remain?

25. If fluid friction be used to retard the motion of a flywheel making V_0 revolutions per minute, the formula $V = V_0 e^{-kt}$ gives the number of revolutions per minute, after the friction has been applied t seconds. If the constant $k = 0.35$, how long must the friction be applied to reduce the number of revolutions from 750 to 50 per minute?

26. The pressure, P, of the atmosphere in pounds per square inch, at a height of z feet, is given approximately by the relation

$$P = P_0 e^{-kz},$$

where P_0 is the pressure at sea level and k is a constant. Observations at sea level give $P_0 = 14.72$, and at a height of 1122 feet, $P = 14.11$. What is the value of k?

27. Assuming the law in problem 26 to hold, at what height will the pressure be half as great as at sea level?

28. If a body of temperature $T_1°$ be surrounded by cooler air of temperature $T_0°$, the body will gradually become cooler and its temperature, $T°$, after a certain time, say t minutes, is given by Newton's law of cooling, that is,

$$T = T_0 + (T_1 - T_0)e^{-kt},$$

where k is a constant. In an experiment a body of temperature 60°C. was left to cool in air whose temperature was 15°C. After 12 minutes the temperature was found to be 24.7°. What is the value of k?

29. Assuming the value of k found in problem 28, what time will elapse before the temperature of the body drops from 24.70° to 20°?

30. If $a = \log_c b$, $b = \log_a c$, $c = \log_b a$, prove that $a \cdot b \cdot c = 1$.

31. In solving an important problem in the elements of mechanics, it turns out that

$$t = \frac{1}{k} \log_e \frac{ks + \sqrt{k^2 s^2 + v_0^2}}{v_0},$$

where s is the distance traversed by a moving point in time t. It is, in general, more useful to have s in terms of t than t in terms of s. Hence, express s in terms of t.

9 QUADRATIC EQUATIONS

72. Typical Form

One of our chief problems is to find the solution of rational integral equations which were defined in Article **31**. In Article **32,** we found the solution of the rational integral equation of the first degree. In this chapter it will be our purpose to find the solution of the rational integral equation of degree 2, the **quadratic equation,** and to discuss some of the properties of this equation and its solutions.

Every quadratic equation, that is, every rational integral equation of degree 2, in one variable x can, by transforming and collecting terms, be arranged in the typical form

$$ax^2 + bx + c = 0,$$

where a, b, c do not involve x, and have any values with the one exception that a is not zero. Since the result of multiplying the members of an equation by any given constant which is not zero is an equivalent equation (Art. **27**), it is possible to select the values for a, b, c in an indefinitely large number of ways.

Illustration: Arrange the equation $3x^2 - x + k = \dfrac{2}{3} x^2 + 2$ in typical form and select the values of a, b, c.

Solution: Arranging all the terms on the left-hand side of the equation in descending powers of x, we have

$$\frac{7}{3} x^2 - x + (k - 2) = 0. \tag{1}$$

Hence we may choose $a = \dfrac{7}{3}$, b $= -1$, $c = k - 2$.

If we multiply both sides of equation (1) by 3, we have the equivalent equation $7x^2 - 3x + 3(k - 2) = 0$. We may now choose $a = 7$, $b = -3$, $c = 3(k - 2)$.

If we multiply both sides of equation (1) by $\dfrac{3}{7}$, we have the equivalent equation $x^2 - \dfrac{3}{7}x + \dfrac{3}{7}(k - 2) = 0$. We may in this case choose $a = 1$, $b = -\dfrac{3}{7}$, $c = \dfrac{3}{7}(k - 2)$.

Usually the second case is the more convenient, for all the coefficients are in integral form.

EXERCISES

Arrange the following equations in typical form with the coefficients in integral form and find the values of a, b, c.

1. $x^2 - 3x + 5 = 0$.

2. $(x - 5)^2 = 2x + 1$.

3. $4x^2 - \dfrac{1}{3}x + \dfrac{3}{8} = 2 - \dfrac{5}{6}x + \dfrac{1}{12}x^2$.

4. $\dfrac{1}{4}x^2 - \dfrac{1}{3}x + \dfrac{1}{2} = \dfrac{1}{3} + \dfrac{1}{4}x - \dfrac{1}{2}x^2$.

5. $x^2 - nx = mn - mx$.

6. $8x^2 + 8kx + 3k - 2 = 0$.

7. $kx^2 + 3kx - 5 = 2x - 3k$.

8. $(k - 1)x^2 + k = kx - 1$.

9. $x^2 - 4 = (x - 1)(x + 2) + (x + 1)(x - 2)$.

10. $gt^2 + 2v_0t + d = 0$.

73. Solution by Factoring

If the left-hand member of a quadratic equation in typical form can be factored readily, the solutions are easily obtained. Take, for example, the equation $x^2 - 4x = 21$ which in typical form is

$$x^2 - 4x - 21 = 0.$$

The factors of the left-hand member are easily found to be $(x + 3)$ and $(x - 7)$, and we may write the equation in the form

$$(x + 3)(x - 7) = 0.$$

We recall (Art. **5**) that if the product of two numbers is zero, then either of the factors must be zero. Hence, either

$$x + 3 = 0 \quad \text{and} \quad x = -3,$$
or $$x - 7 = 0 \quad \text{and} \quad x = 7.$$

If these values of x are substituted in the original equation, it will be found that both values satisfy the equation. Hence the given equation has the two solutions -3 and 7.

EXERCISES

Solve the following quadratic equations by factoring.

1. $(x - 3)^2 = 6 - 2x$.

Solution: Arranged in typical form, this equation becomes

$$x^2 - 4x + 3 = 0.$$

The factors of the left-hand member are $(x - 3)$ and $(x - 1)$ and the equation may be written

$$(x - 3)(x - 1) = 0.$$

The solutions are 3 and 1. The student should check these results by substitution in the given equation.

2. $x^2 + 5x - 14 = 0$.

3. $-3x^2 - 5x + 2 = 0$.

4. $4x^2 + 12x + 9 = 0$.

5. $2x^2 + \dfrac{7}{3} x - \dfrac{20}{3} = 0$.

6. $(x - 2)(x - 3) - 30 = 0$.

7. $3x^2 = 8x$.

8. $5x^2 - 20 = 0$.

9. $\dfrac{3}{8} x^2 - \dfrac{1}{16} x - \dfrac{3}{4} = 0$.

10. $2(x - 1)(x - 3) = (x - 2)(x - 6)$.

11. $x^2 + 16 = 0$.

12. $(2x - 3)(3x + 2) = (2x - 3)$.

13. $(x + 3)^2 - 2(x + 3) = 0$.

14. $(x + 1)^2 - 9 = 0$.

15. $(3x - 1)^2 - 45 = 0$.

16. $(x - 4)^2 + 9 = 0$.

74. Solution by "Completing the Square"

Any quadratic equation may be solved by a method called "completing the square." Before discussing this method, it will be well to note a property of the square of a binomial. From Article **12** we have that $(x \pm a)^2 \equiv x^2 \pm 2ax + a^2$. The property of this identity that is important for our present purposes concerns the right-hand member. We note that the third term of the right-hand member is the square of one-half of the coefficient of x in the second term. Hence, if we know that $x^2 \pm 2ax$ are the first two terms of a perfect trinomial square, then we also know that the third term is a^2. For example, if $x^2 - 18x$ are the first two terms of a perfect trinomial square, then the third term is $\left(\frac{1}{2} \cdot 18\right)^2$ or 81.

Consider the problem of solving the quadratic equation

$$3x^2 + 5x - 2 = 0.$$

First write the equation in the form where the coefficient of x^2 is unity and the constant terms have been removed to the right-hand side, thus

$$x^2 + \frac{5}{3}x = \frac{2}{3}.$$

Add $\left(\frac{1}{2} \cdot \frac{5}{3}\right)^2 = \frac{25}{36}$ to both members, and the left-hand member is a perfect square. We have then

$$x^2 + \frac{5}{3}x + \frac{25}{36} = \frac{2}{3} + \frac{25}{36} = \frac{49}{36},$$

or

$$\left(x + \frac{5}{6}\right)^2 = \frac{49}{36}.$$

Extracting the square root of both sides,

$$x + \frac{5}{6} = \pm \frac{7}{6},$$

$$x = -2 \text{ or } \frac{1}{3}.$$

Both of these values of x satisfy the original equation. Thus

$$3(-2)^2 + 5(-2) - 2 = 3 \cdot 4 - 10 - 2 = 0,$$

$$3\left(\frac{1}{3}\right)^2 + 5\left(\frac{1}{3}\right) - 2 = 3 \cdot \frac{1}{9} + \frac{5}{3} - 2 = 0.$$

Apply this method to the general quadratic equation

$$ax^2 + bx + c = 0.$$

Transpose c and divide through by a,

$$x^2 + \frac{b}{a}x = -\frac{c}{a}.$$

Add $\left(\dfrac{b}{2a}\right)^2$ to both members to make the left-hand member a perfect square,

$$x^2 + \frac{b}{a}x + \left(\frac{b}{2a}\right)^2 = -\frac{c}{a} + \left(\frac{b}{2a}\right)^2 = \frac{b^2 - 4ac}{4a^2},$$

or
$$\left(x + \frac{b}{2a}\right)^2 = \frac{b^2 - 4ac}{4a^2}.$$

Extract the square root, and obtain

$$x + \frac{b}{2a} = \frac{\pm \sqrt{b^2 - 4ac}}{2a},$$

or
$$x = \frac{-b \pm \sqrt{b^2 - 4ac}}{2a}.$$

Hence, the roots of the general quadratic equation

$$ax^2 + bx + c = 0$$

are
$$\frac{-b + \sqrt{b^2 - 4ac}}{2a} \quad \text{and} \quad \frac{-b - \sqrt{b^2 - 4ac}}{2a}.$$

If we denote the first of these roots by r_1 and the second by r_2, we may conveniently use these expressions as formulas for the solution of any quadratic. Thus, to solve the equation

$$3x^2 + 5x - 2 = 0,$$

we substitute in the formula, $a = 3$, $b = 5$, $c = -2$ and find

$$r_1 = \frac{-5 + \sqrt{25 - 4 \cdot 3 \cdot (-2)}}{6} = \frac{-5 + \sqrt{49}}{6} = \frac{1}{3}.$$

Similarly

$$r_2 = \frac{-5 - \sqrt{49}}{6} = -2.$$

EXERCISES

Solve the following equations by the method of completing the square.

1. $3x^2 + 4x - 4 = 0.$

2. $6x^2 - 29x + 35 = 0.$

3. $x^2 - 8x + 21 = 0.$

4. $25x^2 + 40x + 16 = 0.$

5. $x^2 + 2x + 4 = 0.$

6. $9x^2 + 12x + 5 = 0.$

7. $\dfrac{1}{2}gt^2 + v_0 t - s = 0.$

8. $Lm^2 + Rm + \dfrac{1}{C} = 0.$

Use the formula to solve the following equations and verify the results.

9. $2x^2 - 13x + 15 = 0.$

10. $x^2 + x + 1 = 0.$

11. $x^2 + 3x - 4 = 0.$

12. $7x^2 + 5x - 2 = 0.$

13. $4x - 2x^2 + 3 = 0.$

14. $3x - 5x^2 = 0.$

15. $(3x + 5)^2 = 8.$

16. $2x - x^2 = 3.$

17. $9x^2 - 12x + 13 = 0.$

18. $x^2 - \sqrt{2}x + \dfrac{5}{4} = 0.$

19. $ax^2 - (a^2 - 1)x = a.$

20. $kx^2 + x = 1 + kx.$

21. $6x^2 - ix + 15 = 0.$

22. $x^2 - (1 + 2i)x + i = 1.$

Solve by any method.

23. $0.3x^2 + 0.1x = 1.$

24. $0.2x^2 - 0.3x - 0.9 = 0.$

25. $(x - 2)^2 - 6(x - 2) - 7 = 0.$

26. $(x - 3)^2 + (x + 4)^2 = (2 - x)^2.$

27. $\begin{vmatrix} x & a & b \\ a & b & a \\ b & a & x \end{vmatrix} = 0.$

28. $\begin{vmatrix} x & 1 & 2 \\ 3 & 4 & 3 \\ 2 & 1 & x \end{vmatrix} = 0.$

29. $x^2 - \sqrt{2}x + \sqrt{5}x = \sqrt{10}.$

30. $x^2 + 2bx = 3ax + 6ab.$

31. $x^2 - 2nx = n^4 - n^2.$

32. $x^2 + nx - 2x = 2n^2 - 5n + 3.$

33. $x^2 + mx + nx = mnx + m^2n + mn^2.$

34. $(1 - e^2)x^2 - 2mx + m^2 = 0.$ Solve first for x in terms of m and e, then for m in terms of x and e, and finally for e in terms of m and x.

35. Show by substitution that

$$\frac{-b + \sqrt{b^2 - 4ac}}{2a} \quad \text{and} \quad \frac{-b - \sqrt{b^2 - 4ac}}{2a}$$

are roots of $ax^2 + bx + c = 0.$

The solution of the following fractional equations leads to the solution of quadratics. Solve the following equations and check your answers.

36. $\dfrac{5 - 2x}{7 - x} + \dfrac{3x^2 - 24x - 5}{x^2 - 8x + 7} - 6 = 0.$

37. $\dfrac{x}{x + 1} + \dfrac{x + 3}{3x} = \dfrac{11}{6}.$

38. $\dfrac{x-3}{7x-2x^2-6} - \dfrac{3x+5}{2x^2-x-6} + \dfrac{6x+12}{4x^2-9} = 0.$

39. $\dfrac{x-1}{(x-2)(x-3)} + \dfrac{x-2}{(x-1)(x-3)} + \dfrac{1}{x-2} = 0.$

Use logarithms in finding the solutions of the following equations correct to four significant figures.

40. $x^2 + 1.432x - 0.3925 = 0.$

41. $x^2 + 9.803x + 13.20 = 0.$

42. $x^2 - 7.345x + 5.237 = 0.$

43. $0.8763x^2 - 1.563x - 0.05380 = 0.$

The solution of the following equations containing radicals leads to the solution of quadratic equations. Solve the following equations and check your answers.

44. $\sqrt{5x-11} - \sqrt{3x-8} = 1.$

45. $\sqrt{7(x+2)} - \sqrt{x+11} = 3.$

46. $\sqrt{3x+4} - \sqrt{x+5} = 1.$

47. $\sqrt{x-3} + \sqrt{x} = \sqrt{x+5}.$

48. $\sqrt{2x+5} = \sqrt{x+2} + \sqrt{x-1}.$

49. $\sqrt{2x+1} + \sqrt{x-3} + \sqrt{x} = 0.$

75. Equations in the Quadratic Form

If in an equation we can replace an expression containing the variable by a new letter and have a quadratic equation in that letter, then the original equation is said to be in the **quadratic form.** Thus in the equation

$$(x^2 - 1)^2 - 11(x^2 - 1) + 24 = 0$$

if we let $z = x^2 - 1$, we obtain $z^2 - 11z + 24 = 0$. Again, if we let $u = x^{-\frac{3}{2}}$ in the equation $2x^{-3} + x^{-\frac{3}{2}} + 1 = 0$, we have

$$2u^2 + u + 1 = 0.$$

EXERCISES

Solve the following equations and check the results.

1. $x - 3 - \sqrt{x-3} - 2 = 0.$

Solution: Let $u = \sqrt{x-3}$, where the radical stands for the positive square root of the number under it. The equation then becomes

$$u^2 - u - 2 = 0,$$

or $$u = 2 \quad \text{or} \quad -1.$$

Replacing u by its value in terms of x, we have

$$\sqrt{x - 3} = 2,$$
$$\sqrt{x - 3} = -1.$$

Since $\sqrt{x - 3}$ is the positive square root of $(x - 3)$, the equation $\sqrt{x - 3} = -1$ must be discarded. From $\sqrt{x - 3} = 2$ we have $x - 3 = 4$, or $x = 7$.

Check: $7 - 3 - \sqrt{7 - 3} - 2 = 4 - \sqrt{4} - 2 = 4 - 2 - 2 = 0.$

Hence, the result $x = 7$ satisfies the equation.

2. $x^4 - 34x^2 + 225 = 0.$ **4.** $x^6 + 7x^3 - 8 = 0.$

3. $4x^4 - 41x^2 + 100 = 0.$ **5.** $8x^6 + 63x^3 - 8 = 0.$

6. $2(x - 2)^2 + 4(x - 2) - 3 = 0.$

7. $(x^2 - 1)^2 - 23(x^2 - 1) + 120 = 0.$

8. $(x^2 + x)^2 - 14(x^2 + x) + 24 = 0.$

9. $x^4 - 8x^3 + 7x^2 + 36x - 36 = 0.$

Hint: Write the equation in the form

$$(x^4 - 8x^3 + 16x^2) - 9(x^2 - 4x) - 36 = 0.$$

10. $x^4 + 4x^3 - 3x^2 - 14x - 8 = 0.$

11. $4x^4 - 12x^3 + 9x^2 - 4 = 0.$

12. $(x - 2) + \dfrac{4}{x - 2} = 5.$

13. $\sqrt{2x - 3} - \dfrac{6}{\sqrt{2x - 3}} = 5.$

14. $x^3 - 117x^{\frac{3}{2}} - 1000 = 0.$

15. $2x^{-\frac{2}{3}} + x^{-\frac{1}{3}} - 6 = 0.$

16. $2x^{\frac{2}{3}} + 3x^{\frac{1}{3}} - 2 = 0.$

17. $2x + \sqrt{2x + 1} = 19.$

Hint: Write the equation in the form

$$(2x + 1) + \sqrt{2x + 1} = 19 + 1.$$

18. $x - 2\sqrt{x - 3} - 18 = 0.$

19. $3\sqrt{\dfrac{x - 1}{x + 1}} - 2\sqrt{\dfrac{x + 1}{x - 1}} + 5 = 0.$

20. $x + 5\sqrt{x - 1} + 5 = 0.$

21. $\sqrt{x + 5} - 3\sqrt[4]{x + 5} - 18 = 0.$
22. $a(ax + b)^2 + b(ax + b) + c = 0.$
23. $\log^2_{10} x + 4 \log_{10} x - 12 = 0.$
24. $\log^2_{10} x + \log_{10} x^2 + 1 = 0.$
25. $10^{2x} - 5 \cdot 10^x + 6 = 0.$
26. $e^x + e^{-x} = 2.$
27. $e^x - 6e^{-x} + 1 = 0.$
28. $10^x + 10^{-x} = 6.$
29. $e^x + e^{-x} = 4.$

76. Theorems Concerning the Roots of Quadratic Equations

THEOREM I.   *If r is a root of the equation*

$$ax^2 + bx + c = 0, \tag{1}$$

then $(x - r)$ is a factor of $ax^2 + bx + c$. Conversely, if $(x - r)$ is a factor of $ax^2 + bx + c$, then r is a root of the equation.

If r is a root of the equation, then

$$ar^2 + br + c = 0. \quad \text{(Why?)} \tag{2}$$

We may now write

$$ax^2 + bx + c = ax^2 + bx + c - (ar^2 + br + c) \quad \text{(Why?)} \tag{3}$$
$$= a(x^2 - r^2) + b(x - r) \tag{4}$$
$$= (x - r)(ax + ar + b) \tag{5}$$

Hence, $(x - r)$ is a factor of $ax^2 + bx + c$.

Conversely, if $(x - r)$ is a factor of $ax^2 + bx + c$, then the substitution of r for x makes the factor $(x - r)$ vanish. Hence $ax^2 + bx + c$ takes on the value zero and r is a root of

$$ax^2 + bx + c = 0.$$

The student should study the special case for $r = 0$.

EXERCISES

Form quadratic equations which have the following pairs of numbers as roots.

1. 3, 1.

Solution: When the right-hand member of the equation to be formed is 0, the left-hand member has factors $(x - 3)$ and $(x - 1)$. Hence,

$$(x - 3)(x - 1) = x^2 - 4x + 3 = 0$$

is a quadratic equation with roots 1 and 3. There are, of course, an indefinite number of other quadratic equations having 1 and

3 for roots, for we can multiply through by any number; for example, $2x^2 - 8x + 6 = 0$, $3x^2 - 12x + 9 = 0$, have roots 1 and 3.

2. 2, 5.

∠**3.** 2, − 5.

4. − 2, 5.

5. − 2, − 5.

6. 0, − 3.

7. 2, −$\sqrt{2}$.

8. $\dfrac{1}{3}$, $\dfrac{1}{5}$.

9. $\dfrac{2}{5}$, − $\dfrac{3}{4}$.

10. $4 + \sqrt{3}$, $4 - \sqrt{3}$.

11. $3 + \sqrt{2}$, $2 - \sqrt{3}$.

12. $3 + 2i$, $3 - 2i$.

13. $3i$, − $3i$.

14. $1 - 2i$, $3 + i$.

15. $a - b$, $a + b$.

16. $\dfrac{3}{7}$, $\dfrac{7}{3}$.

∠**17.** $\dfrac{a}{b}$, $\dfrac{b}{a}$.

18. Verify by performing the indicated operations that

$$a\left(x - \frac{-b + \sqrt{b^2 - 4ac}}{2a}\right)\left(x - \frac{-b - \sqrt{b^2 - 4ac}}{2a}\right) \equiv ax^2 + bx + c.$$

77. Number of Roots

In order to avoid certain exceptions, an equation $f(x) = 0$ is said to have as many roots as $f(x)$ has factors of the type $(x - r_1)$ where r_1 is any number. A factor $(x - r_1)$ may be repeated. For example, if $(x - r_1)^2$ is a factor of $f(x)$, we say that $f(x) = 0$ has two roots equal to r_1.

We have shown that a quadratic equation has two roots. The question arises: has it *only* two or may it have more? This question is answered by the following

THEOREM II. *A quadratic equation has only two roots.*

Proof. Suppose there is, in addition to

$$r_1 = \frac{-b + \sqrt{b^2 - 4ac}}{2a}, \quad r_2 = \frac{-b - \sqrt{b^2 - 4ac}}{2a}$$

a third root r_3, distinct from r_1 and r_2, of the equation

$$ax^2 + bx + c = 0.$$

By exercise 18, Article **76,** $ax^2 + bx + c \equiv a(x - r_1)(x - r_2)$. Hence if r_3 is a root,

$$a(r_3 - r_1)(r_3 - r_2) = 0.$$

But this is impossible since no one of these factors is zero.

(IV, Art. **5**)

78. Special Forms of Quadratics

In the typical quadratic $ax^2 + bx + c = 0$, c is called the **constant term**, and bx the **term in x.** Either the constant term or the term in x or both may not be present, but we still have a quadratic equation though it consists of only one or two terms. Such quadratics are called **incomplete** quadratics.

If $c = 0$, $ax^2 + bx + c = 0$ becomes $ax^2 + bx = 0$. Since x is a factor of $ax^2 + bx$, we have one root equal to 0. If both b and c are 0, the equation becomes $ax^2 = 0$. Now x^2 is a factor, or x is a factor twice, and we have two roots equal to 0.

If $b = 0$, but $c \neq 0$, $ax^2 + bx + c = 0$ reduces to $ax^2 + c = 0$. In this case, $x = \pm \sqrt{-\dfrac{c}{a}}$. That is, the roots are arithmetically equal, but opposite in sign.

EXERCISES

Determine k so that each of the following equations shall have one root equal to zero. Find the other root.

1. $3x^2 + 6x - 5 + 2k = 0$.

Solution: One root only of the equation $ax^2 + bx + c = 0$ is zero when $c = 0$ and a, b are different from zero. In this exercise, $a = 3$, $b = 6$, $c = -5 + 2k$. In order for c to be zero, k must equal $\dfrac{5}{2}$. The other root is -2.

2. $3x^2 - 4x - 2k + k^2 = 0$.

3. $2x^2 - 8x - 12 + k + k^2 = 0$.

4. $(k - 1)x^2 + 2kx - k^2 + 9 = 0$.

Determine k and m so that each of the following equations shall have two roots equal to zero.

5. $3x^2 + 2mx - 3kx + m + k - 5 = 0$.

6. $(m^2 - k^2)x^2 + (3m - k - 7)x + m + 2k - 21 = 0$.

Determine k so that the roots of the following equations shall be arithmetically equal but opposite in sign. Find the roots.

7. $3x^2 - 2kx + 4x + 2k - 31 = 0$.

8. $(1 + k)x^2 + k^2x - kx - 6x - 5k - 1 = 0$.

79. Nature of the Roots

In Article **74**, we found the two roots of the quadratic equation

$$ax^2 + bx + c = 0$$

to be $r_1 = \dfrac{-b + \sqrt{b^2 - 4ac}}{2a}, \quad r_2 = \dfrac{-b - \sqrt{b^2 - 4ac}}{2a}.$

In case a, b, c are real numbers, the numerical character of these roots depends upon the number $b^2 - 4ac$ under the radical sign. An examination of r_1 and r_2 leads at once to the following conclusions:

(1) If $b^2 - 4ac > 0$, the roots are real and unequal.

(2) If $b^2 - 4ac < 0$, the roots are imaginary and unequal.

(3) If $b^2 - 4ac = 0$, the roots are real and equal.

It should be observed that if the coefficients are real and one root is imaginary, then both roots are imaginary.

The quantity $b^2 - 4ac$ is called the **discriminant** of the equation

$$ax^2 + bx + c = 0.$$

80. Sum and Product of the Roots

If we add together the two roots of $ax^2 + bx + c = 0$, we have

$$r_1 + r_2 = \frac{-b + \sqrt{b^2 - 4ac}}{2a} + \frac{-b - \sqrt{b^2 - 4ac}}{2a} = -\frac{b}{a}.$$

If we multiply the two roots together, we have

$$r_1 r_2 = \left(\frac{-b + \sqrt{b^2 - 4ac}}{2a}\right)\left(\frac{-b - \sqrt{b^2 - 4ac}}{2a}\right) = \frac{c}{a}.$$

Hence:

I. *The sum of the roots of a quadratic equation in x is equal to the coefficient of x with its sign changed, divided by the coefficient of x^2.*

II. *The product of the roots of a quadratic equation in x is equal to the constant term divided by the coefficient of x^2.*

EXERCISES

Determine the nature of the roots of the following equations.

1. $2x^2 + 5x - 12 = 0$.   **4.** $3x^2 + 2x + 1 = 0$.

2. $171x^2 + 53x = 0$.   **5.** $9x^2 + 30x + 25 = 0$.

3. $44x^2 + 235 = 0$.   **6.** $4x^2 - 9x + 5 = 0$.

For what values of k will the following equations have real and equal roots?

7. $8x^2 + 8kx + 3k + 2 = 0$.

Solution: Comparing this equation with the typical quadratic, we find that $a = 8$, $b = 8k$, $c = 3k + 2$. In order for the equation to have equal roots, it is necessary that $b^2 - 4ac = 0$.

Thus
$$64k^2 - 4 \cdot 8 \cdot (3k + 2) = 0,$$

or
$$2k^2 - 3k - 2 = 0,$$

whence
$$(2k + 1)(k - 2) = 0,$$

and
$$k = -\frac{1}{2} \quad \text{or} \quad k = 2.$$

Check: If $k = -\frac{1}{2}$, the quadratic becomes

$$8x^2 - 4x + \frac{1}{2} = 0,$$

or
$$16x^2 - 8x + 1 = 0,$$

which is a perfect square and both roots are equal to $\frac{1}{4}$.

If $k = 2$, the quadratic becomes

$$8x^2 + 16x + 8 = 0,$$

or
$$x^2 + 2x + 1 = 0,$$

which is again a perfect square, and the roots are both equal to -1.

8. $(k + 1)x^2 + kx + (k + 1) = 0$.
9. $x^2 + kx^2 - 5kx + 3k = 0$.
10. $8x^2 + 6x - k = kx$.
11. $k^2x^2 + 4(k - 1)x + 9 = 0$.
12. $(1 + k^2)x^2 + 20kx + 75 = 0$.
13. $4x^2 + 4(k - 1)x + 3 - k = 0$.
14. $kx^2 - kx + k - x^2 - 1 = 0$.
15. $8x^2 + 6kx - k^2 = 8 + 9x^2$.
16. $kx^2 + 2kx - 3x + k - 1 = 0$.
17. $kx^2 - (2k + 1)x + k + 1 = 0$.

First determine by inspection the sum and product of the roots of the following equations. Then solve the equations and check your answers.

18. $2x^2 + 3x = 27$.

19. $8x - 25 = x^2$.

20. $0.2x^2 + 0.9x = 3.5$.

21. $2 - 3x - 4x^2 = 0$.

22. $x^2 + 4x + 13 = 0$.

23. $Lx^2 + Rx + \frac{1}{C} = 0$.

24. $a^2x^2 + b^2x = c^2$.

Determine the value of k in the following equations which are subject to a given condition. Using the determined value of k, find the roots of the equation to check your answer.

25. $2x^2 + 7x - k = 0$, when one root is -5.

Solution 1. By the definition of root (Art. **26**), we have

$$2(-5)^2 + 7(-5) - k = 0,$$

or

$$k = 15.$$

Check: If $k = 15$, the equation becomes $2x^2 + 7x - 15 = 0$, or $(x + 5)(2x - 3) = 0$, whence one root is -5 and the other root is $\dfrac{3}{2}$.

Solution 2. From Article **80**, the sum of the roots is $-\dfrac{7}{2}$, or $r_1 + (-5) = -\dfrac{7}{2}$. Hence $r_1 = \dfrac{3}{2}$. From the same article, $r_1 \cdot r_2 = -\dfrac{k}{2}$ or $-\dfrac{15}{2} = -\dfrac{k}{2}$. Hence $k = 15$. Check as before.

26. $3x^2 + kx + 2 = 0$, where one root is 2.

27. $4x^2 - 20kx + 9k = 0$, where the difference of the roots is 4.

28. $5x^2 - kx + k - 1 = 0$, where the roots are reciprocals.

29. $5x^2 + kx - 27 = 0$, where a quotient of the roots is -15.

30. The sum and the product of the roots of a quadratic equation $ax^2 + bx + c = 0$ are given by

$$(1)\ \ r_1 + r_2 = -\frac{b}{a}, \text{ and } (2)\ \ r_1 r_2 = \frac{c}{a}$$

respectively. Is it possible to find r_1 and r_2 from the equations (1) and (2) without solving the quadratic equation?

31. If a mass of M grams is suspended at the end of an elastic spring in a resisting medium such as air, and if the mass is pulled down a distance of 2 centimeters from its equilibrium position and then released, the mass will oscillate provided the equation $Mx^2 + k_1x + k_2 = 0$ has imaginary roots. The constant k_1 depends on the nature of the medium and k_2 depends on the stiffness of the spring. If $k_1 = 2,000$ and $k_2 = 50,000$, find the range of values for M so that the mass will oscillate.

81. Graph of the Quadratic Function

In Chapter 4 we learned how to plot the graph of a function and in Chapter 5 we saw that the real roots of the equation $f(x) = 0$

are the abscissas of the points where the graph of the function $f(x)$ crosses the X-axis. It can be shown, if a is positive and different from zero, that the graph of the function $ax^2 + bx + c$ has the same general characteristics as the curve in Figure 13. This curve is called a parabola. The real roots of the equation

$$ax^2 + bx + c = 0$$

are given by the abscissas of the points where the curve crosses the X-axis.

FIG. 13

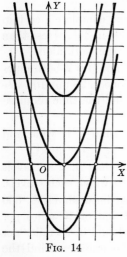

FIG. 14

If the curve has no point in common with the X-axis, then the roots of the equation are imaginary, for we have shown that every quadratic equation has two roots, real or imaginary. If the curve touches (is tangent to) the X-axis, both roots of the equation are real and equal. These three cases are shown in Figure 14, where the graphs of $x^2 - 2x - 3$, $x^2 - 2x + 1$, and $x^2 - 2x + 5$ are given.

EXERCISES

Construct the graphs of the following functions and by measurement determine their zeros if they are real. Choose the vertical unit of such length that the graph will be of convenient proportions for the coordinate paper.

1. $x^2 - 9$.
2. $9 - x^2$.
3. $x^2 + 9$.
4. $x^2 + 3x$.
5. $x^2 - 3x$.
6. $3x - x^2$.
7. $x^2 - 2x - 3$.

8. $x^2 - 7x + 12$.
9. $6x^2 + 5x - 6$.
10. $8 + 10x - 3x^2$.
11. $x^2 - 4x - 1$.
12. $2x^2 - 2x - 1$.
13. $x^2 - 6x + 13$.
14. $2x - 2 - x^2$.

15. What are the general characteristics of the graph of the function $ax^2 + bx + c$ if a is negative? If $b = 0$? If $c = 0$?

PROBLEMS

1. Find two consecutive positive integers whose product is 462.

2. Find two consecutive positive odd integers whose product is 1155.

3. The sum of the squares of two consecutive positive even integers is 452. Find the integers.

4. Working together, a man and his son can complete a certain job in 2 days; working alone the man can do it in 3 days less than the boy. How long would it take each to do the work alone?

5. A tank can be filled by two pipes in 24 minutes if both pipes are open. The larger pipe can fill the tank alone in 20 minutes less time than it takes the smaller pipe alone. Find the time required by each pipe to fill the tank.

6. A rectangular court is 24 feet longer than it is wide and contains 3,456 square feet. Find the dimensions of the court.

7. A travels 780 miles in one hour less time than B. If A travels 5 miles per hour faster than B, find the rate at which each travels.

8. An aviator is flying a straight course between cities 600 miles apart. Outward bound he has a tailwind of 10 miles per hour, while on the return trip he has a headwind of 20 miles per hour. He does the round trip in 7 hours 20 minutes. Find the average cruising speed of the plane.

9. If an object is projected vertically upward with an initial velocity v_0 feet per second, the distance, d, in feet from the point of projection to the object at the end of t seconds is given by the formula

$$d = v_0 t - \frac{1}{2} g t^2,$$

where g is the acceleration due to gravity. The velocity of the object at time t is given by

$$v = v_0 - gt.$$

If the object is projected downward with an initial velocity v_0 feet per second, the distance from the point of projection to the object at the end of t seconds is given by

$$d = v_0 t + \frac{1}{2} g t^2,$$

and its velocity at time t is given by

$$v = v_0 + gt.$$

In order to avoid tedious calculation at this point, we shall sacrifice some accuracy and assume that in the problems in this group $g = 32$ feet per second per second.

(a) A ball is thrown upward with an initial speed of 60 feet per second. At what time will the ball be 36 feet above the ground? Explain the two answers.

(b) At what time is the velocity of the ball zero?

(c) How high will the ball rise?

(d) At what time will it strike the ground?

(e) How far will the ball travel during the third second?

(f) How far will it travel during the second second?

10. From a point 700 feet above the ground, a ball is thrown downward with an initial velocity of 60 feet per second. When and with what speed will it strike the ground? How far will the ball fall during the second second? How far will it fall during the fifth second?

11. If the ball in problem 10 were dropped from rest, that is, if the initial velocity were zero, find how much longer it would take for it to reach the ground.

12. If the ball of problem 10 were thrown upward with an initial velocity of 60 feet per second, how long would it take for the ball to strike the ground?

13. The edges of a cube are each increased in length one inch. It is found that the volume is thereby increased **16** cubic inches. What was the length of an edge of the cube?

14. The diagonal of a cube is one unit longer than an edge of the cube. What is the length of an edge?

15. The radius of a cylinder is 12 inches and its height is 4 inches. How much can be added to either the radius or to the height, and yet give the same increase in volume?

16. By increasing the radius of a sphere 1 inch, its volume is increased by 10 cubic inches. Find the radius of the original sphere to two decimal places.

17. A rectangular sheet of tin whose dimensions are a and b has square corners cut out, and the sides turned up to form a box. The box will have maximum volume if the depth x is a root of

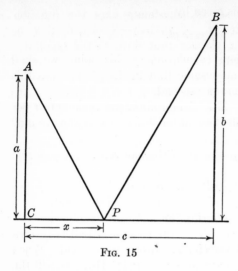

Fig. 15

$12x^2 - 4(a+b)x + ab = 0$. Find this depth. Also find the depth when the rectangle is a square of side a.

18. A ship A rides at anchor a miles offshore (Fig. 15). Further along the shore c miles, another ship B rides at anchor b miles offshore. A boat is to take a passenger from A to the shore and then proceed to B. If the boat lands the passenger at P which is x miles from C, the course of the boat will be minimum in length if x is a solution of

$$\frac{x}{\sqrt{x^2 + a^2}} = \frac{c - x}{\sqrt{b^2 + (x - c)^2}}.$$

Find x.

19. A man in a ship A riding at anchor a miles offshore is directed to proceed immediately to a point B on the shore (Fig. 16). A motor launch at the ship can travel r_1 miles per hour and a car can travel along the shore at the rate of r_2 miles per hour. If B is b miles from C and if the man lands at P which is x miles from C, he can reach B in the shortest possible time if x is a solution of

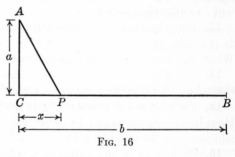

Fig. 16

$$\frac{x}{r_1\sqrt{a^2 + x^2}} = \frac{1}{r_2}.$$

Find x.

20. Show that the equation $x^2 + bx + c = 0$ has one positive root and one negative root if b is real and c is negative.

21. Plot on the same set of coordinate axes the function $2x^2 - 3x + c$, where c takes on the values -5, -2, 0, 1, 3, 5. What effect does changing the constant term in the quadratic function have on the graph?

22. Plot on the same set of coordinate axes the function $ax^2 - 2x - 1$, where a takes the values 8, 3, 1, 0.5, 0.25, 0.1, 0.01. Decreasing the coefficient of x^2 toward zero has what effect on the graph? What is the effect on the roots of the quadratic equation $ax^2 - 2x - 1 = 0$, if a is made to approach zero?

The following three equations occur in some electrical problems.

23. $g = \dfrac{R}{R^2 + X^2}.$ Solve for R.

24. $T = \dfrac{a(n - n')}{1 + b(n - n')^2}.$ Solve for $(n - n')$.

25. $P = \dfrac{RW(r^2 + x^2)}{r(Rr - Xx)}.$ Solve for x.

26. In the course of Steinmetz's solution of the problem of finding the current strength in a divided electric circuit, it is necessary to solve the equation

$$a^2x^2 - as^2 + r^2 = 0$$

for a. His solution is

$$\frac{s^2 \pm q^2}{2x^2},$$

where $q^2 = \sqrt{s^4 - 4r^2x^2}$. Verify the result.

27. In joining together two steel boiler plates with a single row of rivets, the distance p between the centers of the rivets is given by the formula

$$p = 0.56\,\frac{d^2}{t} + d,$$

where t is the thickness of the plate and d the diameter of the rivet holes. In a boiler the rivets are to be placed $1\frac{1}{2}$ inches apart. If the thickness of the plate is $\dfrac{3}{16}$ inch, what is the diameter of the rivet holes?

28. If s is the area in square inches of the flat end of a boiler, and t the thickness of the boiler plate in sixteenths of an inch, then the pressure p per square inch which the flat end plate can safely sustain is given by the formula

$$p = \frac{200(t + 1)^2}{s - 6}.$$

What should be the thickness to the nearest sixteenth of an inch of the boiler plate for the end of a boiler 20 inches in diameter to sustain a pressure of 100 pounds per square inch?

29. Let h be the height and t the thickness (in feet) of a rectangular masonry retaining wall. For very sandy soil with a grade angle of 20°, h and t are connected by the equation

$$t^2 + 0.19t \cdot h - 0.18h^2 = 0.$$

What should be the thickness (to the nearest inch) of a retaining wall four feet high?

30. For loam, the equation in problem 29 would be

$$t^2 + 0.14t \cdot h - 0.13h^2 = 0.$$

What should be the thickness of a retaining wall four feet high?

31. A long horizontal pipe is connected with the bottom of a reservoir. If H be the depth of the water in the reservoir in feet, d the diameter of the pipe in inches, L the length of the pipe in feet, and v the velocity of the water in the pipe in feet per second, then according to Cox's formula

$$\frac{Hd}{L} = \frac{4v^2 + 5v - 2}{1200}.$$

Find the velocity of water in a 5-inch pipe, 1000 feet long, connected with a reservoir containing 49 feet of water.

32. The so-called effective area of a chimney is given by

$$E = A - 0.6\sqrt{A},$$

where A is the measured area. Find A when E is 24 square feet.

33. The electrical resistance of a wire depends upon the temperature of the wire according to the formula

$$R_t = R_0(1 + at + bt^2),$$

where a and b are constants depending on the material, R_0 is the resistance at 0°, and R_t the resistance at $t°$. For copper wire $a = 0.00387$, $b = 0.00000597$, and $R_0 = 0.02057$. At what temperature is the resistance double that at 0°?

34. A stone is dropped into a well, and 4 seconds afterward the report of its striking the water is heard. If the velocity of sound is taken at 1190 feet per second, what is the depth of the well? (Use $g = 32.2$. See problem 9.)

10 SYSTEMS OF EQUATIONS INVOLVING QUADRATICS

82. Quadratic Equations in Two Variables

In Chapter 6 we discussed the solution of a system of n linear equations in n variables, for the cases where $n = 2, 3, 4$. In this chapter, we propose to attempt the solution of two quadratic equations in two variables.

An equation of the form

$$Ax^2 + Bxy + Cy^2 + Dx + Ey + F = 0, \tag{1}$$

in which x and y appear and at least one of the coefficients A, B, or C is not zero, is called a **quadratic equation in x and y.** Equation (1) is called the **general equation of the second degree in x and y.**

We shall see that the problem of solving a system which contains two equations of the type (1) is in general beyond our power at this stage. We will therefore confine our attention to a number of special systems that are of interest in later mathematics and its applications.

ORAL EXERCISES

By comparison with the general equation (1), give the values of A, B, C, D, E, and F in each of the following:

1. $x^2 + y^2 - 16 = 0.$
2. $7x^2 + 4y^2 = 28.$
3. $y^2 - x^2 = 9.$
4. $xy = 16.$
5. $4x^2 - 3y^2 + 8x + 6y = 11.$
6. $xy + 6x - 4y = 0.$
7. $2y = 3x^2 + 4x - 2.$
8. $xy - 3y^2 + 2x = 6.$

83. One Equation Linear and One Quadratic

Any system of two equations in two variables in which one equation is linear and the other is quadratic can be solved by

147

elimination of one of the variables. First solve the linear equation for one variable in terms of the other, say for y in terms of x. Then substitute this expression for y in terms of x in the quadratic equation and obtain a quadratic equation in the variable x, which may be solved for x. The values of x so obtained are then substituted in the *linear* equation in order to obtain the corresponding values of y.

Example 1. Solve the system

$$x^2 + y^2 = 25, \tag{1}$$
$$x - y = 1. \tag{2}$$

Solution: Solving (2) for y in terms of x,

$$y = x - 1. \tag{3}$$

Substituting $x - 1$ for y in (1),

$$x^2 + (x - 1)^2 = 25,$$
or $$x^2 - x - 12 = 0. \tag{4}$$

Equations (3) and (4) form a system that is equivalent to the system formed by equations (1) and (2). The new system may be written in the form

$$(x - 4)(x + 3) = 0,$$
$$y = x - 1.$$

This system of equations is equivalent to two systems of linear equations:

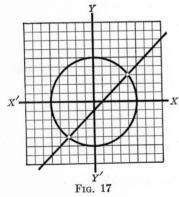

$$x - 4 = 0, \quad \text{or } x + 3 = 0,$$
$$y = x - 1; \qquad y = x - 1.$$

The first system of linear equations yields the solution $x = 4$, $y = 3$. The second gives $x = -3$, $y = -4$. These solutions may be checked by substitution in equations (1) and (2).

Graphical meaning of the two solutions. The graph of

$$x - y = 1 \tag{2}$$

Fig. 17

is the straight line shown in Figure 17, and the graph of

$$x^2 + y^2 = 25 \tag{1}$$

is the circle there shown. To draw the graph of (1), the student may give various values to x and calculate the corresponding values for y from $y = \pm \sqrt{25 - x^2}$.

Any point on the circle (1) has coordinates that satisfy equation (1). Any point on the straight line (2) has coordinates that satisfy equation (2). The points $(4, 3)$ and $(-3, -4)$ lie on both graphs, and satisfy both equations (1) and (2). That is to say, each point of intersection of the graph of (1) with the graph of (2) gives a pair of numbers that is a solution of the system.

Example 2. Solve the system

$$xy = 24, \tag{1}$$
$$y - 2x + 2 = 0. \tag{2}$$

Solution: Solving (2) for y in terms of x,

$$y = 2x - 2. \tag{3}$$

Substituting $2x - 2$ for y in (1), we have

$$x(2x - 2) = 24, \tag{4}$$

which reduces to $\qquad (x - 4)(x + 3) = 0. \tag{5}$

Equations (3) and (5) form a new system which is equivalent to the given system. This new system is equivalent to two systems of two linear equations:

$$x - 4 = 0, \ y = 2x - 2; \tag{6}$$

and $\qquad x + 3 = 0, \ y = 2x - 2. \tag{7}$

The linear system (6) yields the solution

$$x = 4, \ y = 6;$$

while the system (7) yields the solution

$$x = -3, \ y = -8.$$

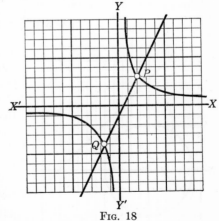

Fig. 18

These pairs of values for x and y may be checked by substitution in the equations (1) and (2).

Graphical meaning of the solutions. The graphs for equations (1) and (2) are shown in Figure 18. The graph of

$$y - 2x + 2 = 0$$

is the straight line, and that of

$$xy = 24$$

is the curve with two branches as shown. This curve belongs to a class of curves called **hyperbolas**. The points of intersection, P and Q, have coordinates that are the solutions of the given system. All points on the graph of (1) have coordinates that satisfy equation (1). All points on the graph of (2) have coordinates that satisfy equation (2). Therefore, the points of intersection have coordinates that satisfy both equations.

Example 3. Solve the system

$$x^2 + y^2 = 25, \tag{1}$$
$$x + y = 10, \tag{2}$$

and draw the graph to explain the fact that the solutions are not real.

If the student carries out the same method as that illustrated in Example 1, he will obtain for solutions

$$x = 5 + \frac{5i}{2}\sqrt{2},$$

$$y = 5 - \frac{5i}{2}\sqrt{2};$$

and

$$x = 5 - \frac{5i}{2}\sqrt{2},$$

$$y = 5 + \frac{5i}{2}\sqrt{2},$$

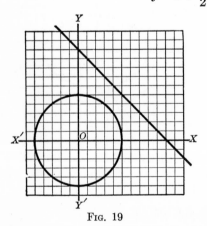

FIG. 19

where $i^2 = -1$. Check these solutions by substitution in (1) and (2).

The graph of equation (1) is the circle shown in Figure 19, and the graph of equation (2) is the straight line there shown. It is to be noted that these graphs do not intersect. This fact means that there exists no pair of real numbers that satisfies both equations (1) and (2).

84. Comments on the Graphs of Quadratic Equations in Two Variables

In analytic geometry, a detailed study is made of the graphs of quadratic equations in two variables. A general notion of the shape of the graph of a quadratic equation in two variables may be given by considering the curve formed by the intersection of a plane and a right circular cone. On this account, the curves are called *conic sections* or merely *conics*. The cone used in this connection is the double cone as shown in Figure 20. A conic may be a circle, an ellipse, a hyperbola, a parabola. In addition, the graphs of certain quadratic equations may be a pair of straight lines, or a point. The graphs of a few equations of standard forms will now be briefly discussed.

FIG. 20

(1) The graph of an equation of the form

$$Ax^2 + Ay^2 = C,$$

in which A and C have the same sign, is a circle with its center at the origin and with its radius equal to $\sqrt{\dfrac{C}{A}}$. Thus, $x^2 + y^2 = 9$ is a circle with its center at the origin and of radius 3.

(2) The graph of an equation of the form

$$Ax^2 + By^2 = C,$$

in which A, B, and C have the same signs, but $A \neq B$, is an oval-shaped figure called an **ellipse** with its center at the origin and with symmetry about the X- and Y-axes. Thus, the

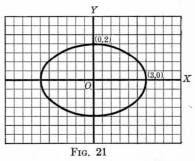

FIG. 21

graph of $4x^2 + 9y^2 = 36$ shown in Figure 21 is an ellipse which crosses the X-axis at $(\pm 3, 0)$ and the Y-axis at $(0, \pm 2)$.

(3) The graph of an equation of the form

$$Ax^2 + By^2 = C,$$

in which A and B have opposite signs, and $C \neq 0$, represents a **hyperbola** with symmetry about the X- and Y-axes. The hyperbola has two separate parts (Fig. 22). Thus, the graph of $4x^2 - 9y^2 = 36$ shown in Figure 22 is a hyperbola which crosses the X-axis at $(\pm\, 3, 0)$.

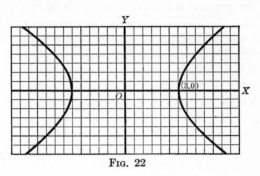

Fig. 22

(4) The graph of an equation of the form

$$y = ax^2 + bx + c$$

represents a **parabola** as explained in Article **81**.

EXERCISES AND PROBLEMS

Solve the following systems, verify each set of roots by substitution in the given equations, and draw the graphs in exercises 1, 2, 3, 4, 5, 6.

1. $x^2 + 9y^2 = 225,$
    $x - 3y = -3.$

2. $x^2 + 9y^2 = 225,$
    $x - 4y = 25.$

3. $x^2 + 9y^2 = 225,$
    $3y - 2x = 45.$

4. $x^2 + y^2 = 20,$
    $y - x = 6.$

5. $3y^2 - 4x^2 = 12,$
    $3x + 2y = 4.$

6. $xy - 18 = 0,$
    $3y - 2x = 12.$

7. $x^2 + y^2 - 4x + 6y + 3 = 0,$
    $x + y = 1.$

8. $xy - 2x + y - 5 = 0,$
    $3x + y + 1 = 0.$

9. $4y + 10x^2 + 7x - 8 = 0,$
    $6x - 8y + 1 = 0.$

10. $x^2 - 5xy + 4y^2 = 0,$
    $2x - 3y = 6.$

11. $3x^2 + y^2 = 14,$
    $2x + y = 7.$

12. $3x^2 + 2y^2 = 77,$
    $3x + y = 7.$

13. $\dfrac{3}{x} + \dfrac{2}{y} = 5,$

$9x - 14y + 5 = 0.$

14. $x^2 + y^2 - 2xy - 2ax - 2ay + a^2 = 0,$

$x + y = a.$

15. $x^2 + y^2 - 2xy - 2ax - 2ay + a^2 = 0,$

$y = x.$

16. $y^2 = 2px,$

$2my = 2m^2x + p.$

17. $\dfrac{(x-1)^2}{9} + \dfrac{(y+2)^2}{4} = 1,$

$y = 2x - 1.$

18. The sum of two numbers is 16 and their product is 63. Find the numbers.

19. The sum of the squares of the two digits of a positive integer is 89. The number itself is 7 more than 6 times the sum of its digits. Find the number.

20. The perimeter of a rectangle is 82 inches. Its area is 364 square inches. Find its length and breadth.

21. The hypotenuse of a right triangle is 39 inches. The difference in the lengths of the legs is 21 inches. Find the lengths of the legs.

Supplementary Exercises

Find the values of a, c, m, or r in the following exercises so that the straight line which is the locus of the first degree equation

(1) cuts the other locus in two distinct points,

(2) is tangent to the curve,

(3) fails to meet the curve.

22. $x^2 + y^2 = r^2,$

$3x + 4y = 5.$

The locus of the first equation is a circle with center at the origin and a radius equal to r.

Solution: From the second equation, we have

$$x = \frac{5 - 4y}{3}.$$

Substituting in the first, we find

$$25y^2 - 40y + 25 - 9r^2 = 0.$$

Solving for y, we obtain, $y = \dfrac{40 \pm 30\sqrt{r^2 - 1}}{50}$.

If y is real, $r^2 - 1$ must be equal to or greater than zero.

Furthermore, if r is any number greater than 1, the two loci intersect in real and distinct points.

If $r = 1$, there is only one value for y, and the line is tangent to the circle. If $r < 1$, the line does not intersect the circle.

23. $x^2 + y^2 = r^2$,
  $2x - y = 4$.

24. $x^2 + y^2 = 16$,
  $y = mx - 6$.

25. $y = 2x^2 - 3x + 2$,
  $y = 5x + c$.

26. $4x^2 - 9y^2 = 36$,
  $ax + 6y = 9$.

27. For what values of b in terms of r and m does the system of equations

$$y = mx + b,$$
$$x^2 + y^2 = r^2$$

have equal solutions?

28. Determine the relation between a, b, m, and k such that the system

$$y = mx + k,$$
$$\frac{x^2}{a^2} + \frac{y^2}{b^2} = 1$$

has equal solutions.

29. Show that the straight line $4x + 5y = 25$ is tangent to the curve $9x^2 + 25y^2 = 225$, and find the point of contact of this tangent.

85. Both Equations Quadratic

When both equations of a system are quadratic, the problem is often so difficult that the system cannot be solved by methods at our disposal.

As illustrated in the following example, the solution of a pair of quadratic equations often reduces to the solution of an equation of the fourth degree.

Example: Solve $x^2 + y^2 + x - 9 = 0$,
    $x^2 + 2y^2 - 3y - 8 = 0$.

Subtracting the second from the first, we have

$$- y^2 + 3y + x - 1 = 0,$$

or
    $x = 1 - 3y + y^2$.

Substituting in the second equation, we have

$$(1 - 3y + y^2)^2 + 2y^2 - 3y - 8 = 0,$$

or $\qquad y^4 - 6y^3 + 13y^2 - 9y - 7 = 0.$

At this stage of his progress in algebra, the student will not be able to solve a general equation of the fourth degree; hence he cannot proceed with the solution of this problem. There are, however, some forms of such equations for which we may easily obtain solutions. In Articles **86, 87,** and **88** we shall consider a few such equations.

When both equations are quadratic, the system ordinarily has **four different solutions.** When each of the four solutions is a pair of real numbers, the graphs intersect in four points whose coordinates are the solutions as in Figure 23. When two of the four solutions are real numbers and two involve imaginary numbers, the graphs intersect in only two points. When each of the four solutions involves imaginary numbers, the graphs do not intersect.

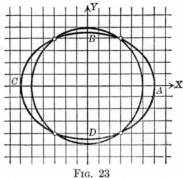

Fig. 23

86. Both Equations of the Form $ax^2 + by^2 + c = 0$

If, instead of considering x and y as the variables, we consider first x^2 and y^2 as the variables, the method of solution is that for linear equations.

EXERCISES

Solve the following systems of equations and give the graphical representations for exercises 1, 2, 3, 4, 5, 6, and 7:

1. $\qquad 16x^2 + 27y^2 = 576,$
$$x^2 + y^2 = 25.$$

Solution: Solving for x^2 and y^2 we have

$$x^2 = \frac{\begin{vmatrix} 576 & 27 \\ 25 & 1 \end{vmatrix}}{\begin{vmatrix} 16 & 27 \\ 1 & 1 \end{vmatrix}} = \frac{-99}{-11} = 9, \qquad y^2 = \frac{\begin{vmatrix} 16 & 576 \\ 1 & 25 \end{vmatrix}}{\begin{vmatrix} 16 & 27 \\ 1 & 1 \end{vmatrix}} = 16.$$

$$x = \pm 3. \qquad\qquad\qquad y = \pm 4.$$

Hence, we find the following four solutions,

$$(3, 4), (-3, 4), (3, -4), (-3, -4).$$

To show these solutions graphically, we plot the graphs of the two equations. Solving each for y, we have

$$y = \pm \sqrt{\frac{576 - 16x^2}{27}},$$

and $$y = \pm \sqrt{25 - x^2}.$$

The first equation has for its graph an ellipse, the second, the circle (Fig. 23). The points of intersection represent graphically the four pairs of solutions.

2. $9x^2 + 4y^2 = 72,$
$x^2 + y^2 = 13.$

3. $9x^2 + 4y^2 = 72,$
$x^2 + 2y^2 = 36.$

4. $9x^2 + 4y^2 = 72,$
$3x^2 + 2y^2 = 48.$

5. $5x^2 + 4y^2 = 80,$
$5x^2 - 3y^2 = 45.$

6. $4x^2 - 9y^2 = 36,$
$9x^2 - 4y^2 = 36.$

7. $225x^2 - 64y^2 = 0,$
$x^2 + y^2 = 289.$

8. $7x^2 + 4y^2 = 64,$
$4x^2 - 5y^2 = 22.$

9. $14x^2 - 15y^2 = -2,$
$18x^2 + 5y^2 = 12.$

10. $4x^2 - 5y^2 = 20,$
$x^2 - y^2 = 9.$

11. $25x^2 - 9y^2 = 225,$
$4x^2 - 9y^2 = 36.$

12. Find four pairs of numbers such that the sum and difference of the squares of each pair are respectively 225 and 63.

87. All Terms Containing Variables Are of the Second Degree

Equations in which each term containing a variable is of the second degree have no first degree terms. Two methods of solution of such equations are illustrated by the following example.

Example: Solve $x^2 + y^2 = 20,$ (1)
$ x^2 + 3xy = 28.$ (2)

First solution: The main feature of the first solution is that we obtain a factorable second degree expression by the elimination of the constant terms. To do this, we treat our example as follows:

Multiply (1) by 7: $\qquad 7x^2 + 7y^2 = 140.$ $\hspace{3em}$ (3)

Multiply (2) by 5: $\qquad 5x^2 + 15xy = 140.$ $\hspace{3em}$ (4)

Subtract, (3) − (4): $\quad 2x^2 - 15xy + 7y^2 = 0;$ or,

$$(y - 2x)(7y - x) = 0. \hspace{3em} (5)$$

By equating each factor of (5) to zero, we obtain two linear equations:

$$y - 2x = 0 \quad \text{and} \quad 7y - x = 0.$$

It remains to solve each of these equations with (1) or (2), say with (1). Thus, we are to solve the two systems:

$$y - 2x = 0, \hspace{3em} (6)$$
$$x^2 + y^2 = 20; \hspace{3em} (7)$$

and

$$7y - x = 0, \hspace{3em} (8)$$
$$x^2 + y^2 = 20. \hspace{3em} (9)$$

Solving (6) and (7), we get the solutions $(2, 4)$, $(-2, -4)$, and solving (8) and (9), we get

$$\left(\frac{7}{5}\sqrt{10}, \frac{1}{5}\sqrt{10}\right), \left(-\frac{7}{5}\sqrt{10}, -\frac{1}{5}\sqrt{10}\right).$$

Second solution: The main feature of the second solution is the substitution of $y = mx$ in both equations.

By setting $y = mx$ in (1), we have

$$x^2 + m^2x^2 = 20,$$

whence $\hspace{6em} x^2 = \dfrac{20}{1 + m^2}.$ $\hspace{3em}$ (10)

By setting $y = mx$ in (2), we have

$$x^2 + 3mx^2 = 28,$$

whence $\hspace{6em} x^2 = \dfrac{28}{1 + 3m}.$ $\hspace{3em}$ (11)

Equating these values of x^2 in (10) and (11), we obtain

$$\frac{28}{1 + 3m} = \frac{20}{1 + m^2}.$$

Clearing of fractions and reducing, we obtain

$$7m^2 - 15m + 2 = 0,$$

or $\hspace{6em} m = 2, \text{ or } \dfrac{1}{7}.$

Substituting these values of m in $x^2 = \dfrac{28}{1+3m}$, we find, for $m = 2$,

$$x^2 = 4,\ x = \pm\, 2,$$
$$y = mx = \pm\, 4.$$

For $m = \dfrac{1}{7}$, we find $\quad x^2 = \dfrac{98}{5},\ x = \pm\, \dfrac{7}{5}\, \sqrt{10} = \pm\, 4.43^+,$

$$y = mx = \pm\, \dfrac{1}{5}\, \sqrt{10} = \pm\, 0.63^+.$$

The solutions are therefore

$$(2,\, 4),\ (-\, 2,\, -\, 4),\ \left(\dfrac{7}{5}\, \sqrt{10}, \dfrac{1}{5}\, \sqrt{10}\right),\ \left(-\, \dfrac{7}{5}\, \sqrt{10}, -\, \dfrac{1}{5}\sqrt{10}\right).$$

The graphs of the two equations of this exercise are shown in Figure 24. The geometrical interpretation of the substitution $y = mx$ is also shown in the figure.

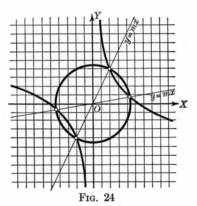

FIG. 24

EXERCISES

Solve each of the following systems of equations and plot the graphs in exercises 1 and 2.

1. $x^2 + y^2 = 1,$
   $25xy = 12.$

2. $x^2 - y^2 = 3,$
   $xy = 2.$

3. $x(x + y) = 35,$
   $y(x + y) = 14.$

4. $x(x + y) = 70,$
   $y(x - y) = 12.$

5. $4x^2 - xy + y^2 = 24,$
   $x^2 + 2y^2 = 12.$

6. $x^2 - xy + y^2 = 7,$
   $2x^2 + 3xy - 4y^2 = -\, 10.$

7. $3x^2 + 2xy - y^2 = 5,$
    $5x^2 - xy - 4y^2 = 9.$

8. $2x^2 + xy - 8y^2 - 2 = 0,$
    $x^2 - 3xy - 4y^2 + 6 = 0.$

9. $4x^2 - 5y^2 = 16,$
    $12x^2 - 8xy - 7y^2 = 32.$

10. $2x^2 - 5xy + y^2 = 1,$
    $x^2 - 3xy + 3y^2 = 1.$

88. Symmetrical Equations

An equation is said to be **symmetrical with respect to x and y** whenever interchanging x and y leaves the equation unchanged. The typical form of a symmetrical quadratic equation in two variables is

$$A(x^2 + y^2) + Bxy + D(x + y) + F = 0.$$

The solution is illustrated in the following.

Example: Solve $\quad x^2 + y^2 + x + y = 8,$ $\qquad\qquad$ (1)
$$xy + x + y = 5. \qquad\qquad (2)$$

Solution: Let $x = u + v$, $y = u - v$. Substituting in the two equations we obtain after reductions

$$u^2 + v^2 + u = 4, \qquad\qquad (3)$$
$$u^2 - v^2 + 2u = 5. \qquad\qquad (4)$$

Eliminating v^2 by adding we obtain an equation in u,

$$2u^2 + 3u = 9,$$

from which $u = \dfrac{3}{2}$ or -3.

The four solutions of (3) and (4) are then

$$\left(\frac{3}{2}, \frac{1}{2}\right), \left(\frac{3}{2}, -\frac{1}{2}\right), (-3, i\sqrt{2}), (-3, -i\sqrt{2}).$$

From the first pair

$$x = u + v = \frac{3}{2} + \frac{1}{2} = 2,$$

$$y = u - v = \frac{3}{2} - \frac{1}{2} = 1.$$

In a similar way we find from the other pairs,

$$\left.\begin{array}{l} x = 1 \\ y = 2 \end{array}\right\}, \qquad \left.\begin{array}{l} x = -3 + i\sqrt{2} \\ y = -3 - i\sqrt{2} \end{array}\right\}, \qquad \left.\begin{array}{l} x = -3 - i\sqrt{2} \\ y = -3 + i\sqrt{2} \end{array}\right\}.$$

Solve the following systems of equations:

1. $x^2 + y^2 = 13$,
$xy + x + y = 11$.

2. $3x^2 + 3y^2 + 2xy + 5x + 5y = 34$,
$2x^2 + 2y^2 - xy + 15x + 15y = 53$.

3. $3x^2 + 3y^2 - 2xy = 19$,
$2xy - x - y = -3$.

4. $x^2 + y^2 + 5xy + 3x + 3y - 16 = 0$,
$2x^2 + 2y^2 - 11xy - x - y + 24 = 0$.

5. $2x^2 + 2y^2 - 3xy + x + y - 29 = 0$,
$x^2 + y^2 - xy - x - y - 9 = 0$.

6. $x^2 + y^2 + 2xy - 4x - 4y = 12$,
$x^2 + y^2 - xy - x - y = 3$.

89. Special Devices

Systems of equations involving quadratics which do not come under the classifications already discussed may frequently be solved by special methods, which will be indicated in the problems at the end of this section. The types of equations already discussed may often be solved more easily by these special devices. Furthermore, many systems of equations of degree higher than two, and systems containing three or more variables may be solved by combinations of the methods already discussed and these special devices. It must, however, be borne in mind that these methods are not sufficient to solve all possible systems that might appear. Whatever method is used, the ultimate test of a solution is substitution in the original equations.

Example: Solve $x^2 + y^2 = 13$ and $xy = 6$.

Solution: This set of equations may be solved by either the method of Article **87** or that of Article **88**. However, if the second equation is multiplied by 2, and if this resulting equation is then added to the first equation and then subtracted from the first equation, the following system is obtained.

$$x^2 + 2xy + y^2 = 25,$$
$$x^2 - 2xy + y^2 = 1.$$

Extracting the square root of each equation of this system, we have

$$x + y = \pm 5,$$
$$x - y = \pm 1.$$

We thus have four systems of linear equations which yield the four pairs of values $(3, 2)$, $(2, 3)$, $(-3, -2)$, and $(-2, -3)$.

MISCELLANEOUS EXERCISES AND PROBLEMS INVOLVING QUADRATICS

Solve the following systems of equations. Check your results in exercises 1–6 by means of graphs.

1. $x^2 + 2y^2 = 8,$
$x + 2y = 6.$

2. $x^2 + 4y^2 = 25,$
$x^2 - 2y^2 = 1.$

3. $xy = 9,$
$y^2 = 3x.$

4. $y^2 = 4x,$
$x^2 = 4y.$

Hint: Subtract the equations and factor the difference.

8. $2x^2 + 2y^2 - 3x - 10y - 2 = 0,$
$x^2 + y^2 - 2x - 6y + 5 = 0.$

9. $\dfrac{1}{x^2} + \dfrac{1}{y^2} = 29,$

$\dfrac{1}{x} + \dfrac{1}{y} = 3.$

10. $\dfrac{9}{x^2} + \dfrac{16}{y^2} = 348,$

$\dfrac{1}{x^2} + \dfrac{1}{y^2} = 27.$

14. $9x^2 + 4y^2 = 36\,x^2y^2,$
$3xy = 1.$

15. $3x^2 + 7xy + 4y^2 = 0,$
$(2y - 3x + 5)(3y + 2x - 6) = 0.$

5. $y^2 + 7y + 3x = 0,$
$x^2 + 7x + 3y = 0.$

6. $y^2 - 16y - 6x = 0,$
$x^2 + 14x + 4y = 0.$

7. $x^2 + y^2 + 2x - 4y - 8 = 0,$
$x^2 + y^2 - 3x - 3y - 2 = 0.$

Hint: Subtract the equations.

11. $x^2 + y^2 = 10,$
$xy = 3.$

12. $x^2 + 2xy - 5y^2 = 3,$
$xy - x + 2y = 2.$

Hint: Factor the second equation.

13. $x^2 + xy - 2y^2 = 20,$
$6x^2 - xy - y^2 = 0.$

16. $x^3 + y^3 = 9,$
$x + y = 3.$

Hint: Divide the first equation by the second.

17. $x^3 - 8y^3 = 8,$
$x^2 + 2xy + 4y^2 = 4.$

18. $x^{-1} + y^{-1} = 5,$
$x^{-2} - x^{-1}y^{-1} + 2y^{-2} = 16.$

19. $x^{\frac{1}{2}} + y^{\frac{1}{2}} = 1,$
$2y = x^{\frac{1}{2}}.$

20. $x^{\frac{1}{2}}y^{\frac{1}{2}} - 3x^{\frac{1}{2}} + 4y^{\frac{1}{2}} = 0,$
$3x^{\frac{1}{2}} - 2y^{\frac{1}{2}} = 4.$

21. $\sqrt{x} - \sqrt{y} = 1,$
$x - 2y + \sqrt{xy} = 7.$

22. $x + \sqrt{y + 2} = 11,$
$x - 1 - \sqrt{y + 2} = 2.$

23. $8x^2 - 8y^2 + 3z^2 = 3,$
$2x + y - z = 1,$
$2x - y + 3z = 9.$

24. $16x^2 + 16y^2 - 9z^2 = 0,$
$x^2 + y^2 + z^2 = 25,$
$x + y = 0.$

25. $x(y + z) = 16,$
$y(x + z) = 21,$
$z(x + y) = 25.$

Hint: Let $y = mx$ and $z = nx.$

26. $x(y - 2z) = 4,$
$y(z - 2x) = 10,$
$z(x - 2y) = -15.$

27. The product of two numbers is 63 and the sum of their squares is 130. Find the numbers.

28. The sum of the reciprocals of two numbers is $\dfrac{8}{45}$. The product of the numbers is 135. Find the numbers.

29. The perimeter of a rectangle is 58 inches. The area is 189 square inches. Find the length and breadth.

30. A rectangular field of 75 acres has a diagonal of 170 rods. Find the lengths of the sides. (An acre is equal to 160 square rods.)

31. Show that the formulas for the length l and width w of a rectangle in terms of its area A and diagonal d are

$$l = \frac{1}{2}\left[(d^2 + 2A)^{\frac{1}{2}} + (d^2 - 2A)^{\frac{1}{2}}\right], \; w = \frac{1}{2}\left[(d^2 + 2A)^{\frac{1}{2}} - (d^2 - 2A)^{\frac{1}{2}}\right].$$

32. Show that the formulas for the length l and width w of a rectangle in terms of its perimeter p and area A are

$$l = \frac{1}{4}\left[p + (p^2 - 16A)^{\frac{1}{2}}\right], \; w = \frac{1}{4}\left[p - (p^2 - 16A)^{\frac{1}{2}}\right].$$

33. *A* travels 360 miles in one hour less time than *B*. If *A*'s average speed is 5 miles per hour greater than *B*'s, find the rate at which each travels.

34. Two men, A and B, buy different grades of coal. Each spends $126, but A obtains 4 tons more than B. If A spends $1 less for 5 tons than B spends for 4 tons, how much does each spend per ton and how many tons does each buy?

35. Strong head winds reduced the average speed of an airliner by 20 miles per hour and hence the liner required $\frac{1}{2}$ hour longer to complete its journey of 720 miles. Find the usual average speed and the time of flight.

36. Two towns on opposite sides of a lake are 33 miles apart by water. At 6 A.M. a ship starts from each town for the other town. Both ships travel at uniform speed. The ships pass each other at 7:30 A.M. One ship arrives at its destination 33 minutes earlier than the other. Find the time it takes each ship to make the trip and their respective speeds.

37. Two men can complete a task in 10 days, but if they work alone it takes one man 10 days longer than the other to do the job. In what time can each do the work alone?

38. It took a number of men as many days to pave a street as there were men, but had there been five more workmen employed, the work would have been done four days sooner. How many men were employed?

39. A rectangular piece of tin containing 400 square inches is made into an open box containing 384 cubic inches by cutting a 6-inch square from each corner of the tin and folding up the sides. Find the dimensions of the box.

40. If the product of two numbers is increased by their sum, the result is 71. If their product is decreased by twice their sum, the result is 26. Find the numbers.

41. After a mowing machine had made the circuit of a 10-acre rectangular field 33 times, cutting a swath 5 feet wide each time, $2\frac{1}{2}$ acres of grass were still standing. Find the dimensions of the field. (1 acre = 43,560 sq. ft.)

42. An airplane, flying at the rate of 120 miles per hour and following a straight road, passed an automobile going in the opposite direction. Three hours later it overtook a second automobile. The automobiles passed each other when the plane was 270 miles away. If both automobiles traveled at the same speed, how far apart were they when the plane passed the second one and what was their speed?

43. The hypotenuse of a right triangle is 150 feet. If the longer leg be increased by 30 feet and the shorter leg be decreased by 10 feet, the hypotenuse would be increased by 20 feet. Find the sides of both triangles.

44. Psychologists assert that the rectangle most pleasing to the human eye is that in which the sum of the two dimensions is to the longer as the longer is to the shorter. If the area of a page of this book remains unchanged, what should its dimensions be?

45. The diagonal of a rectangular parallelepiped is 17 inches long. The sum of the three dimensions is 29 inches. The product of the two smaller dimensions is one-half the square of the largest. What are the dimensions of the parallelepiped?

46. The diagonals of the three faces of a rectangular parallelepiped which meet in a vertex of the solid are 5, 6, and 7 inches respectively. What is the volume of the solid?

11 INEQUALITIES

90. Definition

The expressions, "a is greater than b" ($a > b$) and "c is less than d" ($c < d$), where a, b, c, d are real numbers, mean that $a - b$ is a positive number and $c - d$ is a negative number. Such expressions are called **inequalities.** Two inequalities, $a > b$, $c > d$, which have the signs pointing in the same direction, are said to be **alike in sense.** If the signs point in opposite directions, as $a > b$, $c < d$, they are said to be **different in sense.** The expression $a \leq b$ is read "a is less than or equal to b," and $a \geq b$ is read "a is greater than or equal to b." The continued inequality $a < b < c$ means that $a < b$ and $b < c$, that is, b is between a and c.

If the numbers are plotted on a straight line as in Figure 25, the statement $a > b$ means that a lies to the right of b (Art. **3**).

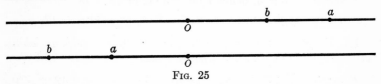

FIG. 25

The symbol $|x|$ is used to denote the numerical value of x, that is, the value of x without regard to sign. For example, $|5| = 5$ and $|-3| = 3$. The expression $|x|$ is read "the absolute value of x."

91. Absolute and Conditional Inequalities

We have seen that there are two kinds of equalities, identical and conditional equalities. Corresponding to these there are two

165

kinds of inequalities. An inequality such as $a^2 + b^2 > -1$, which is valid for all real values of a and b, is called an **absolute** inequality; while an inequality such as $x - 4 > 0$, which holds only when x is greater than 4, is called a **conditional** inequality. In a conditional inequality the letters cannot take all real values.

92. Elementary Principles

The following elementary principles, which follow at once from the definition of an inequality, must be observed in dealing with inequalities.

I. *The sense of an inequality is not changed if both sides are increased or decreased by the same number. In particular, the sense is not changed if we transpose a term, changing its sign.*

Let $\qquad\qquad\qquad a > b.$

Then $\qquad\qquad\quad a - b = n$, where n is positive,

and $\qquad\quad a + k - b - k = n,$

or $\qquad\quad (a + k) - (b + k) = n.$

Hence, $\qquad\qquad a + k > b + k.$

Examples: $7 > 3$, hence $7 + 6 > 3 + 6$, or $13 > 9.$

$\qquad\qquad -5 < -2$, hence $-5 + 10 < -2 + 10$, or $5 < 8.$

II. *The sense of an inequality is not changed if both sides are multiplied or divided by the same positive number.*

Examples: $7 > 3$, hence $7 \cdot 6 > 3 \cdot 6$, or $42 > 18.$

$\qquad\qquad -5 < -2$, hence $-5 \cdot 6 < -2 \cdot 6$, or $-30 < -12.$

III. *The sense of an inequality is reversed if both sides are multiplied or divided by the same negative number.*

Examples: $7 > 3$, hence $7 \cdot (-6) < 3 \cdot (-6)$, or $-42 < -18.$

$\qquad -5 < -2$, hence $-5 \cdot (-10) > -2(-10)$, or $50 > 20.$

$$8 < 16, \text{ hence } \frac{8}{-2} > \frac{16}{-2}, \text{ or } -4 > -8.$$

The proofs of **II** and **III** are very similar to the proof of **I**.

EXERCISES

1. What part of the number scale in Figure 26 is included in each of the following statements?

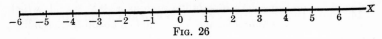

Fig. 26

(a) $-2 \leqq x \leqq 3$,

(b) $-1 < x \leqq 4$,

(c) $-3 \leqq 2x + 1 < 5$,

(d) $-2 < \frac{1}{2}(x - 3) < 1$,

(e) $|x| < 4$,

(f) $x^2 < 4$.

2. If $a > b$ and $c > 0$, prove that $ac > bc$.

3. If $a > b$ and $c < 0$, prove that $ac < bc$.

4. If $a > b$ and if a and b have like sign, prove that $\dfrac{1}{a} < \dfrac{1}{b}$.

5. If $a > b$ and $c > d$, prove that $a + c > b + d$.

6. If $a > b$ and $c < d$, prove that $a - c > b - d$.

7. If a and b are not equal, show that $a^2 + b^2 > 2ab$.

Solution: Since $a \neq b$ and since the square of any real number is positive, $(a - b)^2 > 0$. That is

$$a^2 - 2ab + b^2 > 0.$$

By Principle I, $a^2 - 2ab + b^2 + 2ab > 0 + 2ab$,

or $a^2 + b^2 > 2ab$.

8. If a and b are positive, unequal, real numbers, the arithmetic mean of a and b is $\frac{1}{2}(a + b)$ and the geometric mean of a and b is $\sqrt{ab}$.   Prove that the arithmetic mean is greater than the geometric mean.

9. The harmonic mean of two numbers a and b is $\dfrac{2ab}{a + b}$.   Show that the harmonic mean of two numbers is always less than their geometric mean.

10. If a is positive and not equal to 1, show that the sum of a and its reciprocal is greater than 2.

11. Show that $a^2 + a + 1 > 0$.

Hint: $(a + 1)^2 > a$.

12. If $a^2 + b^2 = 1$ and $c^2 + d^2 = 1$, show that $ab + cd < 1$.

Hint: $(a - b)^2 = a^2 + b^2 - 2ab$.

13. If $\dfrac{a}{b} < \dfrac{c}{d}$, show that $\dfrac{a}{b} < \dfrac{a + c}{b + d} < \dfrac{c}{d}$, where a, b, c, d are positive real numbers.

Hint: $\dfrac{a}{b} + \dfrac{c}{b} < \dfrac{c}{d} + \dfrac{c}{b}$, whence $\dfrac{a + c}{b + d} < \dfrac{c}{d}$.

14. Show that $\dfrac{a-b}{a+b} < \dfrac{a^2-b^2}{a^2+b^2}$, if $b < a$ and a and b are positive real numbers.

15. Prove that $|a| + |b| \geqq |a+b|$.

Hint: Consider two cases, first when a and b have the same sign, second when they have different signs.

16. Prove that $|a| + |b| \geqq |a-b|$.

17. Prove that $|a| - |b| \leqq |a-b|$.

93. Conditional Inequalities

By transposing terms every inequality may be reduced to an inequality of the form $P > 0$, or $P < 0$. If one or both sides involves a variable, say x, it can be put in one of the two forms $f(x) > 0$, or $f(x) < 0$. In this connection the most important problem is to find the range of values of the variable for which the inequality holds. In the case of linear inequalities the solution is easy. Thus, to find the values of x for which the inequality

$$3x + 19 > 12 - x$$

holds, all the terms can be transposed to the left-hand side, and there results

$$4x + 7 > 0.$$

Hence the inequality in question holds only for $x > -\dfrac{7}{4}$.

Graphically,

$$3x + 19 > 12 - x$$

for those values of x for which the graph of the function

$$3x + 19 - 12 + x \equiv 4x + 7$$

Fig. 27

lies above the X-axis (Fig. 27).

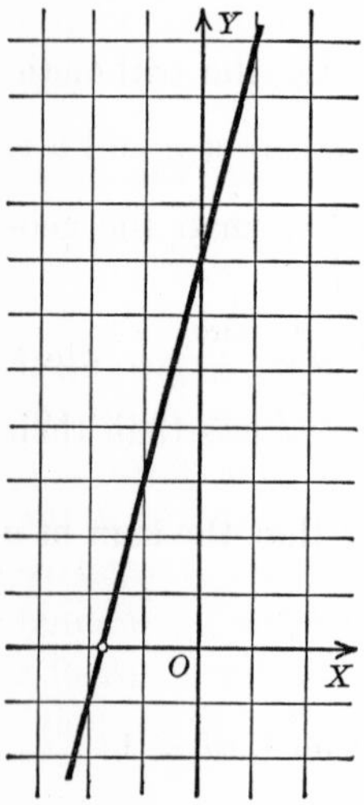

The graph is of great service in determining the values of x for which one function of x is greater or less than another function. Thus, to find the range of values of x for which

$$2x^2 - 3x + 8 > x^2 + 2x + 4,$$

we transpose all terms to one side
and have

$$x^2 - 5x + 4 > 0.$$

The graph of this function is shown
in Figure 28. It crosses the X-axis
at 1 and 4, and for $x > 4$, or $x < 1$,
the function $x^2 - 5x + 4$ is positive;
while for $4 > x > 1$, it is negative;
hence,

$$2x^2 - 3x + 8 > x^2 + 2x + 4$$

for $x > 4$, and $x < 1$, while

$$2x^2 - 3x + 8 < x^2 + 2x + 4$$

for $4 > x > 1$.

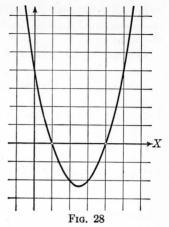

Fig. 28

94. Polynomials in Factored Form

We shall consider polynomials which may be factored into a
product of real, linear factors, and then determine for what values
of the variable the polynomial is either greater than or less than
zero.

Case 1. The factors are all distinct. In this case, the polynomial may be written

$$a(x - r_1)(x - r_2) \cdots (x - r_n),$$

where we shall assume that the factors have been so arranged
that $r_1 > r_2 > \cdots > r_n$. The polynomial is zero only for
$x = r_1$, $x = r_2$, $\cdots$ or $x = r_n$. Let us assume that the constant a
is positive. Then for $x > r_1$ each factor is positive and so is the
polynomial. If $r_1 > x > r_2$, the sign of the first factor is negative
while all the other factors are positive, and hence the polynomial
is negative. By investigating the signs of the factors for values of x
between each of the zeros of the function, the sign of the polynomial can be determined.

Case 2. Some of the factors are repeated. The polynomial may
then be written

$$a(x - r_1)^{k_1}(x - r_2)^{k_2} \cdots (x - r_n)^{k_n},$$

where we assume that $r_1 > r_2 > \cdots > r_n$. Again the sign of
each factor raised to the indicated power may be investigated for

values of x between each zero of the polynomial and the sign of the polynomial may be determined.

Example 1. For what values of x is $2(x-3)\left(x-\dfrac{1}{2}\right)(x+2) > 0$?

Solution: The polynomial is zero for $x = 3$, $x = \dfrac{1}{2}$, $x = -2$.

For $x > 3$, the signs of the factors are $+,+,+$, and $f(x) > 0$.

For $3 > x > \dfrac{1}{2}$, the signs of the factors are $-,+,+$, and $f(x) < 0$.

For $\dfrac{1}{2} > x > -2$, the signs of the factors are $-,-,+$, and $f(x) > 0$.

For $-2 > x$, the signs of the factors are $-,-,-$, and $f(x) < 0$.

Hence the polynomial is greater than zero for $x > 3$ and for $\dfrac{1}{2} > x > -2$.

Example 2. For what values of x is

$$(x-2)^2(x-1)(x+1)^3 < 0?$$

Solution: The function is zero when $x = 2$, $x = 1$, $x = -1$. Investigating the signs of the factors to the indicated powers, we find that

for $x > 2$, the signs are $+,+,+$, and $f(x) > 0$;

for $2 > x > 1$, the signs are $+,+,+$, and $f(x) > 0$;

for $1 > x > -1$, the signs are $+,-,+$, and $f(x) < 0$;

for $-1 > x$, the signs are $+,-,-$, and $f(x) > 0$.

Hence $f(x)$ is less than zero for $-1 < x < 1$.

95. Rational Fractions with Numerator and Denominator in Factored Form

Since a rational fraction is the quotient of two polynomials (Art. **16**), and since the polynomials are presumed to be in factored form, we may apply methods similar to those of Article **94** in order to determine for what values of x the fraction is greater than or less than zero.

Example. Investigate the sign of $f(x) = \dfrac{\left(x+2\right)\left(x-\dfrac{1}{2}\right)^2}{(x-3)(x-1)}$.

Solution: It is shown in more advanced courses in mathematics that this expression can change sign only as x moves across the points where $x = 3$, $x = 1$, $x = \dfrac{1}{2}$, and $x = -2$.

If $\qquad x > 3$, the signs of the factors indicate that $f(x) > 0$;

if $3 > x > 1$, the signs of the factors indicate that $f(x) < 0$;

if $1 > x > \dfrac{1}{2}$, the signs of the factors indicate that $f(x) > 0$;

if $\dfrac{1}{2} > x > -2$, the signs of the factors indicate that $f(x) > 0$;

if $\qquad x < -2$, the signs of the factors indicate that $f(x) < 0$.

Hence $f(x)$ is positive for $x > 3$ and $-2 < x < 1$, and $f(x)$ is negative for $3 > x > 1$ and $x < -2$.

EXERCISES

For what values of x do the following inequalities hold?

1. $3x - 4 > 5$.

2. $3x - 4 < -7$.

3. $3x - 4 > 4x - 3$.

4. $3x - 4 < \dfrac{1}{2}(3x - 4)$.

5. $2x + 7 < 4x - 5$.

6. $x^2 + x - 12 > 0$.

7. $6x^2 < x + 2$.

8. $2x^2 - 3x + 5 > x^2 - 3x + 1$.

9. $3x^2 - 5x - 10 < 2x^2 - 5x - 1$.

10. $4x^2 + 7x \begin{cases} > -3 \\ = -3 \\ < -3. \end{cases}$

11. $12x^3 - 12x^2 - 24x > 0$.

12. $x^3 - 4x < 0$.

13. $5x^4 - 20x^3 > 0$.

14. $(2x - 1)^2(x + 3)(x + 2)^3 > 0$.

15. $(x - 2)(x + 1)^3 < 0$.

16. $2(x - 1)(x + 1)^3 + 3(x - 1)^2(x + 1)^2 < 0$.

17. $3x - \dfrac{3}{x^2} < 0$.

18. $x - \dfrac{a^4}{x^3} > 0$, if $a > 0$.

19. $2x - 1 > \dfrac{1}{x}$.

20. $|x| > \dfrac{1}{x}$.

Discuss the sign of the following fractions as x varies through all the real numbers.

21. $\dfrac{(x - 1)(2 + x)}{(x - 3)}$.

22. $\dfrac{(2x - 3)(3 + x^2)}{(2x + 1)^3}$.

23. For what values of k are the roots of $x^2 + 3kx + k + 7 = 0$ real and unequal? Imaginary?

24. For what values of k are the roots of

$$(k - 1)x^2 + kx + k + 1 = 0$$

real and unequal? Imaginary?

For what values of x do the following inequalities hold?

25. $\begin{vmatrix} 2x & 4 \\ 6 & -3 \end{vmatrix} > 0.$

26. $\begin{vmatrix} x & 1 \\ 1 & 1 \end{vmatrix} < \begin{vmatrix} x & 3 \\ 1 & 2 \end{vmatrix}.$

27. $\begin{vmatrix} x & 0 & 1 \\ 0 & 1 & 1 \\ 1 & 1 & x \end{vmatrix} < 1.$

28. $\begin{vmatrix} x & 1 & 1 \\ 1 & 1 & 1 \\ 1 & 1 & x \end{vmatrix} > \begin{vmatrix} x & 1 & 0 \\ 1 & 2 & 1 \\ 0 & 1 & x \end{vmatrix}.$

29. $\begin{vmatrix} x & 0 & 1 \\ 0 & 1 & 1 \\ 1 & 1 & x \end{vmatrix} > \begin{vmatrix} x & 1 \\ 1 & x \end{vmatrix}.$

12 MATHEMATICAL INDUCTION AND THE BINOMIAL THEOREM

96. Mathematical Induction

Many important theorems in algebra can be proved by a method called **mathematical induction**. The principle on which this method of proof depends may be illustrated as follows. Imagine a line of men at a ticket window seeking to purchase tickets for a football game. Suppose we could show that: (1) the first man in line obtains a ticket; (2) if anyone gets a ticket so does the next in line. We conclude from these propositions that everyone in the line obtains a ticket, regardless of the number of persons in the line. We begin the explanation of this method by applying it to a simple example.

Let it be required to show that $x - y$ is a factor of $x^n - y^n$ for all positive integral values of n. If $n = 1$, we have $x - y$, whose only rational factors are 1 and $x - y$. This corresponds to the condition (1). Let r be any value of n for which the proposition is true. Then

$$x^r - y^r = (x - y)Q, \qquad (1)$$

where Q is a polynomial (Art. **30**) in x and y. Since

$$\begin{aligned}
x^{r+1} - y^{r+1} &= xx^r - yy^r = xx^r - xy^r + xy^r - yy^r \\
&= x(x^r - y^r) + y^r(x - y) \\
&= x(x - y)Q + (x - y)y^r \qquad \text{by (1)} \\
&= (x - y)(xQ + y^r),
\end{aligned}$$

the proposition is true for $r + 1$ whenever it is true for r. This corresponds to condition (2).

Since the proposition holds for $n = 1$, it follows from the second part of the argument that it holds for the next integer, that is,

173

for $n = 2$. Its validity for $n = 3$, 4, and so on follows for the same reasons.

It is no proof simply to show that a theorem is true in a number of cases. For example, the above theorem is not proved by showing that it is true for $n = 1$, $n = 2$, $n = 3$, $n = 4$, and so on for a definite number of cases. The second part of the proof is necessary.

A celebrated example illustrating this point is the expression $n^2 - n + 41$. From the table we see that $n^2 - n + 41$ is a prime

$n =$	1	2	3	4	5	6	7	8	9	10	11	12
$n^2 - n + 41$	41	43	47	53	61	71	83	97	113	131	151	173

number for all integral values of n up to 12. The table could be continued up to $n = 40$ and the lower row would still contain nothing but prime numbers. However we have no proof that $n^2 - n + 41$ is prime for all integral values of n. To prove this it is necessary to take the second step in the proof by mathematical induction, i.e., to prove that if $r^2 - r + 41$ is prime, then $(r + 1)^2 - (r + 1) + 41$ is prime. But this is impossible. In fact, when $n = 41$, we have

$$n^2 - n + 41 = 1681 = 41^2,$$

a number which is not prime.

Again, it is no proof simply to show that if a statement is true for $n = r$ it is true for $n = r + 1$. For example, assuming that the sum of the first r even numbers is an odd number it follows that the sum of the first $r + 1$ even numbers is odd. Though the second part of the proof of this statement by mathematical induction can be correctly presented, we know the statement to be false. The first part of the proof is lacking.

We emphasize the two parts as follows:

Part I. To show by mere verification that the proposition in question is true for some particular case, usually for $n = 1$.

Part II. To show that if it is true for $n = r$, it is then true for $n = r + 1$.

If these two steps are completed it follows that the proposition is true for every positive integral value of n, equal to or greater than the one for which the verification was made in Part I. The verification for values of n beyond $n = 1$ may be satisfying but this is not relevant to the proof.

EXERCISES

Prove by mathematical induction, n being any positive integer.

1. $\qquad 2 + 4 + \cdots + 2(n - 1) + 2n = n(n + 1).$ $\qquad$ (1)

Solution: Part I. If $n = 1$ the series on the left of equation (1) reduces to the single term 2. But $2 = 1(1 + 1)$, so the equation holds if $n = 1$.

Part II. Let r be any value of n for which equation (1) is true. That is,

$$2 + 4 + \cdots + 2(r - 1) + 2r = r(r + 1) = r^2 + r. \qquad (2)$$

We wish to show that the equation obtained from (1) by letting $n = r + 1$ is a consequence of equation (2). We are interested in the question: Is

$$2 + 4 + \cdots + 2r + 2(r+1) = (r + 1)[(r + 1) + 1] = r^2 + 3r + 2? \quad (3)$$

The left side of equation (3) contains all the terms of the left side of equation (2) and the single additional term $2(r + 1)$. Subtracting equation (2) from equation (3) we obtain

$$2(r + 1) = 2r + 2,$$

an identity. Thus equation (3) is implied by equation (2) and the proof of Part II is complete. Equation (1) is therefore valid for all positive integral values of n.

Remark. The proof in Part II can also be made by adding the $(r + 1)$th term of the progression to both sides of equation (2) and reducing the expression on the right to the form $(r + 1)(r + 2)$.

2. $1 + 2 + 3 + \cdots + n = \dfrac{n}{2}(n + 1).$

3. $1 + 3 + 5 + \cdots + (2n - 1) = n^2.$

4. $4 + 7 + 10 + 13 + \cdots + (3n + 1) = \dfrac{n}{2}(3n + 5).$

5. $2 + 2^2 + \cdots + 2^n = 2(2^n - 1).$

6. $\dfrac{1}{2} + \dfrac{1}{4} + \cdots + \left(\dfrac{1}{2}\right)^n = 1 - \left(\dfrac{1}{2}\right)^n.$

7. $\dfrac{1}{1 \cdot 2} + \dfrac{1}{2 \cdot 3} + \cdots + \dfrac{1}{n(n + 1)} = \dfrac{n}{n + 1}.$

8. $1^2 + 2^2 + 3^2 + \cdots + n^2 = \dfrac{1}{6} n(n + 1)(2n + 1).$

9. $1^3 + 2^3 + \cdots + n^3 = \dfrac{n^2(n + 1)^2}{4} = (1 + 2 + \cdots + n)^2.$

10. $x + y$ is a factor of $x^{2n} - y^{2n}$.
11. $x + y$ is a factor of $x^{2n+1} + y^{2n+1}$.
12. $x^n - a^n = (x - a)(x^{n-1} + ax^{n-2} + \cdots + a^{n-2}x + a^{n-1})$.

97. Meaning of $r!$

The symbol $r!$, read "factorial r," * is used to indicate the product $1 \cdot 2 \cdot 3 \cdots r$. Thus, $3! = 1 \cdot 2 \cdot 3 = 6$; $7! = 1 \cdot 2 \cdot 3 \cdot 4 \cdot 5 \cdot 6 \cdot 7 = 5040$.

EXERCISES

Evaluate the following expressions.

1. $\dfrac{5!}{8!}$. **3.** $\dfrac{5!\,7!}{8!}$. **5.** $\dfrac{5! + 4!}{6!}$. **7.** $\dfrac{n!}{(n-3)!}$.

2. $\dfrac{9!}{7!}$. **4.** $\dfrac{5!\,4!}{6!}$. **6.** $\dfrac{(n-1)!}{n!}$. **8.** $\dfrac{n}{n!}$.

98. Binomial Theorem; Positive Integral Exponents

By multiplication, we find

$$(a + x)^2 = a^2 + 2ax + x^2.$$
$$(a + x)^3 = a^3 + 3a^2x + 3ax^2 + x^3$$
$$= a^3 + 3a^2x + \frac{3 \cdot 2}{2!}ax^2 + x^3.$$
$$(a + x)^4 = a^4 + 4a^3x + 6a^2x^2 + 4ax^3 + x^4$$
$$= a^4 + 4a^3x + \frac{4 \cdot 3}{2!}a^2x^2 + \frac{4 \cdot 3 \cdot 2}{3!}ax^3 + x^4.$$

If n represents the exponent of the binomial in any one of the above three cases, we notice:

(1) The first term is a^n.

(2) The second term is $na^{n-1}x$.

(3) The exponents of a decrease by unity from term to term while the exponents of x increase by unity.

(4) If in any term the coefficient be multiplied by the exponent of a and divided by the exponent of x increased by unity, the result is the coefficient of the next term.

For $n < 5$, we may then write

* The symbol $\lfloor r$ is often used to represent factorial r.

$$(a + x)^n = a^n + na^{n-1}x + \frac{n(n - 1)}{2!} a^{n-2}x^2 + \cdots$$

$$+ \frac{n(n - 1) \cdots (n - r + 2)}{(r - 1)!} a^{n-r+1}x^{r-1} + \cdots + x^n.$$

Here the question naturally occurs: Does the expansion hold for $n \geqq 5$? It can be shown by mathematical induction that it holds for any positive integral value of n.

Assume

$$(a + x)^m = a^m + ma^{m-1}x + \frac{m(m - 1)}{2!} a^{m-2}x^2 + \cdots$$

$$+ \frac{m(m - 1) \cdots (m - r + 2)}{(r - 1)!} a^{m-r+1}x^{r-1} + \cdots + x^m.$$

Multiply both members of this assumed equality by $a + x$, and we obtain

$$(a + x)^{m+1} =$$

$$a^{m+1} + ma^m x + \cdots + \frac{m(m - 1) \cdots (m - r + 2)}{(r - 1)!} a^{m-r+2}x^{-1} + \cdots + ax^m$$

$$+ a^m x + \cdots + \frac{m(m-1) \cdots (m-r+3)}{(r - 2)!} a^{m-r+2}x^{r-1} + \cdots + max^m + x^{m+1}$$

$$= a^{m+1} + (m + 1)a^m x + \cdots + \frac{(m + 1)m \cdots (m - r + 3)}{(r - 1)!} a^{m-r+2}x^{r-1} + \cdots$$

$$+ (m + 1)ax^m + x^{m+1}$$

This expansion is the same that would be obtained by substituting $m + 1$ for m in the expansion of $(a + x)^m$. Hence, if the expansion is true for $n = m$, it is true for $n = m + 1$. Since we know it is true for $n = 2$, it is true for $n = 3$, and so on. Hence, when n is any positive integer,

$$(a + x)^n = a^n + na^{n-1}x + \frac{n(n - 1)}{2!} a^{n-2}x^2 + \cdots$$

$$+ \frac{n(n - 1) \cdots (n - r + 2)}{(r - 1)!} a^{n-r+1}x^{r-1} + \cdots + x^n.$$

This expansion of a binomial is called the **binomial theorem**.

99. The General Term of $(a + x)^n$

In the expansion of $(a + x)^n$, the rth term is

$$\frac{n(n - 1)(n - 2) \cdots (n - r + 2)}{(r - 1)!} a^{n-r+1}x^{r-1},$$

which may also be written

$$\frac{n!}{(r-1)!\,(n-r+1)!}\,a^{n-r+1}x^{r-1}.$$

The term involving x^r is

$$\frac{n(n-1)(n-2)\cdots(n-r+1)}{r!}\,a^{n-r}x^r = \frac{n!}{r!\,(n-r)!}\,a^{n-r}x^r.$$

Each of these terms is sometimes called the **general term of the binomial expansion.**

100. Binomial Expansion for Negative and Fractional Exponents

So far in this chapter, the binomial expansion has been limited to positive integral values of the exponent n, and the theorem has been proved on this basis. However, if n is a positive rational fraction or a negative rational number, the following expansion is valid provided that $-1 < x < 1$,

$$(1+x)^n = 1 + nx + \frac{n(n-1)}{2!}\,x^2 + \frac{n(n-1)(n-2)}{3!}\,x^3 + \cdots.$$

In these cases it should be noticed that the series does not terminate but continues indefinitely. The validity of the expansion is proved in more advanced courses in mathematics.

The expansion of $(a+b)^n$ may be made to depend on the above expansion. For if $b > a$, then

$$(a+b)^n = \left[b\left(1+\frac{a}{b}\right)\right]^n = b^n\left(1+\frac{a}{b}\right)^n.$$

EXERCISES

Expand the binomials in exercises 1–10, simplify, and check the result for the special case in which each letter is equal to 1.

1. $(2x - 3y^3)^4$.

Solution:

$$(2x - 3y^3)^4 = (2x)^4 + 4(2x)^3(-3y^3) + 6(2x)^2(-3y^3)^2$$
$$+ 4(2x)(-3y^3)^3 + (-3y^3)^4$$
$$= 16x^4 - 96x^3y^3 + 216x^2y^6 - 216xy^9 + 81y^{12}.$$

Check:
$$(2-3)^4 = 16 - 96 + 216 - 216 + 81.$$
$$1 = 1.$$

2. $(a+x)^5$.
3. $(a-x)^5$.
4. $(2-x)^6$.
5. $\left(\dfrac{1}{2}+a^2\right)^4$.
6. $(x^2+2y^3)^5$.
10. $\left(1+\dfrac{1}{x}\right)^7 - \left(1-\dfrac{1}{x}\right)^7$.

7. $\left(2x^{-1}+\dfrac{1}{2}x^{\frac{1}{2}}\right)^6$.
8. $\left(2y-\dfrac{1}{3x}\right)^4$.
9. $\left(\dfrac{x^2}{2}-\dfrac{3}{y}\right)^5$.

Expand by the binomial theorem and simplify.

11. $(\sqrt{x}+\sqrt{y})^8$.
12. $(a^{\frac{2}{3}}-x^{\frac{2}{3}})^4$.
13. $\left(\sqrt{2}+\dfrac{1}{\sqrt{2}}\right)^6$.
14. $\left(\dfrac{x}{\sqrt{a}}+\dfrac{a}{\sqrt{x}}\right)^6$.
18. $(x^2+x+1)^4$.
19. $\left(\sqrt{x}+1+\dfrac{1}{\sqrt{x}}\right)^3$.

15. $\begin{vmatrix} a & 1 \\ 3 & ab \end{vmatrix}^5$.
16. $\begin{vmatrix} x & 3b \\ y & a \end{vmatrix}^6$.
17. $(a+b+c)^3$.
   Hint: $(a+b+c)^3 = [(a+b)+c]^3$
20. $\left(\dfrac{x^2}{2}-\dfrac{2}{x^2}+1\right)^4$.

Find the first four terms of the following and simplify.

21. $(2x^3+3y^2)^{10}$.
22. $\left(\dfrac{2}{3}a^{\frac{3}{2}}-\dfrac{3}{2}a^{-\frac{3}{2}}\right)^{12}$.
23. $\left(1-\dfrac{x}{k}\right)^{k-1}$.
24. $\left(1+\dfrac{1}{n}\right)^n$.

Find the last three terms of the expansion and simplify.

25. $(x^{-1}-2y^{\frac{1}{2}})^{10}$.
26. $\left(a^2+\dfrac{3}{a}\right)^{15}$.

27. Find the seventh term in the expansion of $(x^{\frac{1}{2}}-2y^2)^{11}$.
Solution: The rth term is given by the expression
$$\frac{n(n-1)\cdots(n-r+2)}{(r-1)!}a^{n-r+1}x^{r-1}.$$

Here $n=11, r=7, a=x^{\frac{1}{2}}, x=-2y^2, n-r+2=6$.

Substituting these in the expression for the rth term, we have

$$\frac{11 \cdot 10 \cdot 9 \cdot 8 \cdot 7 \cdot 6}{6!} (x^{\frac{1}{2}})^5 (- 2y^2)^6 = 29568 x^{\frac{5}{2}} y^{12}.$$

28. Find the fourth term of $(x - 2y)^9$.

29. Find the eighth term of $(2x - 3y)^{15}$.

30. Find the middle term of $(x\sqrt{y} - y\sqrt{x})^{10}$.

31. Find the fourteenth term of $\left(2x - \dfrac{1}{3x^{\frac{1}{2}}}\right)^{19}$.

32. Find the middle term of $\begin{vmatrix} a & 2 \\ 1 & b \end{vmatrix}^8$.

Evaluate the following quantities to four significant figures and check your results by means of logarithms.

33. $(10.2)^5 = (10.0 + 0.2)^5$.   **36.** $(0.99)^4$.

34. $(9.8)^5$.   **37.** $(1.1)^{10}$.

35. $(3.1)^6$.   **38.** $(1.1)^{15}$.

39. Find the first five terms of the binomial expansion for $(1 + x)^{-1}$. Show by actual substitution that this expansion cannot possibly be valid for $x = 1$ and for $x = 2$. If $x = \dfrac{1}{2}$, find the sum of the first five terms of the expansion and determine by how much this sum differs from the value of the function when $x = \dfrac{1}{2}$.

40. Expand $(1 + x)^{\frac{1}{2}}$ to six terms. Find the sum of the first six terms when $x = -\dfrac{1}{2}$ and use this sum to evaluate $\sqrt{2}$. Calculate $\sqrt{2}$ by means of logarithms and compare your results.

Calculate the values of the following quantities to four significant figures and check your results by means of logarithms.

41. $\sqrt{1.1}$.

42. $\sqrt{99} = \sqrt{100 - 1} = \sqrt{10^2(1 - 0.01)} = 10(1 - 0.01)^{\frac{1}{2}}$,

43. $\sqrt[3]{9} = \sqrt[3]{8 + 1} = \sqrt[3]{8(1 + 0.125)} = 2(1 + 0.125)^{\frac{1}{3}}$.

44. $\sqrt[4]{17}$.   **47.** $(1.03)^{-2}$.

45. $\sqrt[5]{63}$.   **48.** $(10)^{-\frac{1}{2}}$.

46. $(1.03)^{\frac{1}{2}}$.   **49.** $(0.9)^{-3}$.

13 COMPLEX NUMBERS

101. Number Systems

The basis of mathematics is the number system. The development of the number system was suggested in Chapter 1 and again in Chapter 7. Here we shall again set down in compact form some of the fundamental ideas concerning that development.

We started with a number system consisting of positive integers only. To these positive integers we applied six operations, namely, addition, subtraction, multiplication, division, raising to powers, and extraction of roots. These processes are to be applied only a finite number of times. The sum of two positive integers is always a positive integer and the product of two positive integers is always a positive integer.

Subtraction, the inverse process of addition, is not always possible if one is restricted to the system of positive integers. For example, if $b > a$, there is no positive integer c such that $a - b = c$. In order to make the process possible at all times, the number system is extended to include the negative integers and zero. In this number system consisting of the positive and negative integers and zero, the processes of addition, subtraction, and multiplication are always possible.

Division, the inverse process of multiplication, is not always possible in the system of the positive and negative integers and zero. In order to have a system in which division is in general possible, the system of rational numbers is introduced. A rational number is defined as a number which may be expressed as the quotient of two integers. In this system, addition, subtraction, multiplication, and division (except division by zero) are always possible.

The process of raising any rational number to an integral power is always possible in the system of rational numbers. However, the inverse process is not always possible in that system. In order to have a system in which the extraction of roots is always possible, it is necessary to extend the system of rational numbers twice. First, irrational numbers are introduced, so that it is always possible to extract the roots of positive numbers and the odd roots of negative numbers.* The totality of rational and irrational numbers comprises the system of real numbers. In this system all processes are possible except the extraction of even ordered roots of negative numbers. In order to remove this restriction, the number $i = \sqrt{-1}$ is introduced.

Every number of the form ib, where b is a real number, is called a **pure imaginary number.** The indicated sum of a real number and a pure imaginary number, $a + ib$, is called a **complex number.** If $b = 0$, the complex number reduces to a real number. If $b \neq 0$, the complex number is called **imaginary.** Complex numbers which differ only in the sign of their imaginary parts are called **conjugate** complex numbers. Thus, $a - ib$ is the conjugate of $a + ib$, and the numbers $3 + 2i$ and $3 - 2i$ are said to be conjugates.

The term "imaginary" is used here in a technical sense. The number i is imaginary in the same sense as -1 is imaginary in the system of positive integers, or as $\sqrt{3}$ is imaginary in the system of rational numbers. The terms used to designate the various kinds of numbers may have been unfortunately chosen, but certainly there is no question as to their existence.

The fundamental problem with which we are concerned in this chapter is the application of the processes of algebra to these complex numbers. The question will then arise as to whether or not the number system will have to be extended again in order that these processes shall always be possible in the system under consideration.

---

* The student should not infer that it is always possible to obtain all irrational numbers by the process of taking roots. For instance, the numbers π and e cannot be obtained in this manner. See Klein — *Famous Problems in Elementary Geometry*, translation by Beman and Smith, p. 68.

102. Graphical Representation of Complex Numbers

We have seen that all real numbers may be represented by points on a straight line. The complex number $x + iy$ depends on two real numbers x and y, and may be represented graphically by a point in a plane. Two lines, $X'X$, $Y'Y$, are drawn perpendicular to each other and intersecting at O, Figure 29. To represent the number $2 + 3i$, measure off on $X'X$ to the right the distance 2, and up the distance 3. In general, the graph of the number $x + iy$ is the point whose coordinates are (x, y). The line $X'X$ is called the axis of "reals" and the line $Y'Y$ the axis of imaginaries.

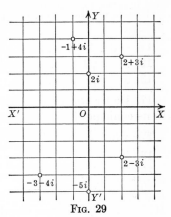

Fig. 29

103. Equal Complex Numbers

If two complex numbers $a + bi$ and $c + di$ are equal, then $a = c$ and $b = d$. For, if

$$a + bi = c + di, \tag{1}$$

by transposing,

$$a - c = (d - b)i. \tag{2}$$

Unless $a - c = d - b = 0$, we should have $a - c$, a real number, equal to $(d - b)i$, an imaginary number.

Conversely, if $a = c$, and $b = d$,

$$a + bi = c + di.$$

Hence, *when any two expressions containing imaginary and real terms are equal to each other, we may equate the real parts and the imaginary parts separately.*

In particular, if $a + bi = 0$, $a = 0$ and $b = 0$.

EXERCISES

Represent the following complex numbers and their conjugates graphically.

1. $5 + 2i$.

2. $5 - 2i$.

3. $-2 + 7i$.

4. $-3 - 4i$.

5. $-6i$.

6. -4.

7. $\dfrac{1}{2} - \dfrac{1}{4}i$.

8. $-\dfrac{1}{4} - \dfrac{1}{2}i$.

9. $2 + 3i$.

10. $\pi + i$.

Which of the following pairs of complex numbers are conjugates?

11. $-3 + 2i$, $3 + 2i$.

12. $1 - 2i$, $1 + 2i$.

13. $5 - 6i$, $-5 + 6i$.

14. -3, -3.

15. $-2i$, $2i$.

16. 4, -4.

17. Under what conditions is a complex number $a + ib$ equal to its conjugate?

For what values of x and y are the following equations true?

18. $(x - y + 1) + i(4x + y - 16) = 0$.

19. $(5x + 3y) + i(3x - 4y) = -9 - 17i$.

20. $2x + i(x - 2y) = y + 5 - 2i$.

21. $2x + 3y + i(xy - 5) = 7 - iy^2$.

22. $2x + 9iy^2 = y + 4 + i(72 - 4x^2)$.

104. Addition and Subtraction of Complex Numbers

We assume that the number i like other numbers obeys all the laws of algebra. Given two complex numbers $a + bi$, $c + di$, we may write the sum and difference:

Thus, $\quad (a + bi) + (c + di) = (a + c) + (b + d)i$,

$\qquad\quad (a + bi) - (c + di) = (a - c) + (b - d)i$.

Hence, to add (or subtract) complex numbers, add (or subtract) the real and imaginary parts separately. The result is a complex number.

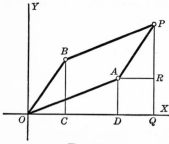

FIG. 30

To add two complex numbers, $a + bi$ and $c + di$, graphically, we represent the numbers as points A and B in Figure 30. Connect each point with the origin O. Complete the parallelogram, having OA and OB for adjacent sides. The vertex P represents the sum of the two given complex numbers. For, from the figure the coordinates of the fourth vertex are OQ and QP. But

$$OQ = OD + DQ = a + c,$$
$$QP = QR + RP = b + d.$$

Hence, P represents the point $(a + c) + (b + d)i$ which is the sum of $a + bi$ and $c + di$.

To subtract one complex number from another graphically, say $c + di$ from $a + bi$, we graph the points which represent $- c - di$ and $a + bi$, and proceed as for addition.

EXERCISES

Perform the following operations algebraically and graphically.

1. $(5 + 2i) + (2 + 3i)$.
2. $(3 + i) + (- 4 + 2i)$.
3. $(4 - 3i) + (- 2 + 3i)$.
4. $(- 2 - 2i) + (3 - 4i)$.
5. $\left(\dfrac{1}{3} - \dfrac{i}{2}\right) + \left(\dfrac{3}{4} + \dfrac{5i}{6}\right)$.

6. $(2 + 3i) - (3 - 2i)$.
7. $(2 - 5i) - 3i$.
8. $- 3 - (5 + 4i)$.
9. $2i - (5 + 3i)$.
10. $(2 + 3i) + (2 - 3i) - (4 + i)$.

11. $(2 - 3i) + (- 3 + i) + (- 2 + 3i)$.
12. $(1 + i) - 5 + (6 - 3i)$.
13. Show that the sum of a complex number and its conjugate is always a real number.
14. Show that the difference of a complex number and its conjugate is always a pure imaginary number.

105. Multiplication and Division of Complex Numbers

Let $a + ib$ and $c + id$ be any two complex numbers. Since we have assumed that i obeys all the laws of algebra, we have

$$(a + ib)(c + id) = ac + ibc + iad + i^2bd$$
$$= (ac - bd) + i(bc + ad).$$

If n is a positive integer, the value of $(a + ib)^n$ may be found by use of the binomial theorem.

The quotient of two complex numbers may be found as follows:

$$\frac{a + ib}{c + id} = \frac{a + ib}{c + id} \cdot \frac{c - id}{c - id} = \frac{ac + bd - i(ad - bc)}{c^2 + d^2}$$
$$= \frac{ac + bd}{c^2 + d^2} - i \frac{ad - bc}{c^2 + d^2}.$$

It should be noticed that in each of these cases the result is a complex number.

EXERCISES

Express the following products as complex numbers.

1. $(4 - 3i)(2 + 5i)$.

Solution: $(4 - 3i)(2 + 5i) = 8 - 6i + 20i - 15i^2$
$$= 8 - 6i + 20i + 15$$
$$= 23 + 14i.$$

2. $(2 + 3i)(3 - 2i)$.

3. $(-4 + 5i)(3 - 2i)$.

4. $i(2 + 5i)$.

5. $(-1 + i\sqrt{3})(-1 - i\sqrt{3})$.

6. $(1 + i)(1 + 2i)(1 + 3i)$.

7. $(-2 + 0i)(3 - i)$.

8. $\left(\dfrac{5}{13} - \dfrac{12}{13}i\right)\left(\dfrac{12}{13} - \dfrac{5}{13}i\right)$.

9. $\left(\dfrac{3}{5} + \dfrac{4}{5}i\right)\left(\dfrac{4}{5} + \dfrac{3}{5}i\right)$.

10. $(2 - 3i)^2(-5i)^2$.

11. $(0 + 3i)^2(0 - 2i)^2$.

Use the binomial theorem to express each of the following as a complex number.

12. $(2 - 3i)^5$.

Solution:

$$(2 - 3i)^5 = (2)^5 + 5(2)^4(-3i) + \frac{5 \cdot 4}{2!}(2)^3(-3i)^2$$

$$+ \frac{5 \cdot 4 \cdot 3}{3!}(2)^2(-3i)^3 + \frac{5 \cdot 4 \cdot 3 \cdot 2}{4!}(2)(-3i)^4 + (-3i)^5$$

$$= 32 - 240i - 720 + 1080i + 810 - 243i$$
$$= 122 + 597i.$$

13. $(3 - 2i)^4$.

14. $(1 + i)^8$.

15. $(-1 + i\sqrt{3})^3$.

16. $\left(\dfrac{1}{2} + \dfrac{i\sqrt{3}}{2}\right)^6$.

Express the following quotients as complex numbers.

17. $\dfrac{3 + 2i}{4 - 3i}$.

Solution:

$$\frac{3 + 2i}{4 - 3i} = \frac{3 + 2i}{4 - 3i} \cdot \frac{4 + 3i}{4 + 3i}$$

$$= \frac{6 + 17i}{25} = \frac{6}{25} + \frac{17}{25}i.$$

18. $\dfrac{3 + 4i}{3 - 4i}$.

19. $\dfrac{3 + 4i}{4 - 3i}$.

20. $\dfrac{1+2i}{3-2i}$.

24. $\dfrac{1+i}{i}$.

21. $\dfrac{5-\sqrt{-4}}{2+3i}$.

25. $\dfrac{i}{1-i}$.

22. $\dfrac{-1+i}{1+i}$.

26. $(1+i)^{-3}$.

$\quad\quad$ *Hint:* $(1+i)^{-3}=\dfrac{1}{(1+i)^3}$.

23. $\dfrac{1-i\sqrt{3}}{1+i\sqrt{3}}$.

27. $(2+3i)^{-2}$.

28. Show that the product of a complex number and its conjugate is always a real number.

29. Under what conditions is the quotient of a complex number and its conjugate equal to a real number? To a pure imaginary number? Where do points representing such complex numbers lie in the plane?

30. Under what conditions is the reciprocal of a complex number equal to its conjugate? Where do the points representing such complex numbers lie in the plane?

31. Show that the conjugate of the product of two complex numbers is equal to the product of their conjugates.

106.* Polar Form of a Complex Number

It is often convenient to represent complex numbers by another method. Connect the point which represents $x+iy$ with the origin as in Figure 31. Let the length of this line be r. The point can then be represented by giving the length r and the angle θ. From the figure, using the definitions of sine and cosine given in trigonometry, we have

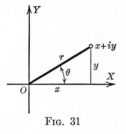

$$x = r\cos\theta,$$
$$y = r\sin\theta,$$
$$x^2 + y^2 = r^2.$$

Fig. 31

Hence, the number $x+iy$ may be written in the form

$$x + iy = r(\cos\theta + i\sin\theta).$$

---

* The remainder of this chapter may be omitted by those who have not yet studied trigonometry.

This form is called the **polar** form of a complex number. The angle θ is called the **argument** or **amplitude,** the length r the **modulus** or **absolute value** of the complex number.

EXERCISES

Represent graphically the following numbers and in each case find the argument and the modulus:

1. $2 - 3i$.

Solution: The number is represented in Fig. 29. The modulus r is given by

$$r = \sqrt{x^2 + y^2} = \sqrt{4 + 9} = \sqrt{13}.$$

To find the argument θ we have

$$\tan \theta = \frac{y}{x} = -\frac{3}{2}, \ \theta = \arctan -\frac{3}{2}; \ \sin \theta = -\frac{3}{\sqrt{13}}.$$

2. $3 + 4i$.

3. $12 - 5i$.

4. $-5 - 12i$.

5. $1 - i$.

6. $8 - 6i$.

7. $-2i$.

8. $5i$.

9. $-3i + 0i$.

10. 6.

11. $0.707 - 0.707i$.

12. $-\frac{1}{2} + \frac{i\sqrt{3}}{2}$.

13. $\sqrt{2 + \sqrt{3}} - i\sqrt{2 - \sqrt{3}}$.

14. $\sqrt{\sqrt{3} - 2} - i\sqrt{\sqrt{3} + 2}$.

Write the following in the rectangular form $x + iy$.

15. $6(\cos 30° + i \sin 30°)$.

16. $2(\cos 150° + i \sin 150°)$.

17. $2(\cos 315° + i \sin 315°)$.

18. $3(\cos 180° + i \sin 180°)$.

19. $\frac{1}{4}(\cos 90° + i \sin 90°)$.

20. $5(\cos 240° + i \sin 240°)$.

21. $3(\cos 120° - i \sin 300°)$.   Find the argument of this complex number.

107. Multiplication of Complex Numbers in Polar Form

Let $a + ib$ and $c + id$ be any two complex numbers, and let them be represented by the points P_1 and P_2 respectively in Figure 32. Reducing the numbers to polar form, we have

$$a + ib = r_1(\cos \theta_1 + i \sin \theta_1),$$
$$c + id = r_2(\cos \theta_2 + i \sin \theta_2).$$

By actual multiplication,

$(a + ib)(c + id)$
$= r_1 r_2 [\cos \theta_1 \cos \theta_2 - \sin \theta_1 \sin \theta_2 + i(\sin \theta_1 \cos \theta_2 + \cos \theta_1 \sin \theta_2)]$
$= r_1 r_2 [\cos (\theta_1 + \theta_2) + i \sin (\theta_1 + \theta_2)].$

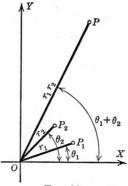

Hence, *the modulus of the product of two complex numbers is the product of their moduli and the argument is the sum of their arguments.*

The point P which represents

$$(a + ib)(c + id)$$

may then be constructed by drawing through O a line making an angle

$$\theta = \theta_1 + \theta_2$$

with the line $X'X$ (Fig. 32) and constructing on this line a segment OP whose length is $r_1 r_2$.

Fig. 32

EXERCISES

Find the following products in both the rectangular and the polar form. Find the arguments and moduli of the products and draw a graph of the product.

1. $(3 + \sqrt{3}i)(2 + 2i).$

Solution:

$(3 + \sqrt{3}i)(2 + 2i) = 6 + 6i + 2\sqrt{3}i + 2\sqrt{3}i^2 = 6 - 2\sqrt{3} + i(6 + 2\sqrt{3}).$

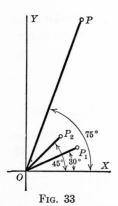

Fig. 33

Putting the numbers in the polar form, we have,

$$3 + \sqrt{3}i = 2\sqrt{3}(\cos 30° + i \sin 30°),$$
$$2 + 2i = 2\sqrt{2}(\cos 45° + i \sin 45°).$$

Hence,

$$r_1 = 2\sqrt{3},\ r_2 = 2\sqrt{2},\ \theta_1 = 30°,\ \theta_2 = 45°.$$

The modulus of the product is, then,

$$r_1 r_2 = 4\sqrt{6},$$

and the argument is 75°.

Let P_1 and P_2 in Figure 33 represent the two given numbers. Through O draw a line making an angle of 75° with the line OX.

On this line measure off the distance

$$OP = 4\sqrt{6}.$$

The point P then represents the product of the two numbers.

2. $(1 + i\sqrt{3})(\sqrt{3} + i)$.

3. $(2 - 2i)(-3 + 3i)$.

4. $(2 - 2i)(2 + 2i)$.

5. $\left(-\dfrac{1}{2} + \dfrac{i\sqrt{3}}{2}\right)\left(-\dfrac{1}{2} - \dfrac{i\sqrt{3}}{2}\right)$.

6. $(1 + i)(-1 + i)$.   **7.** $(1 + i)^2$.   **8.** $(i - 1)^3$.

Find the following products and draw the graphs of the given numbers and their product. Express the product in both rectangular form and polar form.

9. $2(\cos 75° + i \sin 75°) \cdot 3(\cos 60° + i \sin 60°)$.

10. $(\cos 120° + i \sin 120°)(\cos 90° + i \sin 90°)$.

11. $(\cos 180° + i \sin 180°)(\cos 135° + i \sin 135°)$.

12. $(\cos 30° + i \sin 30°)^2$.

13. $[2(\cos 135° + i \sin 135°)]^2$.

14. $(\cos 90° + i \sin 90°)^2$.

15. $(\cos \theta + i \sin \theta)^2$.

16. $(\cos \theta + i \sin \theta)(\cos \theta - i \sin \theta)$.

Hint: $\cos(-\theta) = \cos \theta$, $\sin(-\theta) = -\sin \theta$.

108. Division of Complex Numbers in Polar Form

Let the complex numbers $a + ib$ and $c + id$ be represented by the polar forms $r_1(\cos \theta_1 + i \sin \theta_1)$ and $r_2(\cos \theta_2 + i \sin \theta_2)$ respectively. Then

$$\frac{a + ib}{c + id} = \frac{r_1(\cos \theta_1 + i \sin \theta_1)}{r_2(\cos \theta_2 + i \sin \theta_2)}$$

$$= \frac{r_1(\cos \theta_1 + i \sin \theta_1)(\cos \theta_2 - i \sin \theta_2)}{r_2(\cos \theta_2 + i \sin \theta_2)(\cos \theta_2 - i \sin \theta_2)}$$

$$= \frac{r_1[\cos(\theta_1 - \theta_2) + i \sin(\theta_1 - \theta_2)]}{r_2(\cos^2 \theta_2 + \sin^2 \theta_2)}$$

$$= \frac{r_1}{r_2}[\cos(\theta_1 - \theta_2) + i \sin(\theta_1 - \theta_2)].$$

Hence, *the modulus of the quotient of two complex numbers is the quotient of their moduli, and the argument is the difference of their arguments.*

If, in Figure 34, P_1 and P_2 represent the points $a + ib$ and $c + id$ respectively, the point P which represents the quotient $\dfrac{a + ib}{c + id}$ may be constructed by drawing through O a line making an angle $\theta = \theta_1 - \theta_2$ with the line OX, and constructing on this line a segment OP, whose length is $\dfrac{r_1}{r_2}$.

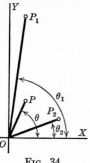

Fig. 34

EXERCISES

Find the quotients of the following pairs of complex numbers both in rectangular and polar form. Draw the graphs.

1. $(4 + 4i) \div \left(2 + \dfrac{2}{3}\sqrt{3}i\right)$.

Solution:

$$\frac{4 + 4i}{2 + \dfrac{2}{3}\sqrt{3}i} = \frac{4 + 4i}{2 + \dfrac{2}{3}\sqrt{3}i} \cdot \frac{2 - \dfrac{2}{3}\sqrt{3}i}{2 - \dfrac{2}{3}\sqrt{3}i} = \frac{3 + \sqrt{3}}{2} + \frac{3 - \sqrt{3}}{2}i.$$

Writing both numbers in the polar form, we obtain

$$4 + 4i = 4\sqrt{2}(\cos 45° + i \sin 45°),$$

$$2 + \frac{2}{3}\sqrt{3}i = \frac{4}{3}\sqrt{3}(\cos 30° + i \sin 30°).$$

Hence, $r_1 = 4\sqrt{2},\ r_2 = \dfrac{4}{3}\sqrt{3},\ \theta_1 = 45°,\ \theta_2 = 30°.$

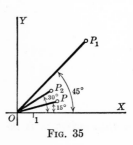

Fig. 35

The modulus of the quotient is then $\dfrac{r_1}{r_2}$ $= \sqrt{6}$, and the argument is $\theta = \theta_1 - \theta_2 = 15°$. Let P_1 and P_2 in Figure 35 represent the two given numbers. Through O draw a line making an angle of 15° with the line OX. Measure off on this line the distance $OP = \sqrt{6}$. The point P then represents the quotient of the two numbers.

2. $(1 - i) \div (1 + i)$.   **3.** $i \div (1 + i)$.

4. $\left(-\dfrac{1}{2} - \dfrac{i\sqrt{3}}{2}\right) \div \left(-\dfrac{1}{2} + \dfrac{i\sqrt{3}}{2}\right)$.

5. $\left(-\dfrac{\sqrt{3}}{2} - \dfrac{i}{2}\right) \div \left(\dfrac{1}{2} + \dfrac{i\sqrt{3}}{2}\right)$.

6. $-2 \div i$.   **8.** $(1 - i) \div 2i$.

7. $2i \div (1 - i)$.   **9.** $(1 + i\sqrt{3}) \div (1 - i\sqrt{3})$.

Find the following quotients. Express the results in both polar and rectangular form and draw the graphs.

10. $6(\cos 120° + i \sin 120°) \div 2(\cos 30° + i \sin 30°)$.

11. $3(\cos 315° + i \sin 315°) \div 2(\cos 270° + i \sin 270°)$.

12. $(\cos 50° + i \sin 50°) \div (\cos 185° + i \sin 185°)$.

13. $(\cos 40° + i \sin 40°) \div (\cos 160° + i \sin 160°)$.

14. Show that $1 \div (\cos \theta + i \sin \theta) = \cos \theta - i \sin \theta = \cos (-\theta) + i \sin (-\theta)$.

Find the reciprocals of the following numbers using both the rectangular and the polar forms. Draw the graph of each number and its reciprocal.

15. $2 + 2i$.   **19.** $\sqrt{3} - i$.

16. $-2 + 2i$.   **20.** -2.

17. $-i$.   **21.** $(\sqrt{3} + i)^2$.

18. $-\dfrac{1}{2} + \dfrac{i\sqrt{3}}{2}$.   **22.** $\left(-\dfrac{1}{2} + \dfrac{i\sqrt{3}}{2}\right)^2$.

109. De Moivre's Theorem

Consider the complex number $r(\cos \theta + i \sin \theta)$. Then

$$[r(\cos \theta + i \sin \theta)]^2 = r^2(\cos \theta + i \sin \theta)^2$$
$$= r^2(\cos^2 \theta + 2i \sin \theta \cos \theta - \sin^2 \theta)$$
$$= r^2(\cos 2\theta + i \sin 2\theta).$$

Again

$$[r(\cos \theta + i \sin \theta)]^3 = r^3(\cos \theta + i \sin \theta)^2(\cos \theta + i \sin \theta)$$
$$= r^3(\cos 2\theta + i \sin 2\theta)(\cos \theta + i \sin \theta)$$
$$= r^3(\cos 3\theta + i \sin 3\theta).$$

It thus appears that

$$[r(\cos \theta + i \sin \theta)]^n = r^n(\cos n\theta + i \sin n\theta).$$

This conjecture is proved by mathematical induction. We have already verified the statement for the cases $n = 2$ and $n = 3$. Let k be any integer for which it is true that

$$[r(\cos \theta + i \sin \theta)]^k = r^k(\cos k\theta + i \sin k\theta).$$

Multiply both sides of this equation by $r(\cos \theta + i \sin \theta)$ and get

$$[r(\cos \theta + i \sin \theta)]^{k+1} = r^{k+1}(\cos \theta + i \sin \theta)^k(\cos \theta + i \sin \theta)$$
$$= r^{k+1}(\cos k\theta + i \sin k\theta)(\cos \theta + i \sin \theta)$$
$$= r^{k+1}[\cos (k + 1)\theta + i \sin (k + 1)\theta].$$

Hence if the statement is true for $n = k$ it is also true for $n = k + 1$. This completes the proof.

The equality $[r(\cos \theta + i \sin \theta)]^n = r^n(\cos n\theta + i \sin n\theta)$ is known as **De Moivre's theorem.**

110. Roots of Complex Numbers

By an nth root of the complex number $a + ib = r(\cos \theta + i \sin \theta)$ we shall mean a complex number $R(\cos \phi + i \sin \phi)$ such that

$$R^n(\cos \phi + i \sin \phi)^n = r(\cos \theta + i \sin \theta).$$

By De Moivre's theorem, we then have

$$R^n(\cos n\phi + i \sin n\phi) = r(\cos \theta + i \sin \theta).$$

Since $\cos (\theta + k360°) = \cos \theta$ and $\sin (\theta + k360°) = \sin \theta$, if k is an integer, we conclude that

$$R = r^{\frac{1}{n}} \text{ and } \phi = \frac{\theta + k360°}{n}.$$

Therefore $(a + ib)^{\frac{1}{n}} = [r(\cos \theta + i \sin \theta)]^{\frac{1}{n}}$
$$= r^{\frac{1}{n}}\left[\cos \frac{\theta + k360°}{n} + i \sin \frac{\theta + k360°}{n}\right].$$

If we let k assume the values $0, 1, 2, \cdots, (n - 1)$, we find n distinct results such that the nth power of any one of them is $a + ib$. We may then state the following

THEOREM. *Every complex number, except zero, has n distinct nth roots.*

EXERCISES

Using De Moivre's theorem, find the indicated powers and roots. Illustrate the given number and its indicated power or roots graphically.

1. $(3 + \sqrt{3}i)^4$.

Solution: Writing $3 + \sqrt{3}i$ in the polar form,

$$3 + \sqrt{3}i = 2\sqrt{3}(\cos 30° + i \sin 30°).$$

By De Moivre's theorem,

$$(3 + \sqrt{3}i)^4 = [2\sqrt{3}(\cos 30° + i \sin 30°)]^4$$
$$= 144(\cos 120° + i \sin 120°)$$
$$= 144\left(-\frac{1}{2} + \frac{1}{2}\sqrt{3}i\right)$$
$$= -72 + 72\sqrt{3}i.$$

2. $(\sqrt{3} + 3i)^3$.

3. $(1 + i\sqrt{3})^{12}$.

4. $(-2 + 2i)^2$.

5. $\left(-\frac{1}{2} - \frac{i\sqrt{3}}{2}\right)^3$.

6. $[2(\cos 105° + i \sin 105°)]^4$.

7. $[3(\cos 150° + i \sin 150°)]^5$.

8. Show that $(\cos \theta + i \sin \theta)^{-n} = \dfrac{1}{(\cos \theta + i \sin \theta)^n}$

$$= (\cos n\theta - i \sin n\theta) = \cos(-n\theta) + i \sin(-n\theta).$$

Use the result of problem 8 to evaluate:

9. $(1 + i)^{-2}$.

10. $(\sqrt{3} + 3i)^{-5}$.

11. $(-1 - i\sqrt{3})^{-1}$.

12. $\left(-\dfrac{\sqrt{3}}{2} + \dfrac{i}{2}\right)^{-3}$.

13. $\sqrt[3]{-2 + 2i}$.

Solution: Writing $-2 + 2i$ in the polar form, we have

$$-2 + 2i = 2\sqrt{2}(\cos 135° + i \sin 135°).$$

By De Moivre's theorem,

$$\sqrt[3]{-2 + 2i} = (-2 + 2i)^{\frac{1}{3}}$$
$$= [2\sqrt{2}\{\cos(135° + k360°) + i \sin(135° + k360°)\}]^{\frac{1}{3}}$$
$$= \sqrt{2}[\cos(45° + k120°)1 + i \sin(45° + k120°)].$$

For $k = 0, 1,$ and 2, this expression reduces to

$$1 + i, \quad \sqrt{2}(\cos 165° + i \sin 165°),$$
and $$\sqrt{2}(\cos 285° + i \sin 285°)$$

respectively. Any one of these three numbers is a cube root of

$-2 + 2i$. The points P_1, P_2, P_3, representing these three numbers lie at equal intervals on a circle of radius $\sqrt{2}$ (Fig. 36).

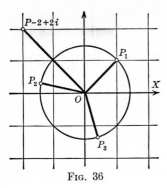

FIG. 36

14. $\sqrt[3]{2i - 2}$.

15. $\sqrt[4]{2\sqrt{3} - 2i}$.

16. $\sqrt[3]{\cos 180° + i \sin 180°}$.

17. $\sqrt[4]{\cos 300° + i \sin 300°}$.

18. $\sqrt[6]{1}$.

Hint: Write 1 in the form $\cos 0° + i \sin 0°$.

19. $\sqrt{i}$.

20. $\sqrt[6]{-i}$.

Find all the roots of the following equations and represent them graphically.

21. $x^3 + 8 = 0$.

22. $x^5 - 243 = 0$.

23. $x^4 - i = 0$.

24. $x^6 + 1 = 0$.

25. $2x^5 + \sqrt{3} - i = 0$.

26. $x^3 - 1 = 0$.

27. If ω represents one of the complex cube roots of unity found in exercise 26 and ω_1 the other, verify that $\omega_1 = \omega^2$, that $\omega = \omega_1{}^2$, and that $1 + \omega + \omega_1 = 0$.

14 THEORY OF EQUATIONS

111. Rational Integral Equations of Degree n

An equation, in one variable x, of the form

$$a_0 x^n + a_1 x^{n-1} + a_2 x^{n-2} + \cdots + a_{n-1} x + a_n = 0, \ (a_0 \neq 0), \quad (1)$$

is called a **rational integral equation of degree n in x** if n is a positive integer and the coefficients of the various powers of x are independent of x (Art. **31**).

If $f(x)$ represents the general polynomial in x of degree n (Art. **30**), then

$$f(x) = a_0 x^n + a_1 x^{n-1} + a_2 x^{n-2} + \cdots + a_{n-1} x + a_n, \ (a_0 \neq 0),$$

and equation (1) can be represented in the more compact form

$$f(x) = 0.$$

In this chapter, we shall agree that the symbol $f(x)$ always represents a polynomial of degree n.

In Article **32** the rational integral equation of degree one, the linear equation $a_0 x + a_1 = 0$, was solved for x in terms of the coefficients a_0 and a_1.

In Chapter 9 the rational integral equation of degree two, the quadratic equation $ax^2 + bx + c = 0$, was discussed and a formula giving the roots in terms of the coefficients a, b, c was derived.

The roots of the linear and the quadratic equations were expressed as functions of the coefficients of the respective equations, but more than this, the functions of the coefficients were *algebraic*. That is, the roots were expressed in terms of the coefficients by applying to the coefficients a finite number of additions, subtractions, multiplications (including raising to powers), divisions, and extractions of roots (Art. **101**). The algebraic solution of an equation is often called the solution by radicals. The mathematician's wish then was to express the solution of any rational integral equation as an algebraic function of the coefficients.

At the end of this chapter, the general cubic

$$a_0x^3 + a_1x^2 + a_2x + a_3 = 0,$$

and the general quartic

$$a_0x^4 + a_1x^3 + a_2x^2 + a_3x + a_4 = 0$$

are solved by radicals.*

The algebraic solution of the general fifth degree equation

$$a_0x^5 + a_1x^4 + a_2x^3 + a_3x^2 + a_4x + a_5 = 0,$$

engaged the attention of mathematicians during the eighteenth and the first quarter of the nineteenth century. The Norwegian mathematician, Abel (1802–1829), proved the impossibility of finding a formula which would express the roots of this equation as algebraic functions of the coefficients, a_0, a_1, a_2, a_3, a_4, a_5. It has been proved that the roots of the rational integral equation of degree n, where $n > 4$, cannot be expressed as algebraic functions of the coefficients a_0, a_1, a_2, $\cdots$, a_n. The student should be clear as to what has actually been stated here. The above statements do not exclude the possibility of solving some special equations of degree greater than 4. For example, the equation $x^6 - 9x^3 + 8 = 0$ is capable of solution by algebraic methods and was one of the exercises in Chapter 9. The essential fact is that given the general equation

$$a_0x^6 + a_1x^5 + a_2x^4 + a_3x^3 + a_4x^2 + a_5x + a_6 = 0,$$

we cannot write a formula giving x as an algebraic function of a_0, a_1, a_2, a_3, a_4, a_5, a_6.

The principal object of this chapter is to present methods which aid in determining exactly or approximately the real roots of special rational integral equations with numerical coefficients.†

---

* For an account of the historical lore connected with the solution of these equations and the men involved, the reader is referred to E. T. Bell — *Development of Mathematics*, pp. 108, 109.

† The term "numerical coefficients" is used here to indicate that the coefficients are not literal.

It is largely for this purpose that we discuss the graphs of polynomials. The zeros of the polynomial are the roots of the equation formed by equating the polynomial to zero. The real roots of the equation may then be looked upon geometrically as the abscissas of the points of the X-axis where the graph of the polynomial meets the X-axis. The remainder theorem (Art. **112**) and synthetic division (Arts. **115, 116**) often save time in carrying out the numerical work necessary in graphing polynomials.

112. Remainder Theorem

If r is some constant and if $f(x)$ is divided by $(x - r)$ until a remainder is obtained that does not involve x, this remainder is equal to $f(r)$.

Let $f(x) \equiv a_0 x^n + a_1 x^{n-1} + a_2 x^{n-2} + \cdots + a_{n-1} x + a_n.$ (1)
Then $f(r) \equiv a_0 r^n + a_1 r^{n-1} + a_2 r^{n-2} + \cdots + a_{n-1} r + a_n,$ (2)
and

$$f(x) - f(r) \equiv a_0(x^n - r^n) + a_1(x^{n-1} - r^{n-1}) + \cdots + a_{n-1}(x - r). \quad (3)$$

Since $(x - r)$ is a factor of each of the expressions $x^n - r^n$, $x^{n-1} - r^{n-1}, \cdots, x - r$, (Art. **96**), it is a factor of the right-hand member of (3). Hence the right-hand member of (3) may be written as $(x - r)Q(x)$, where it should be noted that $Q(x)$ is a polynomial of degree $n - 1$ in x. Then we have

$$f(x) - f(r) \equiv (x - r)Q(x),$$

or $\qquad \dfrac{f(x)}{x - r} \equiv Q(x) + \dfrac{f(r)}{x - r}.$ (4)

This is the symbolic form of the theorem that was to be proved.

Example: Without performing the division, find the remainder when $x^3 + 5x^2 + 3x - 1$ is divided by $(x + 2)$.

Solution: Here $f(x) = x^3 + 5x^2 + 3x - 1,$

$\qquad x - r = x + 2,$ so $r = -2,$
and $\qquad f(r) = f(-2) = (-2)^3 + 5(-2)^2 + 3(-2) - 1 = 5.$

Hence, the remainder is 5.

CoROLLARY. *If $f(r) = 0$, then $f(x)$ is exactly divisible by $(x - r)$.*
This corollary follows immediately from (4).

Example. Without performing the division, show that $x^3 - 7x + 6$ is exactly divisible by $x + 3$.

Solution: Here $f(x) = x^3 - 7x + 6$ and $r = -3$,

and $f(-3) = (-3)^3 - 7(-3) + 6 = 0$.

Hence, by the corollary above, $f(x)$ is exactly divisible by $x + 3$.

113. Factor Theorem

If r is a root of the equation $f(x) = 0$, then $(x - r)$ is a factor of $f(x)$.

Since the hypothesis that r is a root of the equation $f(x) = 0$ means that $f(r) = 0$, this theorem follows directly from the corollary to the remainder theorem (Art. **112**).

114. Converse of the Factor Theorem

If $(x - r)$ is a factor of $f(x)$, then r is a root of the equation $f(x) = 0$.

By hypothesis, $f(x)$ is exactly divisible by $(x - r)$. Thus, in the notation of Article **112**,

$$f(x) = (x - r)Q(x).$$

Hence, $f(r) = 0 \cdot Q(r) = 0$, which means that r is a root of the equation $f(x) = 0$.

EXERCISES

1. Which of the following are rational integral equations in x? For those which are rational integral equations, find the values of n, a_0, a_1, $\cdots$, a_n.

(a) $3x^5 - 2x^3 + 3x^2 - 5 = 0$.

(b) $x^4 + 3x^3 - 2x^2 = 0$.

(c) $2x^5 + \dfrac{1}{2} x^4 - \dfrac{1}{4} x + 3 = 0$.

(d) $3x^3 + \sqrt{2}x^2 + (3 - 2i)x + 7i = 0$.

(e) $x^4 + 2x - 2\sqrt{x} + 3 = 0$.

(f) $x^2 + x + 1 + \dfrac{1}{x} = 0$.

(g) $x^3 + 3x^{-2} + 5x - 6 = 0$.

(h) $3\sqrt{2}x^3 - 2\sqrt{3}x - \sqrt{6} = 0$.

2. Find the remainder when $x^3 - 7x + 6$ is divided by $x - 3$:

(a) by performing the division,

(b) by use of the remainder theorem.

Find the remainder after each of the following divisions by use of the remainder theorem.

3. $(x^3 + 4x^2 - 7x - 10) \div (x - 2)$.

4. $(x^3 + 4x^2 - 7x - 10) \div (x + 2)$.

5. $(x^4 - 3x^2 + 2x + 5) \div (x + 1)$.

6. $(6x^3 + 19x^2 + x - 6) \div \left(x - \dfrac{1}{2}\right)$.

7. $(3x^4 + 5x^3 - 6x + 7) \div x$.

8. $(2x^4 - 7x^3 + 6x) \div x$.

9. Show that $x - 5$ is a factor of $x^3 - x^2 - 16x - 20$.

10. Show that $2x + 3$ is a factor of $6x^3 + 19x^2 + 11x - 6$.

11. Show that $x - \sqrt{2}$ is a factor of $x^3 - 3x^2 - 2x + 6$.

12. Use the factor theorem to show that $x^{2n} - a^{2n}$ is exactly divisible by $x + a$.

13. Use the factor theorem to show that $x^{2n+1} + a^{2n+1}$ is exactly divisible by $x + a$.

14. Determine k so that $3x^4 - 2kx^2 + 3x - 6$ is divisible by $x + 2$.

15. Determine k so that $2x^3 - 3x^2 + k^2x - k - 5$ is divisible by $x - 2$.

115. Synthetic Division

Since we shall often have occasion to divide a polynomial, $f(x)$, by ($x -$ an assigned number), (1) in finding values of $f(x)$ for assigned values of x, (2) in finding factors of $f(x)$, and (3) in solving the equation $f(x) = 0$, it is important to learn a short method of performing the divisions. We shall now illustrate and develop Horner's **method of synthetic division** for dividing $f(x)$ by $(x - r)$.

Illustration: Divide $5x^4 - 6x^3 + 8x^2 - 24x - 6$ by $(x - 2)$.

By the ordinary method

$$
\begin{array}{r}
5x^4 - 6x^3 + 8x^2 - 24x - 6 \,\lfloor\underline{x - 2} \\
\underline{5x^4 - 10x^3} \quad 5x^3 + 4x^2 + 16x + 8 \\
4x^3 + 8x^2 \\
\underline{4x^3 - 8x^2} \\
16x^2 - 24x \\
\underline{16x^2 - 32x} \\
8x - 6 \\
\underline{8x - 16} \\
+ 10
\end{array}
$$

Manifestly, the work can be abridged by writing only the coefficients, thus,

$$5 - 6 + 8 - 24 - 6 \underline{\lfloor 1 - 2}$$
$$5 - 10 \qquad\qquad \overline{5 + 4 + 16 + 8}$$
$$\overline{+ 4 + 8}$$
$$+ 4 - 8$$
$$\overline{+ 16 - 24}$$
$$+ 16 - 32$$
$$\overline{+ 8 - 6}$$
$$+ 8 - 16$$
$$\overline{+ 10}$$

Since the coefficient of x in $x - r$ is unity, the coefficient of the first term of each remainder is the coefficient of the next term to be obtained in the quotient. Further, it is not necessary to write the terms of the dividend as part of the remainder, nor the first term of the partial products.

The work thus becomes:

$$5 - 6 + 8 - 24 - 6 \underline{\lfloor 1 - 2}$$
$$- 10$$
$$\overline{+ 4}$$
$$- 8$$
$$\overline{+ 16}$$
$$- 32$$
$$\overline{+ 8}$$
$$- 16$$
$$\overline{+ 10}$$

We may omit the first term of the divisor and write the work in the following more compact form:

$$5 - 6 + 8 - 24 - 6 \underline{\lfloor - 2}$$
$$- 10 - 8 - 32 - 16$$
$$\overline{5 + 4 + 16 + 8 + 10}$$

If we replace $- 2$ by $+ 2$, we may add the partial products to the numbers in the dividend. Then, we have:

$$5 - 6 + 8 - 24 - 6 \underline{\lfloor 2}$$
$$+ 10 + 8 + 32 + 16$$
$$\overline{5 + 4 + 16 + 8 + 10}$$

The quotient is $5x^3 + 4x^2 + 16x + 8$, and the remainder is 10.

116. Rule for Synthetic Division

To divide $f(x)$ by $(x - r)$, arrange $f(x)$ in descending powers of x, supplying all missing powers by putting in zeros as coefficients.

Detach the coefficients, write them in a horizontal line and in the order a_0, a_1, a_2, $\cdots$, a_n.

Bring down the first coefficient a_0; multiply a_0 by r, and add the product to a_1; multiply this sum by r, and add the product to a_2. Continue this process; the last sum is the remainder, and the preceding sums are the coefficients of the powers of x in the quotient, arranged in descending order.

Proof of Rule. This rule may be established by mathematical induction.

By long division,

$$
\begin{array}{r}
a_0x^{n-1} + (a_1 + a_0r)x^{n-2} + \cdots + (a_{s-1} + ra_{s-2} + \cdots + r^{s-1}a_0)x^{n-s} + \cdots \\
\hline
x - r \mid a_0x^n + a_1x^{n-1} + a_2x^{n-2} + \cdots + a_sx^{n-s} + a_{s+1}x^{n-s-1} + \cdots + a_n \\
a_0x^n -- a_0rx^{n-1} \\
\hline
(a_1 + a_0r)x^{n-1} + a_2x^{n-2} \\
(a_1 + a_0r)x^{n-1} - (a_1r + a_0r^2)x^{n-2} \\
\cdot \cdot \cdot \cdot \cdot \cdot \cdot \cdot \cdot \cdot \cdot \cdot \cdot
\end{array}
$$

We note that the coefficient of x^{n-2} in the quotient is formed according to the rule. Assume that the coefficients in the quotient down to that of x^{n-s} are formed according to the rule. On this hypothesis, proceed by long division to find the coefficient of x^{n-s-1} in the quotient. This may be exhibited as a continuation of the division above as follows:

$$
\begin{array}{l}
(a_{s-1}+ra_{s-2}+\cdots+r^{s-1}a_0)x^{n-s+1} + a_sx^{n-s}+a_{s+1}x^{n-s-1}+\cdots+a_n \\
(a_{s-1}+ra_{s-2}+\cdots+r^{s-1}a_0)x^{n-s+1}-(ra_{s-1}+r^2a_{s-2}+\cdots+r^sa_0)x^{n-s} \\
\hline
(a_s+ra_{s-1}+r^2a_{s-2}+\cdots+r^sa_0)x^{n-s}+a_{s+1}x^{n-s-1}+\cdots+a_n
\end{array}
$$

This shows that if the coefficients in the quotient down to that of x^{n-s} are formed according to the rule, the coefficient of the next lower power is formed according to the rule. Hence, the rule is established.

EXERCISES

Divide by synthetic division and check by ordinary division.

1. $x^4 + 3x^3 - 5x + 3$ by $(x - 4)$.

Solution:
$$
\begin{array}{r}
1 + 3 + 0 - 5 + 3 \mid\underline{4} \\
+ 4 + 28 + 112 + 428 \\
\hline
1 + 7 + 28 + 107 + 431
\end{array}
$$

The quotient is $x^3 + 7x^2 + 28x + 107$ and the remainder is 431. The student should check this result by ordinary division.

2. $(x^4 - 2x^3 + 3x^2 - 5x + 3) \div (x - 1)$.

3. $(x^4 + 5x^3 - 8x + 2) \div (x + 3)$.

4. $(2x^3 - 3x + 5) \div (x - 2)$.

Find the remainder and the quotient in the following by synthetic division.

5. $(6x^3 + 7x^2 - 9x + 2) \div (x - 3)$.

6. $(x^4 - 16) \div (x + 2)$.

7. $(x^5 + x^3 - 5) \div (x + 1)$.

8. $(5x^4 - 3x^2 - 10) \div \left(x + \dfrac{1}{2}\right)$.

9. If $f(x) = 4x^4 + 4x^3 - 11x^2 + 4x - 15$, find $f(-2)$, $f(-1)$, $f(1)$, $f(2)$ by using synthetic division and the remainder theorem.

10. If $f(x) = 6x^3 - x^2 - 10x - 3$, find $f(-2)$, $f(-1)$, $f(0)$, $f(1)$, $f(2)$.

117. Graphical Solution of an Equation $f(x) = 0$

When the coefficients of $f(x)$ are real numbers, the manner in which the function changes as x varies can be most clearly presented by the use of graphical methods (Arts. **22, 23**). To any assigned value of x, there corresponds one and only one value of the polynomial $f(x)$. This fact is sometimes expressed by saying that $f(x)$ is single valued. The fact that the graph of $f(x)$ is a continuous curve (Art. **23**) makes it of much service in the theory of equations.

The graph of the function $f(x)$ shows at least approximately the points at which the function crosses the X-axis. The abscissas of these points are the zeros of the function. They are also the real roots of the equation $f(x) = 0$. It is therefore obvious that in locating the zeros of the function $f(x)$, we are also locating the roots of $f(x) = 0$.

EXERCISES

Construct the graphs of the following functions and locate their real zeros approximately (to within 0.5):

1. $f(x) = x^3 - 6x^2 + 11x - 6$.

As pointed out in Article **115,** synthetic division furnishes a convenient method of evaluating $f(x)$ for different values of x. Thus $f(0.5)$ is obtained as follows:

$$
\begin{array}{r}
1 - 6 \quad + 11 \quad - 6 \quad \underline{|\,0.5} \\
0.5 - \ 2.75 + 4.125 \\
\hline
1 - 5.5 + \ \ 8.25 - 1.875
\end{array}
$$

Hence, $f(0.5) = -1.875$.

In this way the following values are obtained:

$f(-2) = -60.$ $f(1.5) = 0.375.$

$f(-1) = -24.$ $f(2) = 0.$

$f(-0.5) = -13.125.$ $f(2.5) = -0.375.$

$f(0) = -6.$ $f(3) = 0.$

$f(0.5) = -1.875.$ $f(4) = 6.$

$f(1) = 0.$ $f(5) = 24.$

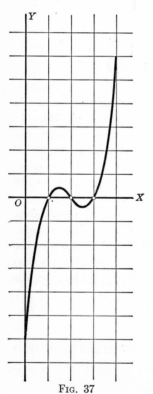

Fig. 37

The graph is shown in Figure 37; it presents to the eye the following facts:

(1) $f(x)$ has zeros at 1, 2, and 3.

(2) $f(x)$ is positive when $2 > x > 1$, and when $x > 3$.

(3) $f(x)$ is negative when $x < 1$ and when $3 > x > 2$.

Query. If x were assigned a numerically very large value, say $x = 100$ or $x = -100$, how would the value of the highest degree term, x^3, compare in numerical value with all the other terms together?

2. $f(x) = 6x^4 + x^3 - 25x^2 - 4x + 4.$

3. $f(x) = x^3 + x^2 - 6x.$

4. $f(x) = 2x^3 - x - 1.$

Use graphical methods to evaluate the real roots of the following to within 0.5.

5. $x^4 + 3x^3 - 3x^2 + 3x - 4 = 0.$

6. $x^4 - 5x^3 + 8x^2 - 7x + 3 = 0.$

7. $2x^3 - 3x^2 - 12x + 12 = 0.$

8. $x^3 - x + 5 = 0.$

118. Number of Roots of an Equation

Every equation, $f(x) = 0$, of the nth degree has n roots and no more.

To prove this proposition we assume the fundamental theorem that every equation, $f(x) = 0$, has at least one root. More explicitly, we assume that

There always exists at least one number, real or complex, which will satisfy an equation of the nth degree, whose coefficients are any real or complex numbers. [*]

Let r_1 be a root of $f(x) = 0$, then (Art. **113**) $(x - r_1)$ is a factor of $f(x)$ and

$$f(x) = 0 \text{ becomes } (x - r_1)f_1(x) = 0, \qquad (1)$$

where $f_1(x)$ is a polynomial of degree $n - 1$, beginning with the term $a_0 x^{n-1}$. By the theorem assumed, $f_1(x) = 0$ has at least one root. Let r_2 be a root; then

$$f_1(x) = 0 \text{ becomes } (x - r_2)f_2(x) = 0$$

and
$$f(x) = 0 \text{ becomes } (x - r_1)(x - r_2)f_2(x) = 0, \qquad (2)$$

in which $f_2(x)$ is a polynomial of degree $n - 2$, beginning with the term $a_0 x^{n-2}$. Continuing this process, we separate out n linear factors with a quotient a_0, so that

$$f(x) = 0 \text{ becomes } a_0(x - r_1)(x - r_2) \cdots (x - r_n) = 0, \qquad (3)$$

where $r_1, r_2, \cdots, r_n$ are n roots of $f(x) = 0$.

If $f(x) = 0$ has another root different from any of these, let r denote such a root. Then, from (3),

$$a_0(r - r_1)(r - r_2) \cdots (r - r_n) = 0. \qquad (4)$$

But here we should have the product of factors equal to zero when no one of the factors is zero. As this is impossible (IV, Art. **5**), there are not more than n roots of $f(x) = 0$. Hence, every equation of the nth degree has n roots and no more. Furthermore, every polynomial of the nth degree is the product of n linear factors. It is not, however, possible, in general, to determine these factors if n exceeds 4 (see Art. **111**). Two or more of the n roots of $f(x) = 0$ may be equal to each other. Equal roots are called **multiple roots.** If the same root occurs twice, it is called a **double root;** if three times, a **triple root;** if m times $(m > 3)$, a root of

---

[*] This fundamental theorem was first proved by Gauss in 1797. For proof, see Fine's *College Algebra*, p. 588

multiplicity m. Thus, $(x - 2)^5 = 0$ has the root 2 of multiplicity 5, and $(x - 1)^2(x - 3)(x - 4)^3 = 0$ has a double root equal to 1, a single root equal to 3, and a triple root equal to 4.

COROLLARY I. *If two polynomials of degrees not greater than n are equal to each other for more than n distinct values of the variable, the coefficients of like powers of the variable are equal.*

Let

$$a_0x^n + a_1x^{n-1} + \cdots + a_n = b_0x^n + b_1x^{n-1} + \cdots + b_n \qquad (4)$$

for more than n values of x.

From (4),

$$(a_0 - b_0)x^n + (a_1 - b_1)x^{n-1} + \cdots + (a_n - b_n) = 0. \qquad (5)$$

Then
$$a_0 - b_0 = 0,$$
$$a_1 - b_1 = 0,$$
$$\cdot \quad \cdot \quad \cdot \quad \cdot$$
$$a_n - b_n = 0.$$

For, if any coefficient in (5) were not equal to zero, we should have an equation of degree equal to or less than n with more than n roots, which is contrary to the theorem just proved.

Hence, $a_0 = b_0$, $a_1 = b_1$, $\cdots$, $a_n = b_n$.

COROLLARY II. *If two polynomials of degrees not greater than n are equal for more than n distinct values of the variable, they are equal for all values, and the equality is an identity.*

119. Forming an Equation with Given Roots

If r_1, r_2, $\cdots$, r_n are given roots of an equation $f(x) = 0$, then it follows from Article **118** that the equation may be written in the form

$$f(x) = a_0(x - r_1)(x - r_2) \cdots (x - r_n) = 0$$

in which we may assign to a_0 any value not equal to 0.

In case all the roots are integers or rational fractions, a_0 may be selected as an appropriate multiple of the denominators of the fractions in such a manner that all the coefficients of the terms of the equation are integers.

Illustration 1. Form an equation that has roots $1, -1, \dfrac{1}{2}, \dfrac{2}{3}$, and no others.

Solution: The equation is of the form

$$a_0(x - 1)(x + 1)\left(x - \frac{1}{2}\right)\left(x - \frac{2}{3}\right) = 0. \tag{1}$$

By choosing $a_0 = 6$, we obtain an equation free from fractional coefficients. This choice of a_0 is equivalent to multiplying the last factor of the left-hand side of (1) by 3, and the preceding factor by 2, thus obtaining

$$(x - 1)(x + 1)(2x - 1)(3x - 2) = 0,$$

or
$$6x^4 - 7x^3 - 4x^2 + 7x - 2 = 0.$$

Illustration 2. Form an equation with integral coefficients that has 1 as a triple root, $\frac{1}{2}$ as a double root, $\frac{1}{3}$ as a single root, and no other roots.

Solution: The equation is, following illustration 1,

$$(x - 1)^3(2x - 1)^2(3x - 1) = 0,$$

or
$$12x^6 - 52x^5 + 91x^4 - 82x^3 + 40x^2 - 10x + 1 = 0.$$

EXERCISES

Find each root of the equation and indicate the multiplicity of each root.

1. $3(x - 1)(x + 2)^3(x - 5)^2 = 0.$

2. $(2x - 1)^2(3x + 1)(5x - 4)^3 = 0.$

3. $(x^2 - 1)(x^2 - 4x + 3) = 0.$

4. $4x^5 + 13x^4 - 12x^3 = 0.$

5. $x^3 - 1 = 0.$

6. $(2x - 3)^3(x^2 + 1)^2 = 0.$

7. Show that -3 is a triple root and $\frac{1}{2}$ is a double root of

$$4x^5 + 32x^4 + 73x^3 + 9x^2 - 81x + 27 = 0.$$

8. Show that -2 and $-\frac{1}{2}$ are both double roots of

$$4x^4 + 20x^3 + 33x^2 + 20x + 4 = 0.$$

9. Form equations that have the following roots:

(a) $2, -4, 4.$

(b) $1, -2, -2, 3.$

(c) $2 + \sqrt{3}, 2 - \sqrt{3}, 2.$

(d) $3 + 2i, 3 - 2i, 2 + 3\sqrt{2}, 2 - 3\sqrt{2}$, where $i^2 = -1.$

10. Form equations with integral coefficients that have the following roots and no others:

(a) double root -2, single roots $\frac{5}{3}$ and $\frac{2}{5}$.

(b) triple root -1, double root 1, and single root 3.

11. If $Q(x)$ is a polynomial of degree 2, determine $Q(x)$ and r and s, so that

$$4x^4 + 20x^3 + 33x^2 + 20x + 4 \equiv (x^2 + 5x + 6)Q(x) + rx + s.$$

Hint: If $Q(x) \equiv Ax^2 + Bx + C$, the right-hand side of the identity may be written

$$Ax^4 + (5A + B)x^3 + (6A + 5B + C)x^2 + (6B + 5C + r)x + (6C + s).$$

Then apply corollary I, Article **118.**

12. If $Q(x)$ is a polynomial of degree 3, determine $Q(x)$ and r and s, so that

$$4x^5 + 13x^4 - 12x^3 \equiv (x^2 + x + 1)Q(x) + rx + s.$$

13. If $f(x)$ is a known polynomial of degree n and $ax^2 + bx + c$ is a known quadratic, and if $Q(x)$ is a polynomial of degree $n - 2$, show that $Q(x)$, r, and s may be determined so that

$$f(x) \equiv (ax^2 + bx + c)Q(x) + rx + s.$$

120. Comments on the Graphs of Factored Polynomials

Given

$$a_0x^n + a_1x^{n-1} + \cdots + a_n = a_0(x - r_1)(x - r_2) \cdots (x - r_n).$$

In the remainder of this chapter, we assume that $a_0, a_1, \cdots, a_n$ are real numbers, and further, for convenience of expression, that a_0 is positive, although this is not a necessary limitation. In this article, we shall assume that the polynomial can be separated into a product of real, linear factors. In Article **94**, we found how to determine the values of x for which such a polynomial is greater than zero or less than zero. We now use that information to draw graphs of polynomials which can be separated into the product of real, linear factors.

1. *When the factors $x - r_1$, $x - r_2$, $\cdots$, $x - r_n$ are all real and distinct.*

Arrange the factors so that $r_1 > r_2 > \cdots > r_{n-1} > r_n$. When $x > r_1$ all the factors are positive and the graph is above the X-axis.

When $r_1 > x > r_2$, one factor is negative and the graph is below the X-axis. When $r_2 > x > r_3$, two factors are negative, and the graph is again above the X-axis. Continuing this process, we see that the graph crosses the X-axis at the n points, $x = r_1$, $x = r_2$, $\cdots$, $x = r_n$, and we obtain a general notion of the nature of the curve. See Figure 38.

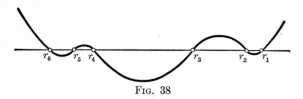

FIG. 38

2. *When the factors are real but some of them repeated.*
To discuss the graph in this case, take for example,

$$f(x) = a_0(x - r_1)^2(x - r_2)(x - r_3)^5,$$

and let $r_1 > r_2 > r_3$.

Since the factors $x - r_2$ and $x - r_3$ occur to powers with odd exponents, it follows as above that the curve crosses the X-axis at $x = r_2$ and $x = r_3$. But it does not cross at $x = r_1$, since the sign of $f(x)$ is the same when $x > r_1$ as when $r_1 > x > r_2$, and the curve touches the axis at $x = r_1$. In general, *if a factor* $(x - r)^m$ *occurs where m is odd, the graph crosses the X-axis at* $x = r$ (See A and B, Fig. 39). *Moreover, if* $m = 1$, *the graph tends to cut the X-axis as at* B, Figure 39, *whereas if m is an odd number greater than* 1, *the graph not only crosses at* $x = r$, *but is tangent to the X-axis at* $x = r$ *as at* A, Figure 39. *If m is even, the graph merely touches the X-axis without crossing* (see C, Fig. 39). These comments, in

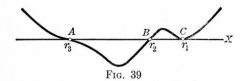

FIG. 39

italics, follow in part from studies in the calculus, and may be accepted here without proof.

Another case is discussed in Article **122**, where imaginary factors occur.

121. Theorem Concerning Imaginary Roots.

If an imaginary number $a + bi$ *is a root of an equation* $f(x) = 0$ *with real coefficients, the conjugate imaginary number* $a - bi$ *is also a root. Thus, imaginary roots occur in conjugate pairs.*

The theorem is established if we can show that $[x - (a - bi)]$ is a factor of $f(x)$ (Art. **114**). Since $[x - (a - bi)]$ is a factor of the quadratic expression

$$D(x) = x^2 - 2ax + a^2 + b^2 = [x - (a + bi)][x - (a - bi)], \quad (1)$$

our theorem is proved if we can show that $D(x)$ is a factor of $f(x)$.

If $Q(x)$ is a polynomial of degree $n - 2$, then we may write the identity

$$f(x) \equiv D(x)Q(x) + cx + d \tag{2}$$

where the coefficients of $Q(x)$ and the constants c and d are real numbers, since $f(x)$ and $D(x)$ have real coefficients. (See problem 13, p. 208.)

Since, by hypothesis, $(a + bi)$ is a root of $f(x) = 0$, we have $f(a + bi) = 0$. From (1),

$$D(a + bi) = 0.$$

Hence, if we substitute $x = (a + bi)$ in (2), we get

$$0 = 0 \cdot Q(a + bi) + c(a + bi) + d,$$

or $\qquad\qquad (ac + d) + bci = 0. \tag{3}$

Equating reals and imaginaries on the two sides of (3), we have

$$ac + d = 0 \text{ and } bc = 0. \tag{4}$$

Since, by hypothesis, $(a + bi)$ is an imaginary number, $b \neq 0$. Hence, $c = 0$. Then from $ac + d = 0$ of (4), we get $d = 0$, and thus the remainder $cx + d$ in (2) is zero, and $D(x)$ is a factor of $f(x)$.

COROLLARY. *Any polynomial* $f(x)$ *with real coefficients can be expressed as a product of real linear and quadratic factors.*

Since imaginary factors of $f(x)$ occur in conjugate pairs when the coefficients in $f(x)$ are real, it follows that in this case $f(x)$ may be regarded as the product of a_0, of real linear factors of the type $(x - r)$, and quadratic factors of the type

$$(x - a)^2 + b^2 = (x - a - bi)(x - a + bi),$$

where a, b, and r are real numbers. When all the roots of $f(x) = 0$ are real, the polynomial $f(x)$ is the product of real linear factors, but if $f(x) = 0$ has imaginary or complex roots, $f(x)$ contains real quadratic factors of the type $(x - a)^2 + b^2$ which cannot be separated into real linear factors.

122. Graphs of $f(x)$ When Some Linear Factors are Imaginary

In Article **120** the graph of $f(x)$ is discussed when the polynomial is the product of real linear factors, and it is shown that, corresponding to each linear factor $(x - r)$, the graph meets the X-axis at $x = r$. It should now be noted that

$$(x - a)^2 + b^2 > 0,$$

for all real values of x, and there is, therefore, corresponding to such quadratic factors of $f(x)$, no intersection of the graph with the X-axis.

Example: Graph
$$f(x) = x^4 - 7x^3 - 4x^2 + 78x$$
$$= x(x + 3)(x^2 - 10x + 26)$$
$$= x(x + 3)[(x - 5)^2 + 1].$$

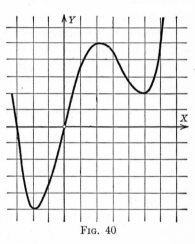

Fig. 40

Corresponding to the linear factors x and $x + 3$, the graph intersects the X-axis at $x = 0$ and $x = -3$ respectively (Fig. 40). Corresponding to the quadratic factor $x^2 - 10x + 26$ there is no intersection with the X-axis. (In Fig. 40 one horizontal space represents one unit, while one vertical space represents twenty units.)

EXERCISES

Plot the graph of each of the following polynomials.

1. $f(x) = (x + 2)(x - 1)(x - 5)$.
2. $f(x) = x(x + 1)^2(x - 3)$.
3. $f(x) = (2x + 1)^4(3x - 2)^3$.
4. $f(x) = x^2(x^2 - 4)$.
5. $f(x) = x^2(x - 2)^2$.
6. $f(x) = x(x - 3)(x^2 + x + 1)$.

Separate the following polynomials into real linear and real quadratic factors and plot the graphs.

7. $f(x) = x^3 - 8.$　　　　　　　**9.** $f(x) = x^4 - 16.$

8. $f(x) = x^3 + 8.$　　　　　　　**10.** $f(x) = x^4 - 8x^2 - 9.$

11. Show that an equation $f(x) = 0$ of odd degree and with real coefficients has an odd number of real roots.

12. Show that an equation $f(x) = 0$ of even degree and with real coefficients has an even number of real roots, or no real roots.

123. Transformation to Multiply Each Root of an Equation by a Constant.

The solution of an equation $f(x) = 0$ is often facilitated by transforming it into an equation whose roots are equal to those of the original equation times a constant. If we make $x = \dfrac{y}{m}$ (or $y = mx$) in $f(x) = 0$, we obtain an equation in y whose roots are m times those of $f(x) = 0$. In particular, if $m = -1$, we make $x = -y$ in $f(x) = 0$, *and obtain $f(-y) = 0$ whose roots are equal in absolute value but opposite in sign to those of $f(x) = 0$.*

These transformations can be performed rapidly by means of the following rules:

1. *To obtain an equation each of whose roots is m times a corresponding root of $f(x) = 0$: multiply the successive coefficients beginning with that of x^{n-1} by m, m^2, m^3, $\cdots$, respectively and replace x by y.*[*]

For example, to find the equation each of whose roots is double the roots of the equation $x^4 - 4x^3 + 3x^2 + 1 = 0$, we make $m = 2$, and obtain

$$y^4 - 2(4y^3) + 2^2(3y^2) + 2^3(0 \cdot y) + 2^4 = 0,$$
$$y^4 - 8y^3 + 12y^2 + 16 = 0.$$

To establish this rule, substitute $x = \dfrac{y}{m}$ in

$$f(x) = a_0 x^n + a_1 x^{n-1} + a_2 x^{n-2} + \cdots + a_{n-1}x + a_n = 0. \quad (1)$$

The result of this substitution is

$$a_0\left(\frac{y}{m}\right)^n + a_1\left(\frac{y}{m}\right)^{n-1} + a_2\left(\frac{y}{m}\right)^{n-2} + \cdots + a_{n-1}\left(\frac{y}{m}\right) + a_n = 0, \quad (2)$$

[*] In carrying out this rule any missing power of x should be supplied with zero as a coefficient.

or $\quad a_0y^n + ma_1y^{n-1} + m^2a_2y^{n-2} + \cdots + m^{n-1}a_{n-1}y + m^na_n = 0,$ (3)

after multiplying by the constant m^n. The rule is thus established.

2. *To obtain an equation each of whose roots is equal in absolute value to a root of $f(x) = 0$, but opposite in sign: change the signs of the odd degree terms in $f(x) = 0$ and replace x by y.*

For example, the roots of the equation

$$x^4 - 2x^3 - 13x^2 + 14x + 24 = 0$$

are 2, 4, $-$ 1, $-$ 3, and the equation with roots $-$ 2, $-$ 4, 1, 3 is

$$y^4 + 2y^3 - 13y^2 - 14y + 24 = 0.$$

The rule follows at once if we substitute $x = -y$ in the given equation.

EXERCISES

Obtain equations in y whose roots are equal to the roots of the following equations multiplied by the number opposite.

1. $x^3 - 4x^2 - 7x + 10 = 0.$ $\hspace{3cm}$ (2)

2. $x^3 - 3x - 2 = 0.$ $\hspace{4cm}$ (-3)

3. $x^4 - 5x^3 - 18x^2 + 20x + 56 = 0.$ $\hspace{2cm}$ ($-$ 1)

4. $x^3 + \dfrac{1}{3} x^2 - \dfrac{17}{12} x + \dfrac{1}{2} = 0.$ $\hspace{2.5cm}$ (6)

Obtain equations in y whose roots are equal to the roots of the following equations multiplied by the smallest number which will make all the coefficients integers and that of the highest power unity.

5. $x^3 + 8x^2 - \dfrac{1}{4} x - 2 = 0.$

6. $x^4 - \dfrac{7}{6} x^2 - \dfrac{10}{3} = 0.$

7. $x^4 + \dfrac{5}{6} x^3 + 3x^2 + \dfrac{10}{3} x - 4 = 0.$

8. $3x^3 - 8 = 0.$

9. $5x^3 - 16x^2 - 47x + 10 = 0.$

10. $4x^5 + x^3 - x^2 = 0.$

11. $8x^4 - 4x^2 + 3x - 1 = 0.$

12. $12x^3 + 4x^2 - 3x + 5 = 0.$

13. Obtain equations in y whose roots are equal in absolute value but opposite in sign to the roots of the equations given in exercises 5 $-$ 12.

124. Descartes' Rule of Signs

In a polynomial arranged in descending powers of x, if two successive terms differ in sign, there is said to be a **variation in sign**. For example,

$$x^4 - 4x^3 + 3x^2 + 4x - 5$$

has three variations of sign, as is shown more clearly by writing the signs $+ - + + -$. By use of the principle of variation of signs of the terms, an upper limit may be established for the number of positive and negative roots of an equation $f(x) = 0$ by means of the following theorem, which is called **Descartes' rule of signs.**

THEOREM. *The number of positive roots of an equation $f(x) = 0$ is either equal to the number of variations of sign in $f(x)$ or to that number decreased by an even integer. The number of negative roots of $f(x) = 0$ is equal to the number of variations of sign in $f(-x)$ or to that number decreased by an even integer.*

The proof of this theorem rightfully belongs in a more advanced course in the theory of equations and hence will be omitted here.

EXERCISES

Without solving, find the maximum number of positive and negative roots, and any other information about the nature of the roots that can be deduced from the use of Descartes' rule of signs and other theorems that have been stated in this chapter.

1. $6x^3 - 11x^2 - x + 6 = 0$.

Solution: There are two variations of sign in the polynomial $f(x)$, and hence there are either two positive roots or no positive root. In $f(-x) = -6x^3 - 11x^2 + x + 6$ there is one variation of sign, and hence there is exactly one negative root. There are then two possibilities: (*a*) two positive roots, one negative root, and no imaginary roots, or (*b*) no positive root, one negative root, and two imaginary roots. However, if the equation is examined just a little more closely, we note that the sum of the coefficients is zero, and hence there is a positive root $x = 1$. Thus the second possibility mentioned above cannot exist.

2. $x^3 + 3x^2 + 5 = 0$.

3. $x^4 - 5x^3 - 8x + 1 = 0$.

4. $2x^4 - 3x^3 + 5 = 0$.

5. $2x^4 - 3x^3 - 5 = 0$.

6. $x^5 + 4x^3 - 5x = 0$.

7. $x^5 + 2x^4 - 5 = 0$.

8. $5x^5 + 4x^4 - 3x^3 + 2x^2 - x + 10 = 0.$

9. $3x^6 - 5x^5 + 4x^3 + 7x^2 - 3x + 2 = 0.$

10. $x^{2n+1} + 1 = 0.$

11. $x^{2n+1} - 1 = 0.$

12. $x^{2n} - 1 = 0.$

The roots of the following equations are real. Find the number of positive and negative roots.

13. $6x^4 - 6x^3 - 11x^2 + 16x - 5 = 0.$

14. $4x^4 + 4x^3 - 51x^2 - 36x + 135 = 0.$

15. $x^3 - 3x^2 + 2 = 0.$

16. $3x^5 + 21x^4 + 20x^3 - 73x^2 - 121x - 30 = 0.$

17. Show that $2x^8 + 6x^5 - 3x^2 - 4 = 0$ has exactly six imaginary roots.

18. Discuss the possible number of imaginary roots of the equation $x^7 - 3x^5 + 2x^4 - 5x^3 + 5 = 0.$

19. Show that the equation $x^6 - x^4 + x^3 - 1 = 0$ has exactly four imaginary roots.

125. Useful Upper and Lower Bounds for Roots

In the present chapter, we are concerned with the graph of $f(x)$ chiefly throughout an interval on x that contains the real roots of $f(x) = 0$. To save unnecessary labor in plotting, it is desirable to know upper and lower bounds of such an interval.

If no real root of $f(x) = 0$ is greater than b, nor less than b_1, the number b is said to be an **upper bound** and the number b_1 a **lower bound** for real roots of $f(x) = 0$.

A useful upper bound can be found by means of the following

THEOREM. *If b is positive or zero, and if each sum in the synthetic division of $f(x)$ by $(x - b)$ is positive or zero, then no real root of $f(x) = 0$ is greater than b.*

The theorem is fairly obvious, since a number greater than b would make the sums still greater. For example, to show that 6 is greater than any real root of

$$f(x) = x^4 - 5x^3 + 3x^2 - 42x - 50 = 0, \tag{1}$$

we divide $f(x)$ by $(x - 6)$ by synthetic division,

$$
\begin{array}{r}
1 - 5 + 3 - 42 - 50 \,\underline{|\,6} \\
6 + 6 + 54 + 72 \\
\hline
1 + 1 + 9 + 12 + 22
\end{array}
$$

and observe that a number greater than 6 would increase each sum.

To find a lower bound of the negative roots of $f(x) = 0$, it is only necessary to find as above, by synthetic division, an upper bound of the positive roots of $f(-x) = 0$.

For example, to find a lower bound for the roots of (1), divide

$$f(-x) = x^4 + 5x^3 + 3x^2 + 42x - 50$$

by $(x - 1)$. We thus find 1 to be an upper bound for roots of $f(-x) = 0$. Hence, -1 is a lower bound for roots of (1).

An upper or a lower bound obtained by the theorem above is not necessarily very close to a root.

For example, consider an upper bound for roots of

$$x^3 - 9x^2 + 23x - 15 = 0. \tag{2}$$

By our theorem, 9 is an upper bound, but 5 is actually the largest root of (2) as shown in exercise 1, Article **127**.

While we may thus cite some examples in which an upper bound obtained by our theorem is not very close to the largest root, the bounds obtained are often close and very useful.

126. Location Theorem

If $f(a)$ and $f(b)$ have contrary signs, the equation $f(x) = 0$ has at least one real root between a and b.

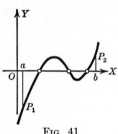

FIG. 41

Thus the points P_1 and P_2 (Fig. 41) which correspond to $x = a$ and $x = b$ are on opposite sides of the X-axis, and any continuous curve connecting P_1 and P_2 crosses the X-axis at least once between a and b. Since, to every intersection of the graph with the X-axis there corresponds a real root of the equation (Art. **120**), we assume this theorem.

EXERCISES

By the method of Article **125**, find integers that are upper and lower bounds of the roots of the equations.

1. $x^4 - 5x^3 + 3x^2 + 2x - 30 = 0$.

2. $x^5 - 6x^3 + 4x^2 - 27x - 35 = 0$.

3. $x^3 - 3x^2 - 36x - 24 = 0$.

4. $x^4 - 2x^3 - 20x^2 - 21x - 8 = 0$.

5. $4x^3 - 12x^2 - 27x + 21 = 0$.

6. $2x^5 - 3x^4 - 5x^3 + 6x + 5 = 0$.

7. $3x^4 + 12x^3 + 5x + 18 = 0$.

8. $3x^4 - 7x^3 - 15x^2 + 7x + 3 = 0$.

9. By means of the location theorem show that the integer obtained in each of the exercises 1–4 is the smallest integer that is an upper bound for the roots.

Find the integral part of each real root.

10. $x^3 - 3x^2 + 2x - 1 = 0$.

11. $x^3 + 2x^2 + 5 = 0$.

12. $x^3 - 2x^2 + 5 = 0$.

13. $x^3 + 2x^2 - 5 = 0$.

14. $x^3 - 2x^2 - 5 = 0$.

15. $2x^3 - 3x^2 + 4x - 5 = 0$.

16. $x^4 + 5x^3 + 5x^2 - 5x - 10 = 0$.

17. $x^3 + x^2 + 2x - 1 = 0$.

127. Theorem Concerning Rational Roots

If an equation

$$f(x) = a_0 x^n + a_1 x^{n-1} + a_2 x^{n-2} + \cdots + a_{n-1} x + a_n = 0 \qquad (1)$$

with integral coefficients, has a rational root $\dfrac{b}{c}$, *where* $\dfrac{b}{c}$ *is in its lowest terms, then b is a factor of a_n and c is a factor of a_0.*

Since $\dfrac{b}{c}$ is in its lowest terms, it is implied that b and c are integers with no common factors except 1 and -1. Since $\dfrac{b}{c}$ is a root of (1), we have

$$a_0 \frac{b^n}{c^n} + a_1 \frac{b^{n-1}}{c^{n-1}} + a_2 \frac{b^{n-2}}{c^{n-2}} + \cdots + a_{n-1} \frac{b}{c} + a_n \equiv 0. \qquad (2)$$

Multiply (2) by c^n. This gives

$$a_0 b^n + a_1 b^{n-1} c + a_2 b^{n-2} c^2 + \cdots + a_{n-1} b c^{n-1} + a_n c^n \equiv 0. \qquad (3)$$

Subtract $a_n c^n$ from each side of (3), and factor b from the remainder in the left side. This gives

$$b(a_0 b^{n-1} + a_1 b^{n-2} c + a_2 b^{n-3} c^2 + \cdots + a_{n-1} c^{n-1}) \equiv -a_n c^n. \qquad (4)$$

Since the left side of (4) is an integer with b as a factor, its right side, $-a_nc^n$, must have b as a factor. Since b has no common factor with c, it must be a factor of a_n.

Next, transpose all the terms of (3) except a_0b^n. This gives

$$a_0b^n = -c(a_1b^{n-1} + a_2b^{n-2}c + \cdots + a_{n-1}bc^{n-2} + a_nc^{n-1}). \qquad (5)$$

Since the right side of (5) is an integer with a factor c, the left side must contain a factor c. Since c has no factor in common with b, it must be a factor of a_0.

Hence, if our original equation (1) with integral coefficients has any rational roots, they may be found by trials that consist in testing which, if any, of the set of fractions whose numerators are factors of a_n and whose denominators are factors of a_0, will satisfy the equation (1).

If the coefficient a_0 of the highest power of x in a rational integral equation is unity, the equation is often written in the form

$$x^n + p_1x^{n-1} + p_2x^{n-2} + \cdots + p_{n-1}x + p_n = 0,$$

and is said to be **expressed in the p-form.**

Corollary. *Any rational root of an equation in the p-form with integral coefficients is an integer and an exact divisor of p_n.*

This important corollary follows at once from the theorem, since $c = 1$ or -1 when it is a factor of $a_0 = 1$, and thus $\dfrac{b}{c}$ must be an integer.

To obtain the rational roots of an equation in the p-form with integral coefficients, it is only necessary to test whether the integers which are the exact divisors of p_n satisfy the equation.[*]

EXERCISES

Find the rational roots by trial. If in the process of finding rational roots, the depressed equation is a quadratic, find all the roots whether they are rational or not.

1. $x^3 - 9x^2 + 23x - 15 = 0$.

Solution: By Descartes' rule of signs, this equation has no negative roots. Hence, we need try only 1, 3, 5, and 15. By synthetic division,

---

[*] If p_n is a number with many factors, this method is likely to become laborious. Similarly, if a_0 or a_n or both of them have a large number of factors, the method suggested directly by the theorem is likely to be laborious.

$$\begin{array}{r} 1 - 9 + 23 - 15 \,\lfloor\underline{1} \\ + 1 - 8 + 15 \\ \hline 1 - 8 + 15 + 0 \end{array}$$

The depressed equation is $x^2 - 8x + 15 = (x - 5)(x - 3) = 0$.
Hence, 1, 3, and 5 are the roots.

2. $108x^3 - 54x^2 + 45x - 13 = 0$.

Solution: In the p-form this equation is

$$x^3 - \frac{1}{2} x^2 + \frac{5}{12} x - \frac{13}{108} = 0. \tag{1}$$

Transform (1) into an equation whose roots are six times those of
(1). This gives

$$x^3 - 3x^2 + 15x - 26 = 0. \tag{2}$$

The rational roots of (2) divided by 6 give the rational roots of (1).
By Descartes' rule, (2) has no negative roots. Hence, we need
try only 1, 2, 13, 26. Depressing the equation,

$$\begin{array}{r} 1 - 3 + 15 - 26 \,\lfloor\underline{1} \\ + 1 - 2 + 13 \\ \hline 1 - 2 + 13 - 13 \end{array}$$

Hence, 1 is not a root.

$$\begin{array}{r} 1 - 3 + 15 - 26 \,\lfloor\underline{2} \\ + 2 - 2 + 26 \\ \hline 1 - 1 + 13 + 0 \end{array}$$

The depressed equation $x^2 - x + 13 = 0$ has roots $\dfrac{1}{2} + \dfrac{i\sqrt{51}}{2}$, and

$\dfrac{1}{2} - \dfrac{i\sqrt{51}}{2}$. Hence, 2 is the only rational root of (2) and $\dfrac{1}{3}$ is the
only rational root of (1).

3. $2x^3 + 3x^2 - 2x - 3 = 0$. $\tag{1}$

Solution: By the theorem, Article **127,** if a rational number $\dfrac{b}{c}$
is a root, the values of b are limited to ± 1 and ± 3; and the
values of c are limited to ± 1 and ± 2. The possible rational
numbers we can form for trial roots are ± 1, $\pm \dfrac{1}{2}$, ± 3, $\pm \dfrac{3}{2}$.

By synthetic division of the left side of (1) by $(x - 1)$, we write

$$\begin{array}{r} 2 + 3 - 2 - 3 \,\lfloor\underline{1} \\ + 2 + 5 + 3 \\ \hline 2 + 5 + 3 + 0 \end{array}$$

Hence, 1 is a root, and the depressed $2x^2 + 5x + 3 = 0$ gives -1, and $-\dfrac{3}{2}$ for the other roots.

4. $x^4 - 15x^2 + 10x + 24 = 0.$

5. $x^4 - x^3 - 7x^2 + x + 6 = 0.$

6. $x^5 - x^4 - 13x^3 + x^2 + 12x = 0.$

7. $18x^3 + 3x^2 - 7x - 2 = 0.$

8. $x^4 - x^3 + x^2 - 3x - 6 = 0.$

9. $x^5 + x^3 - 2x^2 - 12x - 8 = 0.$

10. $x^5 + 3x^4 - 6x^3 - 10x^2 + 21x - 9 = 0.$

11. $x^4 - 5x^3 + 11x^2 + 11x - 78 = 0.$

12. $2x^4 + 7x^3 - 8x + 3 = 0.$

13. $8x^5 - 12x^4 + 6x^3 - 5x^2 + 3 = 0.$

14. $2x^4 - 5x^3 + 3x^2 - x - 2 = 0.$

15. $2x^3 - 17x^2 + 11x + 15 = 0.$

16. $2x^6 + 7x^5 + 6x^4 - x^3 - 10x^2 - 12x + 8 = 0.$

17. $8x^3 - 2x^2 - 4x + 1 = 0.$

18. $9x^4 - 18x^3 - 13x^2 + 8x + 4 = 0.$

19. $3x^4 - 2x^3 - 24x + 16 = 0.$

20. $x^4 - \dfrac{1}{6} x^3 - \dfrac{13}{2} x^2 + \dfrac{2}{3} x + 10 = 0.$

21. $5x^4 - \dfrac{57}{4} x^3 + \dfrac{7}{2} x^2 + \dfrac{91}{4} x + \dfrac{15}{2} = 0.$

22. $x^5 - 4x^4 + 3x^2 + 8x + 4 = 0.$

23. $x^4 - 3x^3 - x + 2 = 0.$

128. Approximations to an Irrational Root of $f(x) = 0$ by Successive Graphs *

The simple geometrical fact that a root of the equation $f(x) = 0$ is a value of x at which the graph of $y = f(x)$ meets the X-axis, enables us to use the location theorem of Article **126** to find closer and closer approximations to an irrational root by selecting a and b (Art. **126**) closer and closer together with the root to be found between them.

While this plan of approximation to a root is simple in principle,

---

* This section is designed especially for those who omit Horner's method. While this graphical method is by no means a full substitute for Horner's method, it is applicable to a broader class of equations as is shown in this article.

the procedure is likely to be found rather laborious. The student may well depend much on his own ingenuity in estimating a root from the graph. The plan can probably be made clearest by examples.

Example 1. Find a root of

$$x^3 + 3x - 20 = 0.$$

Solution: First examine the equation for rational roots (Art. **127**). We find the equation has none. Next, form a table of values of the function $y = f(x) = x^3 + 3x - 20,$

$$x = \ -2, \ -1, \quad 0, \quad 1, \quad 2, \ 3, \cdots$$
$$y = \ -34, \ -24, \ -20, \ -16, \ -6, \ 16, \cdots$$

and plot the function. The first figure of the root is 2. Moreover,

if we assume that the graph is approximately a straight line between the points $(2, -6)$ and $(3, 16)$ we estimate from the graph the approximate value 2.3 for the first two figures of the desired root. Testing this value we find

$$f(2.3) = -.933,$$
$$f(2.4) = 1.024.$$

Thus the root lies between 2.3 and 2.4 by Article **126.** By a repetition of this process [plotting the points $(2.3, -.933)$, $(2.4, 1.024)$ on an *enlarged* scale tenfold that used originally] we infer that the root lies between 2.34 and 2.35. This judgment may be based on the fact that $f(2.3)$ is a little nearer 0 than $f(2.4)$, leading us to expect the root to be about halfway between 2.3 and 2.4 and nearer 2.3. By actual computation* we find

$$f(2.34) = -.167096,$$
$$f(2.35) = +.027875.$$

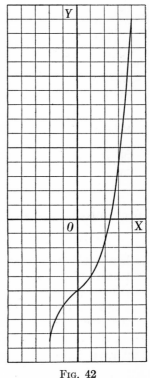

Fig. 42

* These and later computations are greatly facilitated by having at hand a table of cubes.

These figures suggest that the root is near 2.348. As

$$f(2.348) = - .011231808,$$

and $$f(2.349) = + .008314559,$$

it is clear that the root to four figures is 2.348, but the exact value of the root is probably a little nearer to 2.349 than to 2.348. Thus, 2.349 − may be given as an approximation to the root.

It may be noted that the above method is likely to involve laborious arithmetical computations. On this account, some one of several other methods of approximating to the numerical roots of an equation may be preferable. One of these methods applicable to the rational integral equation is called Horner's method. This method is developed in Article **130**. However, any one of the methods of finding a close approximation to the numerical roots of equations is apt to be tedious. The method of this section has one advantage over Horner's method in that it is applicable to an equation $f(x) = 0$ when $f(x)$ is not a rational integral algebraic function as may be shown by the following:

Example 2. Find the positive real root of

$$1 + (x - 2)^{\frac{1}{2}} - (x + 6)^{\frac{1}{3}} = 0.$$

Solution: Obviously the root must be equal to or greater than 2. Form a table of values of $y = f(x) = 1 + (x - 2)^{\frac{1}{2}} - (x + 6)^{\frac{1}{3}}$.

$$x = \quad 2, \qquad 3, \qquad 4, \cdots.$$
$$y = - 1, - 0.08008, + 0.25978, \cdots.$$

We note that a root lies between $x = 3$ and $x = 4$. Since $f(3)$ = − .08008 is less than one-third as much below 0 as $f(4)$ = .25978 is above 0, we estimate 3.2 as the first two figures of the root although it is by no means sure that the first two figures are not 3.3.

To test this estimate, we find

$$f(3.2) = + .000066,$$
$$f(3.3) = + .0372317.$$

From the nearness of $f(3.2)$ to 0, we infer that $x = 3.2$ is a close approximation to the root, the exact root being slightly less than 3.2.

The method of this section may well be called the **method of successively enlarged scales**.

EXERCISES

1. Find correct to three significant figures the positive root of $x^3 + 2x^2 - 5 = 0$ by the method of successively enlarged scales.

2. Find three significant figures of a root of $x^3 + 4x - 7 = 0$.

3. Find correct to three significant figures the real roots of $8x^3 - 2x^2 - 4x + 1 = 0$.

4. The equation $1 + 2\sqrt{x-1} - 2\sqrt[3]{x+5} = 0$ has a root between 1 and 5. Find the first three significant figures of the root.

5. Find a root of $(7x^3 + 4x^2)^{\frac{1}{3}} + [10x(2x-1)]^{\frac{1}{2}} - 28 = 0$, between 4 and 5 correct to two decimal places.

129. Transformation to Diminish the Roots

To obtain an equation each of whose roots is less by h than a corresponding root of a given equation $f(x) = 0$: divide $f(x)$ by $(x - h)$ and indicate the remainder by R_n. Divide the quotient by $(x - h)$, and indicate the remainder by R_{n-1}. Continue this process to n divisions. The last quotient, a_0, and the remainders, $R_1, R_2, \cdots, R_n$ are the coefficients of the transformed equation. The new equation is then,

$$a_0 y^n + R_1 y^{n-1} + R_2 y^{n-2} + \cdots R_{n-1} y + R_n = 0$$

The division should be performed by the method of synthetic division.

For example, find the equation each of whose roots is less by 2 than the roots of the equation

$$x^3 - 4x^2 - 3x + 2 = 0. \tag{1}$$

The work is as follows:

$$
\begin{array}{l}
1 - 4 - 3 + 2 \,\underline{|\,2} \\
+ 2 - 4 - 14 \\
\overline{1 - 2 - 7} - 12 \quad R_3 = -12, \\
+ 2 0 \\
\overline{1 + 0} - 7 \qquad R_2 = -7, \\
2 \\
\overline{1 + 2} \qquad\qquad R_1 = 2, \\
a_0 = 1.
\end{array}
$$

The required equation is

$$y^3 + 2y^2 - 7y - 12 = 0. \tag{2}$$

As a check, the student should use the methods of Article **127** to find the roots of equation (1) and then show that these roots diminished by 2 are roots of equation (2).

To establish the rule, substitute $x = y + h$ in

$$a_0 x^n + a_1 x^{n-1} + \cdots + a_{n-1} x + a_n = 0. \tag{3}$$

This gives the equation in y

$$a_0(y + h)^n + a_1(y + h)^{n-1} + \cdots + a^{n-1}(y + h) + a_n = 0 \tag{4}$$

whose roots are less by h than those of (3). Expanding the binomial powers and arranging in powers of y, we may present the result in the form

$$a_0 y^n + A_1 y^{n-1} + A_2 y^{n-2} + \cdots + A_{n-1} y + A_n = 0. \tag{5}$$

If in (5), we make $y = x - h$, we obtain

$$a_0(x - h)^n + A_1(x - h)^{n-1} + A_2(x - h)^{n-2} + \cdots$$
$$+ A_{n-1}(x - h) + A_n = 0. \tag{6}$$

which is the same as equation (3) arranged in powers of $x - h$. From the form of equation (6), it follows that A_n is the remainder when $f(x)$ is divided by $x - h$; A_{n-1} is the remainder when the quotient of the last-named division is divided by $x - h$; continuing this process to n divisions, A_1 is the last remainder, and a_0 is the last quotient. That is,

$$A_n = R_n,$$
$$A_{n-1} = R_{n-1},$$
$$\cdot \qquad \cdot$$
$$\cdot \qquad \cdot$$
$$A_1 = R_1,$$

which establishes the rule.

EXERCISES

Obtain equations in y whose roots are equal to the roots of the following equations diminished by the number opposite.

1. $f(x) = 2x^4 - 3x^2 + 4x - 5 = 0.$ $\tag{2}$

Solution: We apply synthetic division to divide $f(x)$ by $(x - 2)$ to get the coefficients of the equation in y as explained in Article **129**. Thus, we have

$$2 + \quad 0 - \quad 3 + \quad 4 - \quad 5 \underline{|2}$$
$$+ \quad 4 + \quad 8 + 10 + 28$$
$$\overline{2 + \quad 4 + \quad 5 + 14 + 23} \quad R_4 = 23,$$
$$+ \quad 4 + 16 + 42$$
$$\overline{2 + \quad 8 + 21 + 56} \quad R_3 = 56,$$
$$+ \quad 4 + 24$$
$$\overline{2 + 12 + 45} \quad R_2 = 45,$$
$$+ \quad 4$$
$$\overline{2 + 16} \quad R_1 = 16,$$
$$a_0 = 2.$$

Hence, $2y^4 + 16x^3 + 45x^2 + 56x + 23 = 0$ is the required equation.

2. $2x^3 + 3x - 24 = 0$. (2)

3. $x^3 + 3x^2 - 4x + 1 = 0$. (1)

4. $2x^4 - 3x^3 + 20x - 600 = 0$. (4)

5. $x^3 + 3x^2 - 4x + 1 = 0$. (-1)

6. $8x^3 - 2x^2 - 4x + 1 = 0$. (-0.7)

7. $3x^4 + 8x^3 + 25x^2 + 66x + 56 = 0$. (-2)

8. $x^3 - 9x + 3 = 0$. (2.8)

9. $x^5 - 4.8x^4 + 1.64x^3 + 9.888x^2 - 6.0064x - 0.71552 = 0$.
(-1.2)

10. The roots of the equation $x^4 - 2x^3 - 13x^2 + 14x + 24 = 0$ are $2, 4, -1, -3$. By the method of Article **129,** obtain an equation in y with roots $5, 7, 2, 0$.

130. Irrational Roots. Horner's Method

The irrational roots of a numerical equation can be obtained to any desired number of decimal places by a method of approximation called **Horner's method.** The method is based mainly on successive diminutions of the roots of the equations to be solved (Art. **129**). It can be best explained by first applying it to an example. In case an equation has some rational roots, it should always be depressed by removing such roots before considering irrational roots.

Example: Find the real roots of

$$x^4 - 2x^3 + 4x^2 - 15x + 14 = 0. \tag{1}$$

1. Test for rational roots as in Article **127.** It results that 2 is the only rational root.

$$\dfrac{\begin{array}{r} 1 - 2 + 4 - 15 + 14 \, \lfloor \underline{2} \\ + 2 + 0 + \;\; 8 - 14 \end{array}}{1 + 0 + 4 - \;\; 7 + \;\; 0}$$

The depressed equation is

$$x^3 + 4x - 7 = 0. \tag{2}$$

2. Test for the interval which contains the real roots. From Descartes' rule, equation (2) has not more than one positive root, and it has no negative root. Furthermore, 2 is greater than any root (Art. **125**).

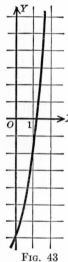

3. Plot $x^3 + 4x - 7$ from $x = 0$ to $x = 2$.

The graph (Fig. 43) shows that 1 is the first figure of the root.

4. Transform to diminish roots by 1; or graphically, change the origin to the point marked 1. The numerical work is as follows:

$$\begin{array}{r} 1 + 0 + 4 - 7 \, \lfloor \underline{1} \\ + 1 + 1 + 5 \end{array}$$
$$\begin{array}{r} \overline{1 + 1 + 5} \, \lvert - 2 \\ + 1 + 2 \lvert \end{array}$$
$$\begin{array}{r} \overline{1 + 2} \, \lvert + 7 \\ + 1 \lvert \end{array}$$
$$\overline{1 + 3}$$

Fig. 43

The first transformed equation is then

$$x_1^3 + 3x_1^2 + 7x_1 - 2 = 0. \tag{3}$$

This equation has a root between 0 and 1, since (2) has a root between 1 and 2. By evaluating $f(x_1) = x_1^3 + 3x_1^2 + 7x_1 - 2$ for successive tenths $(0.0, 0.1, 0.2, \cdots, 0.9)$, we find that this function is negative when $x_1 = 0.2$ and positive when $x_1 = 0.3$. Hence, (3) has a root between 0.2 and 0.3. An approximation to this root is given by neglecting the second and third degree terms in (3) and solving

$$7x_1 - 2 = 0.$$

The root of this equation between 0 and 1 is $x_1 = 0.2 \cdots$. It is important to observe from the graph of $f(x)$ that the sign of the constant term in each transformed equation is to be the same as that of the original equation after the rational roots have been removed.

Transforming (3) into an equation whose roots are less by 0.2, we have *

$$
\begin{array}{rrrr|l}
1 & 3 & 7 & -2 & \underline{\,0.2\,} \\
  & 0.2 & 0.64 & 1.528 & \\
\hline
1 & 3.2 & 7.64 & -0.472 & \\
  & 0.2 & 0.68 & & \\
\hline
1 & 3.4 & 8.32 & & \\
  & 0.2 & & & \\
\hline
1 & 3.6 & & &
\end{array}
$$

or
$$x_2{}^3 + 3.6x_2{}^2 + 8.32x_2 - 0.472 = 0 \qquad (4)$$

as the second transformed equation. The root of equation (4) which we seek lies between 0 and 0.1. Neglecting powers of x_2 higher than the first, it appears from the equation

$$8.32x_2 - 0.472 = 0$$

that x_2 lies between 0.05 and 0.06. That the root is in this interval may be tested by evaluating $x_2{}^3 + 3.6x_2{}^2 + 8.32x_2 - 0.472$ for $x_2 = 0.05$ and 0.06.

Transforming (4) by synthetic division into an equation whose roots are less by 0.05, we obtain

$$x_3{}^3 + 3.75x_3{}^2 + 8.6875x_3 - 0.046875 = 0. \qquad (5)$$

Neglecting powers of x_3 higher than the first, it appears from the equation

$$8.6875x_3 - 0.046875 = 0$$

that x_3 lies between 0.005 and 0.006.

Transforming (5) by synthetic division into an equation whose roots are less by 0.005, we have

$$x_4{}^3 + 3.765x_4{}^2 + 8.725075x_4 - 0.003343625 = 0. \qquad (6)$$

The root of this equation between 0 and 0.001 can be obtained at least as far as the first figure by neglecting powers of x_4 above the first. This gives

$$x_4 = 0.0003^+.$$

Transforming (6) into an equation whose roots are less by 0.0003, we obtain

$$x_5{}^3 + 3.7659x_5{}^2 + 8.72733427x_5 - 0.000725763623 = 0.$$

* In carrying out successive synthetic divisions, no confusion should result if the plus sign is omitted before positive coefficients, provided the work is properly spaced and arranged in tabular form.

The root of this equation between 0 and 0.0001 can be obtained at least so far as the first significant figure by neglecting powers of x_5 above the first. This gives

$$x_5 = 0.00008^+.$$

Taking the sum of successive diminutions of the roots of (2), we obtain as the approximate value of the root sought

$$x = 1.25538^+.$$

The above computation is compactly arranged on page 229. The process can evidently be continued to find the root to any required number of decimal places.

If a root of an equation is known to be small, one important point to note is that such a root can, in general, be well estimated by dividing the constant term, with its sign changed, by the coefficient of the first degree term. The coefficient of the first degree term is, for this reason, sometimes called the **trial divisor** in obtaining approximate roots. A still better estimate of a root can, in general, be obtained by dropping terms of degree higher than the second, and solving the quadratic.

When an equation has more than one irrational root, each is treated separately as we have treated the single irrational root in this example.

If two roots of an equation $f(x) = 0$ are nearly equal, their separation may become laborious, but the separation may be accomplished by assigning values to x sufficiently near each other in plotting the graph of $f(x)$. For example,

$$4x^3 - 24x^2 + 44x - 23 = 0,$$

has two roots between 2 and 3. By assigning successively the values $x = 2$, 2.1, 2.2, 2.3, 2.4, 2.5, 2.6, 2.7, 2.8, 2.9, 3, in plotting the graph we find that one of these roots is between 2.2 and 2.3, while the other is between 2.8 and 2.9. For $f(2.2) = +0.232$ and $f(2.3) = -0.092$ indicates a root between 2.2 and 2.3, while $f(2.8) = -0.152$ and $f(2.9) = +0.316$ indicates a root between 2.8 and 2.9.

On the following page, the solution of the depressed equation $x^3 + 4x - 7 = 0$, which has been given in detail earlier in this article, is arranged in tabular form. The successive diminutions of the roots and the successive transformed equations are printed in heavy type.

```
1   0       4  − 7    |1.
    1       1    5
    ‾‾      ‾‾‾‾‾
1   1       5  − 2
    1       2
    ‾‾      ‾‾
1   2       7
    1
    ‾
1   3       7    − 2          |0.2
    0.2     0.64   1.528
    ‾‾‾     ‾‾‾‾‾‾‾‾‾‾
1   3.2     7.64   − 0.472
    0.2     0.68
    ‾‾‾     ‾‾‾‾
1   3.4     8.32
    0.2
    ‾‾‾
1   3.6     8.32   − 0.472        |0.05
    0.05    0.1825   0.425125
    ‾‾‾‾    ‾‾‾‾‾‾‾‾‾‾‾
1   3.65    8.5025  − 0.046875
    0.05    0.1850
    ‾‾‾‾    ‾‾‾‾‾‾
1   3.70    8.6875
    0.05
    ‾‾‾‾
1   3.75    8.6875    − 0.046875       |0.005
    0.005   0.018775    0.043531375
    ‾‾‾‾‾   ‾‾‾‾‾‾‾‾‾‾‾
1   3.755   8.706275  − 0.003343625
    0.005   0.01880
    ‾‾‾‾‾   ‾‾‾‾‾‾‾
1   3.760   8.725075
    0.005
    ‾‾‾‾‾
1   3.765   8.725075    − 0.003343625        |0.0003
    0.0003  0.00112959    0.002617861377
    ‾‾‾‾‾‾  ‾‾‾‾‾‾‾‾‾‾‾
1   3.7653  8.72620459  − 0.000725763623
    0.0003  0.00112968
    ‾‾‾‾‾‾  ‾‾‾‾‾‾‾‾‾‾
1   3.7656  8.72733427
    0.0003
    ‾‾‾‾‾‾
1   3.7659  8.72733427    − 0.000725763623      |0.00008
    0.00008 0.0003012784    0.000698210843872
    ‾‾‾‾‾‾‾ ‾‾‾‾‾‾‾‾‾‾‾‾
1   3.76598 8.7276355484 − 0.000027552779128
```

131. Negative Roots

The negative roots of $f(x) = 0$ are obtained by finding the positive roots of $f(-x) = 0$, and changing their signs. It is therefore sufficient to discuss the method of obtaining positive roots.

132. Summary

In solving a numerical equation $f(x) = 0$ for all its real roots, the following procedure may be found helpful in systematizing the work:

1. *Test for rational roots; and if any exists, depress the equation by removing the corresponding factors.*

2. *Determine an interval which contains the positive irrational roots* (Art. **125**).

3. *Plot the depressed polynomial to locate a root between consecutive integers. The smaller integer is the integral part of the root.*

4. *To approximate more closely to the root, apply either the method of successively enlarged graphs* (Art. **128**), *or Horner's method* (Art. **130**). *If Horner's method is chosen, the following summary of steps is likely to be helpful: fix the attention upon some positive root whose location is known to be between two consecutive integers. Obtain by synthetic division* (Art. **129**) *an equation whose roots are less than those of the given equation by the smaller of these two integers. The new equation has a root between 0 and 1. Locate this root between two successive tenths; and decrease the roots by the smaller of these tenths. The equation thus obtained has a root between 0 and 0.1. Locate this root between two successive hundredths, and again decrease the roots by the smaller of these hundredths. Continue this process to any required number of decimal places.*

Add together all the diminutions of the roots to obtain the required root.

If more than one root is contained between two consecutive integers, separate them by means of the location principle.

5. *Treat negative roots in the same manner as positive roots after changing* $f(x) = 0$ *into* $f(-x) = 0$.

EXERCISES AND PROBLEMS

Find, by Horner's method, the prescribed root of each equation to two decimal places.

    1. $x^3 - 3x^2 - 2x + 5 = 0$, root between 1 and 2.

    2. $x^3 - 3x^2 - 2x + 5 = 0$, root between 3 and 4.

    3. $x^4 - 8x^3 + 14x^2 + 4x - 8 = 0$, root between 5 and 6.

    4. $x^5 + 12x^4 + 59x^3 + 150x^2 + 201x - 207 = 0$, root between 0 and 1.

Find, to two decimal places, the prescribed roots using either the method of successively enlarged graphs, or Horner's method.

5. $3x^3 - 11x^2 + 6x + 7 = 0$, root between 2 and 3.

6. $x^3 + 10x^2 + 8x - 120 = 0$, root between 2 and 3.

7. $3x^3 + 14x^2 + 13x - 2 = 0$, root between 0 and 1.

8. $x^3 + 3x^2 - 4x + 1 = 0$, two roots between 0 and 1.

9. $x^4 + 10x - 100 = 0$, root between 2 and 3.

10. $x^3 - 9x - 5 = 0$, root between -3 and -2.

11. $x^4 + 10x - 100 = 0$, root between -4 and -3.

Find the rational roots, and the value of each irrational real root to two decimal places, by any method.

12. $x^3 - 100 = 0$.

13. $x^5 - 1000 = 0$.

14. $8x^3 - 12x^2 + 1 = 0$.

15. $x^3 + 4x^2 + 4x + 3 = 0$.

16. $x^4 - 3x^3 + 3 = 0$.

17. $x^3 - 3x - 1 = 0$.

24. $x^3 + 6 = 3x^2 + 2x$.

18. $2x^4 - 12x^3 + 12x - 3 = 0$.

19. $3x^4 + 11 = 2x^3 + 21x^2 + 4x$.

20. $x^3 + 4x^2 = 5x + 20$.

21. $x^3 + 13 = 3x^2 + 4x$.

22. $x^3 + 3x^2 + 4x + 5 = 0$.

23. $x^3 + 30x = 420$.

25. A sphere of yellow pine 1 foot in diameter floating in water sinks to a depth x given by

$$2x^3 - 3x^2 + 0.657 = 0.$$

Find the depth to three significant figures.

26. A sphere of ice 1 foot in diameter floating in water sinks to a depth x given by the equation

$$2x^3 - 3x^2 + 0.93 = 0.$$

Find the depth to three significant figures.

27. A cork sphere 1 foot in diameter floating in water sinks to a depth x given by the equation

$$2x^3 - 3x^2 + 0.24 = 0.$$

If the sphere is 2 feet in diameter, the immersed depth is given by

$$2x^3 - 6x^2 + 1.92 = 0.$$

Find the depths to two significant figures.

28. An open box is made of a rectangular piece of tin 10 inches by 20 inches by cutting equal squares from the corners and turning up the sides. Find (to two decimal places) the side of a square cut out if the volume of the box is 187 cubic inches.

29. The speed in feet per second of a 1-inch manila rope transmitting 4 horsepower, under a tension of 300 pounds on the tight side, is given by the equation

$$v^3 - 19200v + 211200 = 0.$$

Find the velocity to three significant figures.

30. The diameter of a water pipe whose length is 200 feet, and which is to discharge 100 cubic feet per second under a head of 10 feet, is given by the real root of the equation

$$x^5 - 38x - 101 = 0.$$

Find the diameter to three significant figures. (Merriman and Woodward, *Higher Mathematics*, p. 13.)

31. The algebraic treatment of the trisection of an angle whose sine is a involves the solution of the cubic equation

$$4x^3 = 3x - a.$$

The variable, x, is the sine of one third the given angle. When $a = \dfrac{1}{2}\sqrt{2}$, find x to three significant figures.

32. A vat in the form of a rectangular parallelepiped is $8 \times 10 \times 12$ feet. If the volume is increased 500 cubic feet by equal elongations of the dimensions, find elongations in feet to two decimal places.

33. In problem 32 if the volume is increased by elongations proportional to the dimensions, find each elongation.

34. The width of the strongest beam which can be cut from a log 12 inches in diameter is given by the positive irrational root of the equation

$$x^3 - 144x + 665 = 0.$$

Find the width to three significant figures.

133. Coefficients in Terms of Roots

Let $r_1, r_2, \cdots, r_n$ be the roots of

$$x^n + p_1x^{n-1} + p_2x^{n-2} + \cdots + p_n = 0. \tag{1}$$

Then, from Article **118**,

$$x^n + p_1x^{n-1} + p_2x^{n-2} + \cdots + p_n$$
$$= (x - r_1)(x - r_2) \cdots (x - r_n),$$
$$= x^n - (r_1 + r_2 + \cdots + r_n)x^{n-1} + (r_1r_2 + r_1r_3 + \cdots + r_{n-1}r_n)x^{n-2}$$
$$- (r_1r_2r_3 + \cdots + r_{n-2}r_{n-1}r_n)x^{n-3} + \cdots + (-1)^n r_1r_2r_3 \cdots r_n, \tag{2}$$

by actual multiplication of the binomial factors of the second member.

Equating coefficients in (2) (Art. **118**, Cor. I), we have

$$\left.\begin{array}{l} -p_1 = r_1 + r_2 + \cdots + r_n, \\ p_2 = r_1 r_2 + r_1 r_3 + \cdots + r_{n-1} r_n, \\ -p_3 = r_1 r_2 r_3 + \cdots + r_{n-2} r_{n-1} r_n, \\ \qquad \cdots \cdots \cdots \cdots \cdots \\ (-1)^n p_n = r_1 r_2 r_3 \cdots r_n. \end{array}\right\} \qquad (A)$$

That is, $-p_1 = $ sum of the roots,

$\qquad p_2 = $ sum of products of roots taken two at a time,

$\qquad -p_3 = $ sum of products of roots taken three at a time,

$\cdot \quad \cdot \quad \cdot \quad \cdot \quad \cdot \quad \cdot \quad \cdot \quad \cdot \quad \cdot \quad \cdot \quad \cdot \quad \cdot \quad \cdot \quad \cdot \quad \cdot \quad \cdot$

$\qquad (-1)^n p_n = $ product of the roots.

If certain relations among the roots are given, the expressions (A) of the coefficients in terms of the roots may aid in solving the equation.

Example 1.   Solve $x^3 - 2x^2 - 4x + 8 = 0$, the sum of two of the roots being 4.

Solution: Let r_1, r_2, r_3 be the roots and let

$$r_1 + r_2 = 4. \qquad (1)$$

From equations (A),

$$r_1 + r_2 + r_3 = 2, \qquad (2)$$

and $\qquad\qquad r_1 r_2 r_3 = -8. \qquad (3)$

From equations (1) and (2) we learn that $r_3 = -2$.   Substituting this value in (3), we have

$$r_1 r_2 = 4. \qquad (4)$$

By solving (1) and (4) simultaneously, we find

$$r_1 = 2 \quad \text{and} \quad r_2 = 2.$$

Hence the three roots are 2, 2, -2.

Example 2.   Transform $4x^3 + 24x^2 - x - 27 = 0$ into an equation in which the second degree term is missing.

Solution: By equations (A), the sum of the roots is -6.   In the required equation, the sum of the roots must be zero.   Hence, the sum of the three roots of the given equation must be increased by 6.   This will be accomplished by increasing each of the three roots by 2.

Using the method of Article **124**, we perform the following calculations:

$$4 \quad 24 - \ 1 - 27 \ \underline{|-2}$$
$$\underline{\ - \ 8 - 32 \quad \ 66 \ }$$
$$4 \quad 16 - 33| \quad 39$$
$$\underline{\ - \ 8 - 16|}$$
$$4 \quad \ \ 8|-49$$
$$\underline{\ - \ 8|}$$
$$4 \quad \ \ 0$$

The required equation is $4y^3 - 49y + 39 = 0$.

EXERCISES

By use of the equations (A) in Article **133,** write an equation with each of the following sets of prescribed roots.

1. $2, -1, -3$.

2. $1, 3, -5$.

3. $\dfrac{1}{2}, \dfrac{2}{3}, -2$.

4. $3, 0, -2$.

For each of the following equations, find the root that is not given and write the complete equation.

5. $4x^3 - 6x^2 \cdots = 0$, if 1 and $-\dfrac{3}{2}$ are roots.

6. $6x^3 + ax^2 - 5x + b = 0$, if $\dfrac{1}{2}$ and $-\dfrac{2}{3}$ are roots.

7. $3x^3 + \cdots = 0$, if $-\dfrac{2}{3}$ and $-1 + \sqrt{2}$ are roots.

Transform each of the following equations into an equation with the next to the highest degree term missing.

8. $2x^3 + 12x^2 - 4x + 6 = 0$.

9. $2x^4 - 16x^3 + 45x^2 - 56x + 23 = 0$.

10. $2x^3 - 3x^2 + 4x - 7 = 0$.

11. Solve $x^3 - 3x^2 + 4x - 12 = 0$ if the sum of two of the roots is zero.

12. Solve $9x^3 + 6x^2 - 25x - 2 = 0$ if $\dfrac{2 + \sqrt{5}}{3}$ is a root.

13. Solve $x^3 - 4x^2 - 20x + 48 = 0$ if the product of two of the roots is -8.

14. Solve $12x^3 - 25x^2 - 4x + 12 = 0$ if the product of two of the roots is $-\dfrac{1}{2}$.

134. The Cubic Equation

The general cubic equation is

$$a_0x^3 + a_1x^2 + a_2x + a_3 = 0. \qquad (1)$$

By making

$$x = y - \frac{a_1}{3a_0}, \qquad (2)$$

equation (1) is transformed into

$$a_0y^3 + \left(a_2 - \frac{a_1^2}{3a_0}\right)y + \frac{2a_1^3}{27a_0^2} - \frac{a_1a_2}{3a_0} + a_3 = 0,$$

or

$$y^3 + \frac{3a_0a_2 - a_1^2}{3a_0^2}y + \frac{2a_1^3}{27a_0^3} - \frac{a_1a_2}{3a_0^2} + \frac{a_3}{a_0} = 0, \qquad (3)$$

which has no term of the second degree.

Let

$$3H = \frac{3a_0a_2 - a_1^2}{3a_0^2}, \qquad (4)$$

and

$$G = \frac{2a_1^3}{27a_0^3} - \frac{a_1a_2}{3a_0^2} + \frac{a_3}{a_0}. \qquad (5)$$

Then (3) takes the form,

$$y^3 + 3Hy + G = 0. \qquad (6)$$

Now assume

$$y = u^{\frac{1}{3}} + v^{\frac{1}{3}}, \qquad (7)$$

and

$$-H^3 = uv. \qquad (8)$$

From (6), (7), and (8),

$$-G = u + v. \qquad (9)$$

Eliminating v from (8) and (9), we have

$$u^2 + Gu - H^3 = 0, \qquad (10)$$

and solving this quadratic in u, we find for a solution,

$$u = \frac{-G + \sqrt{G^2 + 4H^3}}{2}. \qquad (11)$$

From (8) and (11) we have

$$v = -\frac{H^3}{u} = \frac{-G - \sqrt{G^2 + 4H^3}}{2}. \qquad (12)$$

The double sign before the radical in the solution of the quadratic in u is omitted because taking the negative sign before the radical would simply interchange the values of u and v. Since

$$y = u^{\frac{1}{3}} + v^{\frac{1}{3}},$$

the three values of y are:

$$\left.\begin{array}{l} y_1 = u^{\frac{1}{3}} - \dfrac{H}{u^{\frac{1}{3}}}, \\[2ex] y_2 = \omega u^{\frac{1}{3}} - \dfrac{H}{\omega u^{\frac{1}{3}}}, \\[2ex] y_3 = \omega^2 u^{\frac{1}{3}} - \dfrac{H}{\omega^2 u^{\frac{1}{3}}}, \end{array}\right\} \tag{13}$$

where $u^{\frac{1}{3}}$ is any one of the three cube roots of u, and ω is a complex cube root of unity (Art. **110**).

Exercise. Test the solution by substitution of these values of y in (6).

By means of (2) and (13), the roots of equation (1) are

$$\left.\begin{array}{l} x_1 = u^{\frac{1}{3}} - \dfrac{H}{u^{\frac{1}{3}}} - \dfrac{a_1}{3a_0}, \\[2ex] x_2 = \omega u^{\frac{1}{3}} - \dfrac{H}{\omega u^{\frac{1}{3}}} - \dfrac{a_1}{3a_0}, \\[2ex] x_3 = \omega^2 u^{\frac{1}{3}} - \dfrac{H}{\omega^2 u^{\frac{1}{3}}} - \dfrac{a_1}{3a_0}. \end{array}\right\} \tag{14}$$

When the coefficients of the equation are real numbers, the numerical character of the roots depends upon the number under the radical sign in (11) and (12).

When $G^2 + 4H^3$ is negative, u is a complex number. In this case, to obtain y from (7) would involve the extraction of the cube root of complex numbers. As we have no general algebraic rule for extracting such a cube root, the case in which $G^2 + 4H^3$ is negative is called the **irreducible** case. These roots may, however, be obtained by a method involving trigonometry (Art. **110**). Even when $G^2 + 4H^3$ is positive, the solution presented above is not, in general, so well adapted to obtaining real roots of numerical equations as the methods of Articles **127–132**.

135. The Quartic Equation

The general quartic

$$a_0x^4 + a_1x^3 + a_2x^2 + a_3x + a_4 = 0$$

may be written in the p-form (Art. **127**) as

$$x^4 + p_1x^3 + p_2x^2 + p_3x + p_4 = 0. \tag{1}$$

Adding $(mx + b)^2$ to both members of (1), we have

$$x^4 + p_1x^3 + (p_2 + m^2)x^2 + (p_3 + 2mb)x + p_4 + b^2 = (mx + b)^2. \quad (2)$$

Assume the identity,

$$x^4 + p_1x^3 + (p_2 + m^2)x^2 + (p_3 + 2mb)x + p_4 + b^2 \equiv \left(x^2 + \frac{p_1}{2}x + q\right)^2. \quad (3)$$

Equating coefficients of like powers of x, we have

$$p_2 + m^2 = \frac{p_1^2}{4} + 2q, \quad (4)$$

$$p_3 + 2mb = p_1q, \quad (5)$$

$$p_4 + b^2 = q^2. \quad (6)$$

Eliminating m and b from (4), (5), and (6), we obtain

$$(p_1^2 + 8q - 4p_2)(q^2 - p_4) = (p_1q - p_3)^2, \quad (7)$$

or $\quad 8q^3 - 4p_2q^2 + (2p_1p_3 - 8p_4)q + 4p_2p_4 - p_1^2p_4 - p_3^2 = 0. \quad (8)$

This is a cubic in q. Since the general cubic is solved by radicals in Article **134**, we may assume a value of q known. When q is known, the values of m and b are obtained from (4) and (6). From (2) and (3), we have

$$\left(x^2 + \frac{p_1}{2}x + q\right)^2 = (mx + b)^2, \quad (9)$$

which is equivalent to the two quadratic equations

$$x^2 + \frac{p_1}{2}x + q - mx - b = 0,$$

and $\qquad\qquad x^2 + \frac{p_1}{2}x + q + mx + b = 0.$

The solutions of these two quadratics give the four roots of (1).

EXERCISES

1. Solve $x^3 - 4x^2 + 6x - 4 = 0$ and verify the results by substitution.

Solution: Here $a_0 = 1$, $a_1 = -4$, $a_2 = 6$, $a_3 = -4$. From (4) and (5), Article **134**.

$$G = -\frac{20}{27}, \quad H = \frac{2}{9}.$$

From (11), Article **134** $u = \dfrac{10 + 6\sqrt{3}}{27}$,

$$u^{\frac{1}{3}} = \frac{1 + \sqrt{3}}{3}.$$

From (14), Article **134** the roots of the given equation are

$$2,\ 1 + i,\ 1 - i.$$

Substitution for x shows that each of these numbers satisfies the equation to be solved.

2. Solve $x^4 - 6x^3 + 12x^2 - 20x - 12 = 0.$ \hfill (1)

Solution: Adding $(mx + b)^2$ to both members of this equation gives

$$x^4 - 6x^3 + (12 + m^2)x^2 + (2mb - 20)x + b^2 - 12 = (mx + b)^2. \quad (2)$$

Assume the identity

$$x^4 - 6x^3 + (12 + m^2)x^2 + (2mb - 20)x + b^2 - 12 \equiv (x^2 - 3x + q)^2. \quad (3)$$

Equating coefficients, we obtain

$$12 + m^2 = 9 + 2q, \hfill (4)$$
$$2mb - 20 = -6q, \hfill (5)$$
$$b^2 - 12 = q^2. \hfill (6)$$

Eliminating m and b from these three relations, we have the cubic

$$q^3 - 6q^2 + 42q - 68 = 0. \hfill (7)$$

This cubic has a root $q = 2$. From (4), (5), and (6), the corresponding values of m^2, b^2, and mb are

$$m^2 = 1,\ b^2 = 16,\ mb = 4. \hfill (8)$$

From (2), (3), and (8), $(x^2 - 3x + 2)^2 = (x + 4)^2.$ \hfill (9)

This equation is equivalent to the two quadratic equations

$$x^2 - 3x + 2 - (x + 4) = 0, \hfill (10)$$

and $\qquad\qquad x^2 - 3x + 2 + x + 4 = 0.$ \hfill (11)

The roots of (10) are $2 \pm \sqrt{6}$, and those of (11) are $1 \pm i\sqrt{5}$. These four values satisfy the given quartic.

Solve the following equations by the methods of Articles **134, 135.**

3. $x^3 - 2x^2 + 3 = 0.$

4. $x^4 + x^3 - x^2 = 7x + 6.$

5. $x^3 + 4x^2 + 4x + 3 = 0.$

6. $2x^3 + 1 = 5x^2.$

7. $x^4 + 2x^3 + x^2 + 3 = 0.$

8. $x^3 + 3x = 6x^2 + 18.$

9. $x^3 = x^2 + 4x + 6.$

10. $x^4 - 3x^2 + 6x = 2.$

15 RATIO, PROPORTION, AND VARIATION

136. Ratio

The **ratio** of a number a to a number b is the quotient $\dfrac{a}{b}$ obtained by dividing a by b. The ratio a to b is also written $a : b$.

It is clear from the above definition that any ratio is a fraction and any fraction may be regarded as a ratio. Thus, $\dfrac{2}{3}, \dfrac{3}{4}$, and $\dfrac{c}{d}$ are ratios.

137. Ratios Involved in Measurement

It is good usage and is often convenient to speak of the ratio of two quantities if they have a common unit of measure. Thus, the ratio of 6 feet to 2 feet is $\dfrac{6}{2}$.

To measure a quantity is to find its ratio to a given unit of measure. Thus, when we say a bar is 3 yards long, we mean that the ratio of the length of this bar to that of the standard yard is 3.

138. Proportion

A **proportion** is a statement of the equality of two ratios. Thus,

$$\frac{a}{b} = \frac{c}{d}$$

is a proportion and is often written

$$a : b = c : d.$$

It is read "a is to b as c is to d."

The four numbers a, b, c, and d are said to be in proportion, a and d being called the **extremes** and b and c the **means** of the proportion.

EXERCISES

Find the value of x in the following proportions.

1. $\dfrac{x}{5} = \dfrac{8}{15}$.

2. $\dfrac{5}{x} = \dfrac{8}{15}$.

3. $-\dfrac{2}{3} = \dfrac{x}{8}$.

4. $\dfrac{3}{4} = \dfrac{15}{x}$.

5. $5 : -12 = 3 : x$.

6. $x : 4 = 5 : 3$.

7. If $\dfrac{a}{b} = \dfrac{c}{x}$, then x is said to be a **fourth proportional** to a, b, c.

Find a fourth proportional to the following sets of numbers.

(a) $3, -6, 7$.
(b) $11, 3, -5$.
(c) $8, -5, -6$.

8. If $\dfrac{a}{x} = \dfrac{x}{d}$, then x is said to be a **mean proportional** between a and d. Find a mean proportional between the following sets of numbers.

(a) 8 and 2.
(b) 4 and -1.
(c) -3 and -75.

9. If $\dfrac{a}{b} = \dfrac{b}{x}$, then x is said to be a **third proportional** to a and b.

Find a third proportional to the following pairs of numbers.

(a) $5, 3$.
(b) $5, -3$.
(c) $3, 5$.
(d) $-7, -4$.

Given $\dfrac{a}{b} = \dfrac{c}{d}$, prove the following:

10. $ad = bc$; the product of the means is equal to the product of the extremes.

11. $\dfrac{b}{a} = \dfrac{d}{c}$; said to be obtained by **inversion**.

12. $\dfrac{a}{c} = \dfrac{b}{d}$; said to be obtained by **alternation**.

13. $\dfrac{(a-b)}{b} = \dfrac{(c-d)}{d}$; said to be obtained by **division.**

14. $\dfrac{(a+b)}{b} = \dfrac{(c+d)}{d}$; said to be obtained by **composition.**

15. $\dfrac{(a+b)}{(a-b)} = \dfrac{(c+d)}{(c-d)}$; said to be obtained by **composition and division.**

PROBLEMS INVOLVING SIMILAR FIGURES

Similar polygons are those which (1) are mutually equiangular and (2) have their corresponding sides proportional.

Similar polyhedrons are those which (1) have the same number of faces similar each to each and similarly placed and (2) have corresponding polyhedral angles equal.

16. The legs of a right triangle are 3 and 4 inches respectively. In a similar right triangle the shortest side is 5 inches. What are the lengths of the other sides? (Fig. 44).

17. The sides of a triangle are 7, 10, and 12 inches respectively. If the longest side is increased by 3 inches, what changes must be made in the lengths of the other two sides so that the new triangle is similar to the old?

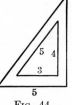

FIG. 44

18. The areas of the faces of a tetrahedron are 20, 25, 30, and 35 square inches respectively. If the area of the smallest face of a similar tetrahedron is 48 square inches, find the areas of the other corresponding faces.

19. The area of a triangle whose base is 12 inches is 60 square inches. Find the area of a similar triangle whose base is 18 inches.

Hint: The areas of two similar triangles are to each other as the squares of the corresponding sides. Prove this statement first.

20. The volume of a tetrahedron is 184 cubic inches. One edge is 10 inches. Find the volume of a similar tetrahedron whose corresponding edge is 15 inches.

Hint: What is the companion theorem to the hint of problem 19?

21. If on a map the distances between two points 350 miles apart is 4 inches, what is the distance between two points which are $5\frac{1}{4}$ inches apart on the map?

139. Variation

In Chapter 4 we have seen that if y is a function of x, written

$$y = f(x),$$

then in general y changes when x changes. We may say that y varies when x varies, but the word "varies" has come to have a more restricted meaning when used in this connection. Each of the statements

"y varies as x,"
"y varies directly as x,"
"y is proportional to x,"
"y is directly proportional to x,"

means that y is equal to the product of x by a constant. That is,

$$y = kx.$$

The constant k is called the **constant of variation.**

The expression "y varies as x" is sometimes written

$$y \propto x.$$

The area of a circle varies as the square of its radius. That is,

$$A = kr^2,$$

if A represents the area and r the radius. With our restricted meaning of the word "varies," it is not correct to say that the area of a circle varies as the radius, for, in the equality

$$A = kr,$$

k is not a constant for different values of r.

If a train moves with a uniform speed, the distance s traversed varies as the time t. That is,

$$s = kt.$$

140. Inverse Variation

Each of the statements

"y varies inversely as x,"
"y is inversely proportional to x,"

means that y is equal to the product of the reciprocal of x and a constant. That is,

$$y = \frac{k}{x}.$$

The volume of air in the cylinder of a bicycle pump varies inversely as the pressure on the piston. That is,

$$V = \frac{k}{p},$$

if V represents volume and p pressure.

141. Joint Variation

The statement "z varies jointly as x and y" means that z is equal to the product of x, y, and a constant. That is,

$$z = kxy.$$

The distance, which a train moving with a uniform speed travels, varies jointly as the speed and the time, or

$$d = kvt,$$

where d is the distance covered, v the speed, and t the time. In this case $k = 1$, if v and d are measured with the same unit of length.

142. Combined Variation

The statement "z varies directly as x and inversely as y" means that z varies jointly as x and the reciprocal of y. That is,

$$z = \frac{kx}{y}.$$

If T varies directly as x, directly as the square of y, inversely as W and inversely as the cube of v, we have

$$T = k\,\frac{xy^2}{Wv^3}.$$

The attraction F of any two masses m_1 and m_2 for each other varies as the product of the masses and inversely as the square of the distance r between the two bodies. That is,

$$F = \frac{km_1m_2}{r^2}.$$

143. Comments on Problems of Variation

Problems of variation frequently arise in experimental work.

Illustration 1. The time of vibration, t, of a simple pendulum varies as the square root of its length, l. It is found by experiment that a pendulum 39.1 inches long makes one vibration per second. Find the time of vibration of a pendulum of length 13 feet.

Solution. The law of variation is $t = k\sqrt{l}$.

To find k, put $t = 1$, $l = 39.1$. Then $k = \dfrac{1}{\sqrt{39.1}}$.

Hence, the law may be written

$$t = \sqrt{\frac{l}{39.1}}.$$

To find t when $l = 13$ feet $= 156$ inches, we have

$$t = \sqrt{\frac{156}{39.1}} = 2^- \text{ seconds.}$$

Illustration 2. The safe load of a horizontal beam supported at both ends varies jointly as the breadth, b, and square of the depth, d, and inversely as the length, l. If a 2×6 white pine joist safely holds up 800 pounds, what is the safe load of a 2×8 joist of same length?

Solution. The law of variation may be written

$$L = \frac{kbd^2}{l}.$$

From the given data, k is determined by the relation $800 = \dfrac{2 \cdot 6^2 \cdot k}{l}$. Thus,

$$k = \frac{800l}{2 \cdot 6^2}.$$

The required safe load, $L = \dfrac{2 \cdot 8^2 k}{l} = \dfrac{8^2}{6^2} \cdot 800 = 1422\tfrac{2}{9}$ lbs.

EXERCISES AND PROBLEMS

Write each of the statements in exercises 1–7 in the form of an equation, using k as a constant.

1. The volume, V, of a cube varies as the cube of its edge, e.

2. The volume, V, of a sphere varies as the cube of its radius, r.

3. The area, S, of the surface of a sphere varies as the square of its radius, r.

4. The volume, V, of a right circular cone varies jointly as the altitude, h, and the square of the radius, r, of the base.

5. The volume, v, of a gas at constant temperature varies inversely as the pressure, p.

6. The attraction, A, of two particles of matter varies inversely as the square of the distance, d, between them.

7. The height, h, of a column of mercury in a thermometer varies directly as the temperature, T.

8. Divide 300 into three parts proportional to 3, 5, 7.

9. A company's stock is divided into five parts proportional to 2, 3, 5, 5, and 9. If there are 20,000 shares of stock issued, how many shares are in each part?

10. Write in the form of an equation, the law: the safe load, w, of a horizontal beam supported at both ends varies jointly as the breadth, b, and the square of the depth, d, and inversely as the length, l, between the supports.

11. A beam 15 feet long, 2 inches wide, and 6 inches deep, when supported at both ends, can bear safely a load of 1200 pounds. What is the safe maximum load for a beam of the same material 15 feet long, 3 inches wide, and 4 inches deep? (See problem 10.)

12. Which of the beams in problem 11 will bear the greater load if the widths and depths are interchanged?

13. Write in the form of an equation, the law: the crushing load, L, of a solid oak square pillar varies directly as the fourth power of its thickness, t, and inversely as the square of its length, l.

14. If a four-inch oak pillar 8 feet high is crushed by a weight of 100 tons, what weight will crush a four-inch oak pillar 6 feet high?

15. Would a six-inch oak pillar 7 feet high be capable of supporting a load of 650 tons?

16. The deflection, D, of a rectangular beam of fixed length varies inversely as the product of the breadth, b, and the cube of the depth, d. Write this statement in the form of an equation.

17. In the formula $s = \dfrac{kbd}{l}$, s denotes the strength of a rectangular beam, b, d, and l, the breadth, depth, and length respectively, of the beam, and k is a constant. State the formula in words, using the language of variation.

18. The number of feet a body falls varies directly as the square of the number of seconds occupied in falling. If the body falls 16.1 feet the first second, how many feet will it fall in 5 seconds?

19. How far will a body fall during the fifth second?

20. The velocity of a falling body at any time varies directly as the number of seconds occupied in falling. What is the velocity at the end of 5 seconds if the velocity at the end of the first second is 32.2 feet per second?

21. An object dropped from a tower struck the ground in 6 seconds. From what height was the object dropped? With what velocity did it strike the ground?

22. A wrench is dropped from an automobile at a height of 3 feet while the automobile is traveling at the rate of 65 miles per hour. How far does the automobile move while the wrench is falling?

23. The time for one vibration of a pendulum at a given place varies as the square root of the length of the pendulum. In Chicago a pendulum 4 feet long requires 1.1 seconds for a vibration. What is the time of vibration of a pendulum 3 feet long?

24. What is the length of a pendulum which vibrates every second at Chicago?

25. A weight is suspended by a wire 94 feet long. How many vibrations will such a pendulum make in 24 hours at Chicago?

26. A pendulum supposed to vibrate every second at Chicago registers 90,000 vibrations in 24 hours. How much must the pendulum be lengthened?

27. The volume of a gas enclosed in a vessel varies inversely as the pressure upon it. Thirty-six cubic inches of air under a pressure of 100 pounds will have what volume when the pressure is decreased to 50 pounds?

28. In a pump, the volume of air enclosed by the walls of the cylinder and a movable piston varies inversely as the pressure. The radius of the cylinder is $\frac{3}{4}$ inches. When the piston is 12 inches from the base of the cylinder, the pressure of the air is 10 pounds per square inch. What is the pressure when the piston has been moved 8 inches nearer the base?

29. The force of the wind on a sail varies jointly as the area of the sail and the square of the wind velocity. When the wind velocity is 15 miles per hour, the force on one square foot of sail is 1 pound. What is the wind velocity when the force acting on the sail is 8 pounds per square foot?

30. The pressure of gas in a tank varies jointly as its density and its absolute temperature. When the density is 1 and the temperature is 300°, the pressure is 15 pounds per square inch. What is the temperature when the density is 1.5 and the pressure is 30 pounds per square inch?

31. The weight, w, of a body above the surface of the earth is inversely proportional to the square of its distance, s, from the center of the earth. If an experiment gives $w = 250$ pounds when $s = 4,000$ miles, find w when $s = 10,000$ miles.

32. The elongation, E, in a brass wire when a mass, m, is hung at its free end varies jointly as the mass and the length, L, of the wire and inversely as the area, A, of cross section of the wire. If $E = 0.060$ centimeters when $m = 944.8$ grams, $L = 213.2$ centimeters, and $A = 0.3127$ square centimeters, find E when $m = 500.0$ grams, $L = 315.2$ centimeters, and $A = 0.2585$ square centimeters.

33. If s be the length of the arc subtended by a chord of length, c, in a circle of radius, r, then the difference between the length of the arc and the length of the chord is approximately proportional to the cube of the arc length and inversely proportional to the square of the radius. The constant of proportionality is $\dfrac{1}{24}$.

(a) Write the formula and check its accuracy by finding the arc of a quadrant of a circle of radius 2 inches.

(b) In a circle of radius 2 inches, use the formula to find the length of a chord which subtends an arc 1.5 inches long.

(c) In the same circle, find the length of the arc subtended by a chord 2 inches long.

34. If x_0 grams of a radioactive substance decompose to x grams in time t, it is known that the time required for the decomposition is proportional to the natural logarithm of the ratio of the number of grams remaining at time t to the initial number of grams. If one-half the initial amount is decomposed in 5 years, how long will it take before one-fourth the initial amount remains? What part of the initial amount will remain 25 years after the decomposition started?

16 PROGRESSIONS

144. Sequences

A succession of numbers which follow each other according to a definite law is called a **sequence**. The successive numbers are called the **terms** of the sequence. For example, each of the following successions of numbers is a sequence.

(a) 2, 5, 8, 11, 14, $\cdots$.

(b) 9, 5, 1, -3, -7, -11, $\cdots$.

(c) 3, 6, 12, 24, 48, 96, 192, $\cdots$.

(d) 9, -3, 1, $\dfrac{-1}{3}$, $\dfrac{1}{9}$, $\dfrac{-1}{27}$, $\dfrac{1}{81}$, $\cdots$.

(e) $\dfrac{2}{3}$, $\dfrac{2}{5}$, $\dfrac{2}{7}$, $\dfrac{2}{9}$, $\dfrac{2}{11}$, $\cdots$.

(f) $\dfrac{1}{2}$, $\dfrac{1}{4}$, $\dfrac{1}{6}$, $\dfrac{1}{8}$, $\dfrac{1}{10}$, $\cdots$.

In the example (a), each term except the first is formed by adding 3 to the preceding term. In example (d), each term except the first is formed by multiplying the preceding term by $\dfrac{-1}{3}$.

Exercise. State the law of formation for the successive terms of the sequences in examples (b), (c), (e), and (f) above.

145. Arithmetic Progressions

An **arithmetic progression** is a sequence of numbers in which any term after the first may be obtained from the preceding term by adding to it a fixed number, called the **common difference**.

Example (a) in the preceding article is an arithmetic progression. Are there any other arithmetic progressions included among the examples of Article **144?**

146. The *n*th Term of an Arithmetic Progression

Let a_1, a_2, a_3, $\cdots$, a_n, $\cdots$ be the terms of an arithmetic progression and let d be the common difference. Then, from the law of formation, it follows that

$$a_2 = \text{the second term} = a_1 + d,$$
$$a_3 = \text{the third term} = a_1 + 2d,$$
$$a_4 = \text{the fourth term} = a_1 + 3d,$$
$$a_5 = \text{the fifth term} = a_1 + 4d.$$

It would seem reasonable then to guess that

$$a_{12} = \text{the twelfth term} = a_1 + 11d$$

and that

$$a_n = \text{the } n\text{th term} = a_1 + (n - 1)d.$$

The conjecture concerning a_{12} could be verified by continuing to form terms of the progression until the twelfth term has been reached.   The conjecture concerning the nth term must be proved by mathematical induction (Art. **96**).   We shall now prove that

$$a_n = a_1 + (n - 1)d. \qquad (A)$$

Part I.   The formula is true for the case $n = 2$, since it follows from the law of formation that

$$a_2 = a_1 + d.$$

Part II.   Let k be any integer for which it is true that

$$a_k = a_1 + (k - 1)d.$$

Add d to both sides of this equation, and get

$$a_k + d = a_1 + (k - 1)d + d.$$

From the law of formation, we know that $a_k + d = a_{k+1}$, and hence

$$a_{k+1} = a_1 + kd.$$

Thus, if the rule is true for $n = k$, it is true for $n = k + 1$. We have already shown that the rule is true for $n = 2$, hence it is true for $n = 3$.   Since it is true for $n = 3$, it is true for $n = 4$, and so on.   The proof of the rule is now complete.

147. The Sum of the First n Terms of an Arithmetic Progression

The sum, s_n, of the first n terms of an arithmetic progression may be written in each of the following forms:

$$s_n = a_1 + (a_1 + d) + (a_1 + 2d) + \cdots + [a_1 + (n-2)d] + [a_1 + (n-1)d].$$
$$s_n = a_n + (a_n - d) + (a_n - 2d) + \cdots + [a_n - (n-2)d] + [a_n - (n-1)d].$$

By addition

$$2s_n = (a_1 + a_n) + (a_1 + a_n) + (a_1 + a_n) + \cdots + (a_1 + a_n) + (a_1 + a_n),$$

or
$$2s_n = n(a_1 + a_n).$$

Therefore,

$$s_n = \frac{n}{2}(a_1 + a_n). \qquad (B)$$

We shall call the five numbers a_1, d, n, a_n, and s_n the elements of an arithmetic progression. If any three elements are known, the remaining two may be determined by using the equations (A) and (B) of Articles **146** and **147**.

Example. In an arithmetic progression $d = -3$ and $s_7 = 28$. Find a_1 and a_7 and write the progression.

Solution: From equation (A), Article **146**,

$$a_7 = a_1 + (6)(-3),$$

and from equation (B), Article **147**,

$$28 = \frac{7}{2}(a_1 + a_7).$$

These equations reduce to

$$a_1 - a_7 = 18,$$

and
$$a_1 + a_7 = 8.$$

Solving these two equations, we find $a_1 = 13$ and $a_7 = -5$. The progression is 13, 10, 7, 4, 1, -2, -5.

148. Arithmetic Means

The terms of an arithmetic progression which lie between any two given terms are called the **arithmetic means** between those terms. The two given terms are called the **extremes**.

Example. Insert six arithmetic means between 3 and 8.

Solution: We are here concerned with 8 terms of an arithmetic progression, the two extremes and the six means. From equation (A), Article **146**,

$$8 = 3 + 7d,$$

and hence
$$d = \frac{5}{7}.$$

The six arithmetic means between 3 and 8 are then $\dfrac{26}{7}, \dfrac{31}{7}, \dfrac{36}{7},$
$\dfrac{41}{7}, \dfrac{46}{7}, \dfrac{51}{7}.$

EXERCISES

Continue each of the following sequences to three additional terms.

1. $2, 7, 12, \cdots$.
2. $11, 8, 5, \cdots$.

4. $-\dfrac{5}{3}, -1, -\dfrac{1}{3}, \cdots$.

3. $\dfrac{2}{3}, \dfrac{1}{2}, \dfrac{1}{3}, \cdots$.

In problems 5 through 14, find the designated quantities for the arithmetic progressions and write out the progressions.

5. If $a_1 = 3$ and $d = 7$, find a_8 and s_8.

6. If $a_1 = -7$ and $s_8 = 56$, find d and a_8.

7. If $a_1 = 5$ and $a_6 = 17$, find d and s_6.

8. If $s_9 = 90$ and $d = -7$, find a_1 and a_9.

9. If $a_1 = -1$, $a_n = \dfrac{3}{2}$, and $s_n = \dfrac{7}{4}$, find n and d.

10. If $a_1 = 10$, $s_n = 40$, and $d = \dfrac{-4}{3}$, find n and a_n.

11. If $a_n = 4$, $d = \dfrac{2}{5}$, and $s_n = 22$, find n and a_1.

12. If $a_1 = 2$, $d = 3$, $s_n = 57$, find n and a_n.

13. If $a_3 = \dfrac{1}{2}$ and $a_6 = \dfrac{1}{3}$, find s_{10}.

14. If $s_5 = 10$ and $s_8 = 25$, find a_{11}.

15. Insert three arithmetic means between 5 and 20.

16. Insert six arithmetic means between -3 and 10.

17. Find the sum of all the odd numbers between 78 and 246.

18. Find the sum of all the numbers between 54 and 189 which are divisible by 7.

19. Derive a formula for the sum of the first n even integers.

20. Derive a formula for the sum of the first n odd integers.

149. Geometic Progressions

A **geometric progression** is a sequence of numbers in which any term after the first may be obtained from the preceding term by multiplying it by a fixed number, called the **common ratio**. Sequences (c) and (d) of Article **144** are examples of geometric progressions.

150. The *n*th Term of a Geometric Progression

Let $a_1, a_2, a_3, \cdots, a_n, \cdots$ be the terms of a geometric progression and let r be the common ratio. Then, from the law of formation, it follows that

$$a_2 = \text{the second term} = a_1 r,$$
$$a_3 = \text{the third term} = a_1 r^2,$$
$$a_4 = \text{the fourth term} = a_1 r^3.$$

It then seems reasonable to suppose that

$$a_n = \text{the } n\text{th term} = a_1 r^{n-1}. \tag{C}$$

This conjecture must be proved by mathematical induction. The proof is left to the student.

151. The Sum of the First *n* Terms of a Geometric Progression

The sum of the first n terms of a geometric progression may be written in the following form:

$$s_n = a_1 + a_1 r + a_1 r^2 + \cdots + a_1 r^{n-2} + a_1 r^{n-1}. \tag{1}$$

Multiply equation (1) by r and get

$$r s_n = a_1 r + a_1 r^2 + a_1 r^3 + \cdots + a_1 r^{n-1} + a_1 r^n. \tag{2}$$

If equation (2) is subtracted from equation (1), we have

$$(1 - r)s_n = a_1 - a_1 r^n,$$

or
$$s_n = \frac{a_1(1 - r^n)}{1 - r}. \tag{D}$$

We shall call the five numbers a_1, r, n, a_n, and s_n the elements of a geometric progression. If any three elements are known, the remaining two may be determined by using the equations (C) and (D).

Example. In a geometric progression $a_1 = 2$, $a_n = \dfrac{81}{8}$, and $r = \dfrac{3}{2}$. Find n and s_n.

Solution: From equation (C), Article **150**,

$$\frac{81}{8} = 2\left(\frac{3}{2}\right)^{n-1},$$

or

$$\frac{81}{16} = \left(\frac{3}{2}\right)^{n-1},$$

or

$$\left(\frac{3}{2}\right)^4 = \left(\frac{3}{2}\right)^{n-1},$$

whence $\qquad\qquad n - 1 = 4$

and $\qquad\qquad\quad n = 5.$

From equation (D),

$$s_5 = \frac{2\left[1 - \left(\dfrac{3}{2}\right)^5\right]}{1 - \dfrac{3}{2}},$$

whence $\qquad\qquad s_5 = \dfrac{211}{8}.$

152. Geometric Means

The terms of a geometric progression which lie between any two given terms are called the **geometric means** between those terms. The two given terms are called the **extremes.** To insert k geometric means between two given numbers is to find a geometric progression of $k + 2$ terms having the two given numbers for extremes.

Example. Insert two geometric means between 2 and 1024.

Solution: We must find r when $a_1 = 2$, $n = 4$, and $a_4 = 1024$. From equation (C), Article **150**,

$$1024 = 2r^3,$$

or $\qquad\qquad\qquad r^3 = 512.$

This equation has three roots, 8, $4(-1 + i\sqrt{3})$, and $4(-1 - i\sqrt{3})$. If we are restricted to real numbers, the problem has only one solution: the two geometric means between 2 and 1024 are 16 and 128.

If complex numbers are permitted, there are three solutions, namely, the one mentioned above and the two which follow:

$$8(-1 + i\sqrt{3}), \ 64(-1 - i\sqrt{3});$$

or $\qquad 8(-1 - i\sqrt{3}), \ 64(-1 + i\sqrt{3}).$

EXERCISES

Continue each of the following sequences to three additional terms.

1. $\dfrac{1}{12}, \dfrac{1}{6}, \dfrac{1}{3}, \cdots$.

2. $2, -6, 18, \cdots$.

3. $3, -\dfrac{3}{2}, \dfrac{3}{4}, \cdots$.

4. $\dfrac{125}{16}, \dfrac{25}{8}, \dfrac{5}{4}, \cdots$.

In problems 5 through 12 find the designated quantities for the geometric progressions and write out the progressions.

5. If $a_1 = \dfrac{1}{8}$ and $r = \dfrac{2}{3}$, find a_6 and s_6.

6. If $a_1 = 1$, $r = 5$, and $s_n = 19,531$, find n and a_n.

7. If $r = -3$, $a_n = 162$, and $s_n = 122$, find n and a_1.

8. If $r = \dfrac{3}{4}$ and $s_5 = \dfrac{781}{288}$, find a_1 and a_5.

9. If $a_1 = 6$, $r = \dfrac{1}{2}$, and $s_n = \dfrac{189}{16}$, find n and a_n.

10. If $r = -\dfrac{1}{3}$, $a_n = \dfrac{1}{45}$, and $s_n = \dfrac{61}{45}$, find n and a_1.

11. If $a_3 = 1$, $a_6 = -8$, and all the terms are real, find s_7.

12. If $a_3 = 3$ and $a_4 = 7$, find a_1.

13. Insert one geometric mean between 4 and 256. Give two solutions.

14. Insert two geometric means between $\dfrac{1}{9}$ and -3. How many solutions are there if imaginary numbers are permitted?

15. Insert three geometric means between 5 and 3125. Imaginary numbers are permitted. Give all possible solutions.

16. Insert three geometric means between $\dfrac{a^2}{2}$ and $\dfrac{8}{a^2}$.

17. In a geometric progression containing only real terms $a_1 = \dfrac{1}{4}$ and $s_5 = \dfrac{11}{4}$. Find r.

18. In a geometric progression $a_1 = 1$ and $s_3 = 3$. Find r.

19. In a geometric progression containing only real terms $a_1 = 1$ and $s_4 = 10$. Find r.

20. Find the seventh term and the sum of the first seven terms of the sequence

$$(3x - 16y),\ (8x + 8y),\ (13x - 4y),\ \cdots.$$

153. Infinite Geometric Progressions

Consider the geometric progression

$$\frac{1}{2},\ \frac{1}{4},\ \frac{1}{8},\ \frac{1}{16},\ \cdots.$$

It may at first thought appear that the sum of the first n terms of this progression could be made to exceed any previously assigned finite number by making n large enough. That this is not the case and that the sum cannot exceed unity, will be seen from the following illustration. Consider a particle moving in a straight line toward a point one unit distant in such a way as to describe $\dfrac{1}{2}$ the distance in the first second, $\dfrac{1}{2}$ the remaining distance in the second second, $\dfrac{1}{2}$ the remaining distance in the third second, and so on indefinitely. This is represented in Figure 45.

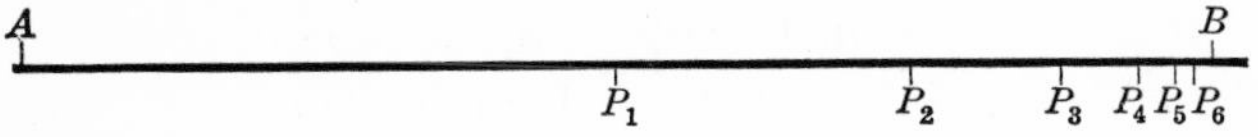

Fig. 45

The distance AB represents one unit. In the first second the particle moves from A to P_1. In the second second it moves from P_1 to P_2, and so on. The total distance traversed by the particle in n seconds is given by the sum

$$\frac{1}{2} + \frac{1}{4} + \frac{1}{8} + \frac{1}{16} + \cdots \text{ to } n \text{ terms,}$$

or

$$s_n = \frac{\dfrac{1}{2}\left[1 - \left(\dfrac{1}{2}\right)^n\right]}{1 - \dfrac{1}{2}} = 1 - \left(\frac{1}{2}\right)^n. \tag{1}$$

It is obvious both from the figure and from this formula that the sum of n terms can neither exceed nor even equal one. Furthermore, as n increases through the positive integers without bound, the value of s_n approaches closer and closer to one. As a matter of fact, the difference between 1 and s_n can be made as small as we please provided n is chosen sufficiently large. For example, suppose that we ask that the difference between 1 and s_n be less than 10^{-3}. From equation (1), $1 - s_n = \left(\dfrac{1}{2}\right)^n$ and we are then asking that $2^{-n} < 10^{-3}$. This inequality will be satisfied if $n > 10$. The reader may check this statement.

Since the difference between 1 and s_n can be made as small as we please by choosing n sufficiently large, we say that s_n approaches the limit 1 as n increases through the positive integers without bound and we write this statement in the symbolic form

$$\lim_{n \to \infty} s_n = 1.$$

We shall call a geometric progression with an infinite number of terms an infinite geometric progression. Furthermore, if $\lim\limits_{n \to \infty} s_n$ exists, we shall call this limit the sum of the infinite geometric progression and designate it by s.

For any geometric progression in which $|\, r\, | < 1$, the sum of the first n terms is given by

$$s_n = \frac{a_1(1 - r^n)}{1 - r} = \frac{a_1}{1 - r} - \frac{a_1 r^n}{1 - r}. \tag{2}$$

We now seek to find the limit of s_n as n increases through all the positive integers without bound. The first term on the right side of equation (2) does not contain n and hence its value remains fixed as n changes. Since $|\, r\, | < 1$, $\lim\limits_{n \to \infty} r^n = 0$, and so the second term on the right side of equation (2) approaches zero as n increases through all the positive integers without bound. We then conclude that if $|\, r\, | < 1$,

$$s = \lim_{n \to \infty} s_n = \frac{a_1}{1 - r}.$$

154. Repeating Decimals

Every repeating decimal can be expressed as the sum of an infinite geometric progression in which $|r| < 1$. By the method of Article **153,** the sum of such a progression may be expressed as the quotient of two integers. Hence, the limiting value of a repeating decimal can be expressed as the quotient of two integers and consequently is a rational number. For example, the repeating decimal, $0.333 \cdots$, may be written as the progression

$$0.3 + 0.03 + 0.003 + \cdots,$$

where $a_1 = 0.3$ and $r = 0.1$. The sum of this infinite geometric progression is

$$s = \frac{0.3}{1 - 0.1} = \frac{0.3}{0.9} = \frac{1}{3}.$$

Again, the repeating decimal $0.9828282 \cdots$ may be written

$$0.9 + 0.082 + 0.00082 + 0.0000082 + \cdots,$$

where the terms after the first form a geometric progression in which $a_1 = 0.082$ and $r = 0.01$. The limiting value of the decimal is

$$0.9 + \frac{0.082}{0.990} = \frac{9}{10} + \frac{82}{990} = \frac{973}{990}.$$

EXERCISES

1. Find the sum of the infinite geometric progression

$$1 - \frac{1}{2} + \frac{1}{4} - \frac{1}{8} \cdots,$$

and draw a figure similar to Figure 45 showing how the sum approaches its limit.

Find the sum of each of the following infinite geometric progressions:

2. $1, \dfrac{2}{3}, \dfrac{4}{9}, \cdots.$

3. $1, -\dfrac{2}{3}, \dfrac{4}{9}, \cdots.$

4. $80, 20, 5, \cdots.$

5. $4, 2\sqrt{2}, 2, \cdots.$

6. $36, -12, 4, \cdots.$

7. $3, 3(10)^{-1}, 3(10)^{-2}, \cdots.$

Find the limiting value of the following repeating decimals.

8. $0.4444\cdots$. **11.** $0.6070070070\cdots$.

9. $0.404040\cdots$. **12.** $2.3353535\cdots$.

10. $0.2575757\cdots$. **13.** $1.52741741\cdots$.

155. Harmonic Progressions

Three or more numbers are said to form a **harmonic progression** if their reciprocals form an arithmetic progression. The term "harmonic" as here used comes from a property of musical sounds. If a set of strings of uniform tension whose lengths are proportional to $1, \frac{1}{2}, \frac{1}{3}, \frac{1}{4}, \frac{1}{5}, \frac{1}{6}$ be sounded together, the effect is harmonious to the ear. The sequence

$$1, \frac{1}{2}, \frac{1}{3}, \frac{1}{4}, \frac{1}{5}, \cdots$$

is a harmonic progression since the reciprocals from the arithmetic progression

$$1, 2, 3, 4, 5, \cdots.$$

156. Harmonic Means

To find n harmonic means between two numbers, find n arithmetic means between the reciprocals of these numbers. The reciprocals of the arithmetic means are the harmonic means.

EXERCISES

Show that the following sequences are harmonic progressions and continue each of them for three more terms.

1. $\frac{8}{7}, \frac{4}{3}, \frac{8}{5}, 2, \cdots$.

2. $4, 2, \frac{4}{3}, \cdots$.

3. $3, 4, 6, \cdots$.

4. Insert two harmonic means between $\frac{3}{7}$ and $\frac{3}{13}$.

5. Insert three harmonic means between $\frac{5}{3}$ and $\frac{1}{7}$.

6. Insert four harmonic means between 6 and 1.

7. What is the harmonic mean between a and b?

PROBLEMS

1. A ball rolls down an inclined plane 8.05 feet the first second, 24.15 feet the second second, 40.25 feet the third second, and so on. How far will it roll in 10 seconds?

2. How many ancestors has a person in the ten preceding generations counting his two parents, four grandparents, eight great grandparents, and so on? Assume no duplicates.

3. If a falling body descends 16.1 feet the first second, three times this distance the next second, five times the next second, and so on, how far will it fall during the twentieth second and what distance will it have traversed during the entire 20 seconds?

4. The cost of digging a well is $25 per foot for the first 10 feet, $35 per foot for the next 10 feet, $45 per foot for the next 10 feet, and so on. How deep a well might be dug for $24,000?

5. A person contributes a dime and sends letters to three friends asking that each contribute a dime to a certain charity and that each write a similar letter to three friends, each of whom is expected to contribute and to write three letters, and so on until 10 sets of letters have been written. If all respond, how much money will the charity receive?

6. Twelve stones are placed in a straight line on the ground at intervals of 4 feet. A basket is placed 10 feet from the end of the row. A runner starts from the basket and picks up the stones and carries them, one at a time, to the basket. How far does he run altogether?

7. A swinging pendulum gradually is brought to rest by the friction of the air. If the length of the first swing of the pendulum bob is 25 centimeters and the length of each succeeding swing is 0.1 less than the preceding one, what is the distance passed over in the tenth swing? What is the total distance passed over in ten swings? Approximately how far will the bob travel before coming to rest?

8. An elastic ball is dropped from a height of 30 feet. Each time it strikes the ground it rebounds $\frac{3}{5}$ of the height from which it has just fallen. How high does it rise on the sixth rebound? How far has it traveled when it strikes the ground for the sixth time? Approximately how far will the ball travel before coming to rest?

9. Find the sum of the infinite geometric progression
$$(1 + x)^{-1}, (1 + x)^{-2}, (1 + x)^{-3}, \cdots, \text{ where } x > 0.$$

10. A bag containing 25 pounds of grass seed was passed in succession among 6 neighbors. Each man used $\frac{1}{5}$ of the seed that was in the bag when he received it. How much seed remained after the sixth man had removed the amount he used? How many pounds of seed did the sixth man use?

11. A vat contains pure alcohol. One-eighth of the alcohol is drawn off and replaced with water. The mixture is thoroughly stirred and then one-eighth of the mixture is drawn off and replaced with water. This process is carried out until five drawings and replacements have been made. What part of the remaining mixture is alcohol?

12. What is the equation whose roots are the arithmetic and harmonic means between the roots of $x^2 - 8x + 12 = 0$?

13. The arithmetic mean of two numbers is 10 and their geometric mean is 8. Find the numbers.

14. The harmonic mean of two numbers is 4 and their geometric mean is 5. Find the numbers.

15. The sides of a right triangle are in arithmetic progression. Show that the triangle is similar to the triangle whose sides are 3, 4, 5.

16. The roots of $x^3 - 6x^2 + 3x + 10 = 0$ are in arithmetic progression. Find them.

Hint: Let the roots be $r_1 = a - d$, $r_2 = a$, $r_3 = a + d$ and use Article **133.**

17. The roots of $x^3 - 7x^2 + cx - 8 = 0$ are real and are in geometric progression. Find the roots and the coefficient c.

18. If a, b, c are in geometric progression, show that $b - a$, $2b$, $b - c$ are in harmonic progression.

19. If A, G, and H stand respectively for the arithmetic, geometric, and harmonic means between two numbers a and b, show that $G^2 = AH$.

20. If $y = ab^x$, $(a > 0, b > 0, b \neq 1)$, and if the numbers x are in arithmetic progression, show that the corresponding values of y are in geometric progression.

21. Consider the geometric progression a, ar, ar^2, $\cdots$ where $a > 0$, $r > 0$, $r \neq 1$. Show that the logarithms of the terms in this geometric progression are in arithmetic progression.

17 INTEREST AND ANNUITIES*

157. Interest

If an individual or business organization lends money, it is expected that at some future date the borrower will not only return the amount borrowed but an additional sum called the **interest**. The amount borrowed is called the **principal**. The **rate of interest** is the interest charged for the use of one unit of money for one unit of time.

158. Simple Interest

If interest is computed on the original principal throughout the life of the transaction, the interest is called simple interest. Thus, if P is the principal, r is the rate per year, and n is the number of years, then the simple interest on P for n years at rate r is

$$I = Pnr. \tag{1}$$

The amount due at the end of n years is

$$S = P + I,$$
or
$$S = P(1 + nr). \tag{2}$$

159. Compound Interest

When interest due is added to the principal at stated intervals, say annually, semiannually, or quarterly, the interest is said to be **compounded** or **converted** into principal. The **conversion**

* For a more complete and detailed discussion of these topics see *Mathematics of Finance*, by Rietz, Crathorne, and Rietz, Henry Holt and Company.

period is the time between two successive conversions of interest into principal. If no conversion period is named, it is ordinarily understood to be one year.

If P is the original principal, i the rate per conversion period, the sum S, called the **compound amount,** to which P will accumulate at the end of n conversion periods is

$$S = P(1 + i)^n. \tag{3}$$

To prove this we proceed as follows:

Interest due at the end of the first period is Pi. The amount at the end of the first period is

$$P + Pi = P(1 + i).$$

Interest due at the end of the second period is $Pi(1 + i)$. The amount due at the end of the second period is thus

$$P(1 + i) + Pi(1 + i) = P(1 + i)^2.$$

The equation (3) has thus been verified for the cases $n = 1$ and $n = 2$.

Let k be any integer for which it is true that the compound amount at the end of k periods is $P(1 + i)^k$. Then the amount at the end of the $(k + 1)$st period is

$$P(1 + i)^k + Pi(1 + i)^k = P(1 + i)^{k+1}.$$

Hence, if formula (3) is true for $n = k$, it is true for $n = k + 1$. The proof is now complete.

The compound amount diminished by the original principal is called the **compound interest.**

160. Present Value

The principal P which invested now will amount to S at the end of n periods at rate i per period is called the **present value** of S due at the end of n periods at the rate i per period. The problem of finding the present value of an amount S when n and i are given is solved by solving equation (3) for P in terms of S, n, and i. Thus

$$P = \frac{S}{(1 + i)^n}. \tag{4}$$

In courses in the mathematics of finance, compound interest tables are used to facilitate the computations involved in equations (3) and (4). Our purpose here is to offer more problems for practice in the use of logarithms.

EXERCISES

1. A man borrows $300 for 90 days at 4% simple interest. Find the interest and the amount due at the end of 90 days.

(a) Assume there are 365 days in the year. The interest so calculated is called exact simple interest.

(b) Assume there are 360 days in the year. The interest so calculated is called ordinary simple interest.

2. A man borrows $500 and signs a note agreeing to pay at the end of 6 months the sum of $512.50, which will cancel the debt, including the interest. What rate of simple interest is he being charged?

3. Find the amount of $1000 in 10 years at 3% interest compounded annually.

In this case, $S = \$1000 \ (1.03)^{10}$.

Form for solution by logarithms:

$$\begin{aligned} \log 1.03 \quad &= \underline{} \\ \log (1.03)^{10} &= \\ \log 1000 \quad &= \underline{} \\ \log S &= \\ S &= \end{aligned}$$

4. What principal will amount to $2000 in 10 years at the rate .03 compounded annually?

Form for solution: $\qquad P = \dfrac{\$2000}{(1.03)^{10}}.$

$$\begin{aligned} \log 1.03 \quad &= \underline{} \\ \log 2000 \quad &= \\ \log (1.03)^{10} &= \underline{} \\ \log P &= \\ P &= \end{aligned}$$

5. Find the amount of $1000 in 8 years at 4% compounded annually.

6. Find the amount of $1000 in 8 years at 4% compounded semiannually.

Hint: 4% compounded semiannually means that the rate of interest during each conversion period is 2%. Hence

$$S = 1000 \ (1.02)^{16}.$$

7. Find the amount of $1000 in 8 years at 4% compounded quarterly.

8. Find the present value of $1000 due in 8 years at 4% compounded annually.

9. Find the present value of $1000 due in 8 years at 4% compounded semiannually.

10. Find the present value of $1000 due in 8 years at 4% compounded quarterly.

11. At the birth of his son a father invests at rate 3.5% compounded semiannually, a sum sufficient to provide $3000 on the son's twentieth birthday. How much did the father invest?

12. In how many years will any sum double itself if invested at the rate 4% compounded quarterly?

13. A man borrows $2000 and agrees to repay principal and interest at the end of 5 years by making a single payment of $2560.17. What rate of interest compounded semiannually does he pay?

14. A United States Savings bond selling for $75 is redeemable at the end of 8 years, 11 months for $100. What rate of interest compounded semiannually do these bonds bear if held to the date of maturity?

15. Draw on the same set of axes the amount of $100 for n years at 4% simple interest and the amount of $100 for n years at 4% compounded annually. Plot points for integer values of n from 1 to 5. Simple interest is used generally only for periods of time less than one year. Can you offer any reason for this restriction?

16. Draw on the same set of axes a graph showing at the end of each year for five years the amount of $100 at 4% compounded annually and at 4% compounded semiannually.

17. Draw on the same axes a graph showing at the end of each year for five years the amount of $100 at 5% compounded semiannually and at $5\frac{1}{2}$% compounded annually.

18. Find the rate i compounded annually such that $100 invested at rate i for one year will be equivalent to $100 invested for one year at 5% compounded semiannually. The rate i is called the effective rate.

19. If you could invest money at 2% compounded quarterly or $2\frac{1}{2}$% compounded semiannually, which investment would you choose?

161. Annuities Certain

An **annuity certain** is a set of equal payments made at equal intervals over a fixed period of time. For example, suppose a fraternity is in debt on a chapter house, and is to pay $2500 at the end of each year for 20 years to discharge the debt, both interest and principal. The set of payments constitute an annuity certain.

Two questions about annuities naturally arise:

(1) To what amount would the payments accumulate at the end of the paying period?

(2) What is the present value of the payments?

For simplicity, we shall limit our answers to these questions to cases in which the payments are made at the end of the interest conversion periods. To take up the problem involved in question (1) let R be the periodic payment and let i be the rate of interest earned during each interest conversion period.

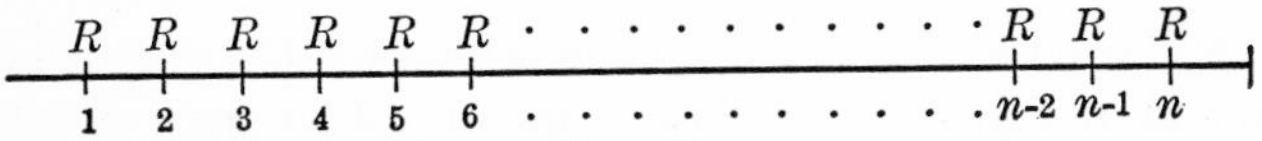

Fig. 46

The first payment of R will accumulate to $R(1 + i)^{n-1}$.

The second payment of R will accumulate to $R(1 + i)^{n-2}$.

The third payment of R will accumulate to $R(1 + i)^{n-3}$.

The next to the last payment of R will accumulate to $R(1 + i)$.

The last payment of R will accumulate to R.

Reversing the order and adding, and letting K be the sum, we have

$$K = R[1 + (1 + i) + \cdots + (1 + i)^{n-2} + (1 + i)^{n-1}].$$

The right-hand member is a geometric progression of n terms in which the first term is R and the common ratio is $1 + i$. The sum, called the **amount of the annuity,** is then (Art. **151**)

$$K = R \frac{(1 + i)^n - 1}{i}. \tag{5}$$

To take up the problem involved in question (2), we define the **present value of an annuity** as the sum of the present values (Art. 160) of the separate payments. The present values of the payments of R each beginning with the first one are

$$R(1 + i)^{-1}, \ R(1 + i)^{-2}, \cdots, \ R(1 + i)^{-n}.$$

We have then for the present value of the annuity

$$P = R[(1 + i)^{-1} + (1 + i)^{-2} + \cdots + (1 + i)^{-n}],$$

a geometric progression whose first term is $R(1 + i)^{-1}$, last term $R(1 + i)^{-n}$, and common ratio $(1 + i)^{-1}$. Summing the series we have (Art. **151**)

$$P = R \frac{1 - (1 + i)^{-n}}{i}. \tag{6}$$

EXERCISES AND PROBLEMS

1. A man sets aside $200 at the end of each year toward a fund for his son's college expenses. He invests the money at rate .04 compounded annually. Calculate the amount at the end of 15 years as nearly as you can using a five-place table of logarithms to find $(1.04)^{15}$.

Solution: From (5) we have the amount

$$S = 200 \frac{(1.04)^{15} - 1}{.04}.$$

By five-place logarithms $(1.04)^{15}$ is found to be 1.801.
Hence $(1.04)^{15} - 1 = .801$.

$$S = \frac{200}{0.4}(.801) = \$4005,$$

correct somewhat accidentally to the nearest dollar.

2. A man pays $26.08 paving tax at the end of each year for 10 years. If the interest charge is 5%, what is the actual tax for the paving to the nearest dollar?

Solution: From (6), we have for the present value of the annuity certain

$$P = 26.08 \frac{1 - (1.05)^{-10}}{.05}.$$

By four-place logarithms, $(1.05)^{-10} = .6137$, hence $1 - (1.05)^{-10} = .3863$.

$$\text{Hence, } P = \frac{(26.08)(.3863)}{.05} = \$201.$$

3. Find the amount and present value of an annuity of $500 paid at the end of each year for 8 years at the rate of 5% per year.

4. A man wants to accumulate $2000 in 5 years by making deposits in a savings account at the end of each six months. The account bears interest at the rate of 2% compounded semiannually. If he makes deposits on the interest conversion dates, find the amount of each deposit.

5. On January 1 and July 1 of each year a man deposits $150 in a Savings and Loan Association which pays interest at the rate of $4\frac{1}{4}$% compounded on January 1 and July 1. If the man made his first deposit on January 1, 1950, how much would he have to his credit on January 1, 1960, just after he had made the deposit on that date?

6. The beneficiary of an insurance policy has the choice of receiving $10,000 in cash or an annuity paid at the end of each year for ten years. If the insurance company operates on an interest rate of $2\frac{1}{2}$% compounded annually, what should be the annual payment to the beneficiary, assuming the present value of both benefits equal?

7. A man buys a $10,000 house. He pays $2,000 cash and agrees to pay the remainder by making equal payments at the end of each six months for 15 years. If the rate of interest is 5% converted on the dates the payments are made, what is the semiannual payment made by the purchaser?

8. A man buys a house priced at $8000. He pays $2000 cash and agrees to pay $1000 at the end of each year until the debt is extinguished. If the rate of interest charged is 5% compounded annually, how many full payments of $1000 must the man make? Can you find the amount of the last payment?

Hint: Let n be the number of $1000 payments and let R be the last payment. Then the present value of the annuity of $1000 per year for n years plus the present value of R for $n + 1$ years must be equal to $6000.

9. How many payments of $200 each made at the end of each three months would be necessary to amount to $1000 at rate 4% compounded quarterly? Can you find the amount of the last payment necessary to bring the fund to exactly $1000?

10. A television set sells for $325 cash or $25 down and $18.50 payable at the end of each month for 18 months. Write an equation whose solution will give the rate of interest charged per month. Show that the rate of interest being charged is about $13\frac{1}{2}$% compounded monthly.

18 PERMUTATIONS AND COMBINATIONS

162. Introduction

Two positions are to be filled in an office — one that of stenographer and the other that of messenger. There are 12 applicants for the position of stenographer, and 3 for that of messenger. In how many ways can the two positions together be filled?

The position of stenographer can be filled in 12 ways, and with each of these there is a choice of 3 messengers. Hence, the two positions can be filled in $12 \times 3 = 36$ ways.

This example illustrates the following

FUNDAMENTAL PRINCIPLE. *If one thing can be done in m different ways; and if, after this is done in one of these ways, a second thing can be done in n ways, then the two together can be done in the order stated in mn ways.*

For, corresponding to each of m ways of doing the first thing, there are n ways of doing the second thing. In other words, there are n ways of doing the two together for each way of doing the first thing. Hence, there are in all mn ways of doing the two things together.

A convenient and evident extension of the fundamental principle may be stated in the following form:

If one thing can be done in m_1 ways, a second in m_2 ways, a third in m_3 ways, and so on, the number of different ways in which they can be done when taken all together in the order stated is $m_1 m_2 m_3 \cdots$.

163. Meaning of a Permutation

*Each different arrangement which can be made of all or part of a number of things is called a **permutation**.*

By the expression "number of permutations of n things taken r at a time" is meant the number of permutations consisting of r things each which can be formed from n different things. Thus, the permutations of the letters abc taken all at a time are

$$a\,b\,c, \quad a\,c\,b, \quad b\,a\,c, \quad b\,c\,a, \quad c\,a\,b, \quad c\,b\,a$$

The permutations of the four letters $a\,b\,c\,d$ taken three at a time are

$a\,b\,c$	$b\,a\,c$	$c\,a\,b$	$d\,a\,b$
$a\,c\,b$	$b\,c\,a$	$c\,b\,a$	$d\,b\,a$
$a\,c\,d$	$b\,c\,d$	$c\,b\,d$	$d\,b\,c$
$a\,d\,c$	$b\,d\,c$	$c\,d\,b$	$d\,c\,b$
$a\,b\,d$	$b\,a\,d$	$c\,a\,d$	$d\,a\,c$
$a\,d\,b$	$b\,d\,a$	$c\,d\,a$	$d\,c\,a$

164. Permutations of Things All Different

In Article **163** we found there were six permutations of the letters a, b, c taken three at a time by writing out the possible permutations. We could have arrived at the number of permutations without writing out each arrangement of the letters. For the first position we had a choice of three letters, a, b, or c. After this choice had been made, there remained a choice of two letters for the second position. After the second position was filled, there remained only one letter for the third position. By the fundamental principle of Article **162,** the number of arrangements is thus $3 \cdot 2 \cdot 1$ or 6.

If there are n distinct objects, we shall designate the number of permutations of these n objects taken n at a time by the symbol $P(n, n)$. For the first position there are n choices, for the second position $(n - 1)$ choices, for the third position $(n - 2)$ choices, and so on, until for the nth position only one object remains. Hence, by the fundamental principle

$$P(n, n) = n(n - 1)(n - 2) \cdots 2 \cdot 1 = n! \qquad (1)$$

Consider now the number of permutations of the four letters a, b, c, d, taken three at a time. In Article **163,** we found the number of permutations by writing them out. The following reasoning will give the number of arrangements without writing them out. For the first position there is a choice of four letters, for the second a choice of three letters, for the third a choice of two letters. Then by the fundamental principle, the number of permutations of four letters taken three at a time is $4 \cdot 3 \cdot 2$ or 24.

In general, the number of permutations of n distinct objects taken r at a time is designated by the symbol $P(n, r)$. For the first position there are n choices, for the second $(n - 1)$ choices, for the third $(n - 2)$ choices, for the fourth $(n - 3)$ choices, and so on, until at the rth there are $(n - r + 1)$ choices. Again using the fundamental principle, we have

$$P(n, r) = n(n - 1)(n - 2)(n - 3) \cdots (n - r + 1),$$

or
$$P(n, r) = \frac{n!}{(n - r)!}. \tag{2}$$

If $r = n$, the formula (2) must reduce to equation (1). From (2), $P(n, n) = \dfrac{n!}{0!}$. Up to this point, the symbol $0!$ has not been defined, so we are permitted to define it in any manner which will be consistent with our previous work. Since obviously the value of $P(n, n)$ should be the same under all circumstances, we are forced to define $0! = 1$.

165. Permutations of n Things Not All Different

Consider the number of permutations of the letters in the word *book*. It gives no new permutation to interchange the o's. Let P be the number of permutations. If we should replace oo by dissimilar characters $o_1 o_2$, there would be $2!$ permutations of $o_1 o_2$ corresponding to each of the P permutations. But if the letters were all different the number of permutations would be $4!$. Hence,

$$4! = 2! \, P, \quad P = \frac{4!}{2} = 12.$$

This example illustrates the

THEOREM. *If P is the number of permutations of n things taken all at a time, of which n_1 are alike, n_2 others alike, n_3 others alike, and so on, then*

$$P = \frac{n!}{n_1! \, n_2! \, n_3! \cdots}.$$

To establish the theorem, suppose we should replace n_1 like things by n_1 unlike things, there would be $P \cdot n_1!$ permutations obtained from the original P permutations. In each of these permutations there would be n_2 things alike, and n_3 others alike. Similarly, replacing the n_2 like things by n_2 dissimilar things, we get $P \cdot n_1! \cdot n_2!$ permutations in each of which there would be n_3 alike. Continuing this argument, we find that the number of permutations of n things taken all at a time, when n_1 are alike, n_2 others alike, n_3 others alike, and so on, is given by

$$P = \frac{n!}{n_1! \, n_2! \, n_3! \cdots}.$$

EXERCISES

1. How many integers consisting of four distinct digits may be formed from the digits 1, 2, 3, 4, 5, 6, 7, 8, 9?

2. How many integers consisting of four digits may be formed from the digits 1, 2, 3, 4, 5, 6, 7, 8, 9, repetition of digits being permitted?

3. What would be the maximum number of Greek letter fraternities having distinct names consisting of three different letters (the Greek alphabet contains 24 letters)?

4. How many Greek letter fraternities may be organized having names of three letters, repetitions of the letters being allowed?

5. How many Greek letter fraternities are possible having either two or three letters in their names?

6. A woman invites six of her friends to luncheon. In how many different ways may she and her guests be arranged around a circular table?

7. A man and his wife invite four women and four men to dinner. The host and hostess sit opposite each other and no persons of the same sex sit beside each other. In how many ways may the group be arranged around the table?

8. A man and his wife invite four married couples to dinner. The group is arranged around a circular table so that each man sits diametrically opposite his wife and no persons of the same sex sit beside each other. In how many ways can the group be arranged around the table?

9. In how many ways may four algebra texts, three geometry texts, and five trigonometry texts be arranged on a shelf, keeping the books on each subject together?

10. In problem 9, if two of the algebras are identical and three of the trigonometries are identical, in how many ways can the books be arranged, keeping those on each subject together?

11. If $P(n, 9) = 20P(n, 7)$, find n.

12. If $P(6, r) = 20P(6, r - 2)$, find r.

13. If $P(7, r) = 84P(5, r - 3)$, find r.

14. How many integers less than 100,000 contain the digits 345 in that order?

166. Combinations

A set of things or elements without reference to the order of individuals within the set is called a **combination.**

Thus, *abc, acb, bac, bca, cab, cba* are the same combination. By the "number of combinations of n things taken r at a time" is meant the number of combinations of r individuals which can be formed from n things.

Thus, the combinations of $a\,b\,c$ taken two at a time are ab, ac, bc.

167. Combinations of Things All Different

Let $C(n, r)$ denote the number of combinations of n things taken r at a time. Then a formula can be derived for $C(n, r)$ by establishing the relation between $C(n, r)$ and $P(n, r)$.

Take one combination of r things; with this $r!$ permutations can be made. Take a second combination; with this $r!$ permutations can be made. There are thus $r!$ permutations for each combination. Hence, there are in all $C(n, r) \cdot r!$ permutations of n things taken r at a time. That is,

$$C(n, r) \cdot r! = P(n, r)$$

whence
$$C(n, r) = \frac{P(n, r)}{r!}.$$

Since
$$P(n, r) = n(n - 1) \cdots (n - r + 1), \qquad \text{(Art. 164)}$$

we have
$$C(n, r) = \frac{n(n - 1) \cdots (n - r + 1)}{r!}.$$

Multiplying numerator and denominator by $(n - r)!$, we get

$$C(n, r) = \frac{n!}{r!(n - r)!}.$$

Since $\quad C(n, n - r) = \dfrac{n(n - 1) \cdots (r + 1)}{(n - r)!} = \dfrac{n!}{(n - r)! \, r!},$

it follows that the number of combinations of n things taken r at a time is the same as the number taken $n - r$ at a time.

168. Binomial Coefficients

In Article **98**, we found the expansion of $(a + x)^n$ when n is a positive integer. In that article, the coefficients in the expansion were obtained by inspecting several special cases and then mathematical induction was employed to show that the expansion so obtained is correct. Let us now obtain these coefficients by another method.

First we recognize the fact that

$$(a + x)^n = (a + x)(a + x)(a + x) \cdots (a + x) \text{ to } n \text{ factors.}$$

Secondly we require that $(a + x)^n$ be expressible as a polynomial of degree n in x, that is

$$(a + x)^n = a^n + c_1 a^{n-1}x + c_2 a^{n-2}x^2 + c_3 a^{n-3}x^3 + \cdots + c_{n-1}ax^{n-1} + c_n x^n.$$

The problem then is to determine the coefficients.

The coefficient of a^n is obviously 1.

Now we shall determine the coefficient of $a^{n-1}x$. In order to get $a^{n-1}x$, we have to select an x from one factor and an a from each of the others. The number of ways in which an x can be chosen from one factor is $C(n, 1)$ or n ways. Hence $c_1 = C(n, 1)$.

In order to obtain the term $a^{n-2}x^2$, we must select an x from two factors and an a from each of the others. The number of ways in which an x can be selected from two factors is $C(n, 2)$.

The process continues in this fashion and so we reach the conclusion that

$$(a + x)^n = a^n + C(n, 1)a^{n-1}x + C(n, 2)a^{n-2}x^2 + C(n, 3)a^{n-3}x^3 + \cdots + C(n, n - 1)ax^{n-1} + C(n, n)x^n.$$

The student may show that this result is identical with that given in Article **98**. The following question will be left for the student to discuss with his instructor and classmates: "Has the binomial expansion been *proved* by finding the coefficients in this manner?"

169. Total Number of Combinations

The total number of combinations of n things taken 1, 2, 3, $\cdots$, *n at a time is* $2^n - 1$. If we write the binomial theorem as in the last section, we obtain

$$(1+x)^n = 1 + C(n, 1)x + C(n, 2)x^2 + \cdots + C(n, n-1)x^{n-1} + C(n, n)x^n.$$

Putting $x = 1$, we get

$$2^n - 1 = C(n, 1) + C(n, 2) + \cdots + C(n, n-1) + C(n, n).$$

EXERCISES AND PROBLEMS

1. A committee of three is to be selected from the twenty-four members of an organization. In how many ways may the committee be chosen?

2. A chairman, secretary, and treasurer are to be chosen from the twenty-four members of an organization. Every member is eligible for any office but no member may hold two offices. In how many ways may the officers be chosen?

3. Five men and three women are candidates for a debating team. If the team consists of three members and if there is one woman on the team, in how many ways may the team be chosen?

4. How many straight lines may be drawn through seven distinct points, no three of which are collinear? Is there any difference if we consider seven points in a plane or seven points in a three-dimensional space?

5. In a group of distinct points every point is connected with every other point by a straight line and no three points lie on the same straight line. There are 120 distinct straight lines. How many points are there?

6. Seven lines, no two of which are either parallel or coincident and no three of which pass through the same point, lie in a plane. How many points of intersection are there?

7. How many circles may be drawn through seven distinct points in a plane if no three of the points are collinear and no four lie on the same circle?

8. An examination is divided into four parts. The first part contains four problems, the second three problems, the third five problems, and the fourth two problems. The students are directed to answer ten problems, excluding one problem from each part of the examination. In how many ways may a student select his ten problems?

9. In an examination with twelve questions, the student is directed to answer ten questions, which include at least one of the first two. In how many ways may the student choose the ten questions?

10. If $C(n, 3) = 220$, find n.

11. If $P(n, r) = 120$ and $C(n, r) = 20$, find n and r.

12. If $P(n, 3) = 4C(n + 1, 4)$, find n.

13. If $14C(6, r) = 3C(8, r)$, find r.

14. In how many ways may 5 objects be divided into groups of 2 and 3? In how many ways may 7 objects be divided into groups of 3 and 4? In how many ways may 9 objects be divided into groups of 4 and 5?

Hint: In the case of the five objects, after three are selected, in how many ways may the remaining pair be chosen?

15. In how many ways may 6 objects be divided into two equal groups? In how many ways may 8 objects be divided into two equal groups? In how many ways may 10 objects be divided into two equal groups? Compare your results with those of problem 14.

Hint: In dividing the 4 letters a, b, c, d, into 2 groups of 2 each, we might at first say that we can choose the first pair in 6 ways and the second pair in 1 way, and hence there are 6 such groupings into pairs. If, however, we write out these 6 groupings, and consider that we are not at all interested in the order of the pairs, we see that there are only 3 such groupings.

16. Show that the number of ways in which $2n$ objects may be divided into two equal groups is the same as the number of ways in which $2n - 1$ objects may be divided into groups of n and $n - 1$.

17. In how many ways may six boys who want to play croquet be divided into two teams of three each?

18. A team of three women is playing croquet against a team of three men. If no player follows his partner, in how many orders may they start to play?

19. In how many ways may three teams of two players be chosen from a group of six players?

20. Two fellows and their dates are playing a bowling game called boccie. Each fellow and his date form a team. The participants play in order and no player is followed by his teammate. In how many orders may they start play?

21. In how many ways can a pack of 52 playing cards be divided into four hands, the order of the hands, but not the cards in the hands, to be regarded?

22. How many different sums of money can be formed with a penny, a nickel, a dime, a quarter, a half dollar, and a dollar?

23. How many different combinations can be formed with the following weights: a one pound, a half pound, a quarter pound, a two ounce, and a one ounce weight?

24. Find the number of permutations of four things taken three at a time where two of the objects are identical. For example, consider the group of letters a, a, b, c.

Hint: Divide the arrangements into two groups, those containing distinct letters and those containing two identical letters. In the second grouping, the third letter may be chosen in $4 - 2$ ways and for each of these choices there are permutations equal in number to the permutations of three things taken three at a time when two are identical.

25. Find the number of permutations of n objects taken three at a time when two of the objects are identical.

26. Find the number of permutations of n objects taken r at a time when two of the objects are identical and $2 < r \leq n - 1$.

27. Find the number of permutations of n objects taken r at a time when three of the objects are identical and $3 < r \leq n - 2$.

28. Find the number of permutations of n objects taken three at a time when three of the objects are identical.

29. In problems 24 through 28 replace the word *permutations* by *combinations* and solve.

19 RELATIVE FREQUENCY AND PROBABILITY

170. Meaning of Relative Frequency

A bag contains white and black balls alike except as to color and thoroughly mixed. The drawing of a ball and replacing it is called a **trial**. Suppose we make 100 trials and obtain 31 white balls. Then we say $\frac{31}{100}$ is the relative frequency of white balls in this set of drawings.

In making a trial we often call the happening of the event in question a **success**. In the above case the drawing of a white ball may be called a success and the drawing of a black ball a **failure**. In general, if we make n trials resulting in m successes and $n - m$ failures, we say that $\frac{m}{n}$ is the relative frequency of successes and $\frac{n - m}{n}$ is the relative frequency of failures in the n trials.

The sum of the relative frequencies of successes and of failures is clearly equal to $\frac{m}{n} + \frac{n - m}{n} = 1$.

Query. What was the relative frequency of deaths in a year among 10,000 persons of equal age if there were 50 deaths within a year?

171. Meaning of Probability of Success

If we increase the number of trials described in Article **170** from 100 to any larger number, say to 1000 or more, we would not necessarily find exactly the same relative frequency of successes. Next, if we conceive of increasing the number of trials and of calculating a new value of the relative frequency of successes after each trial we may find that the sequence of relative frequencies approaches a limiting value (Art. **192**). If there is such a limiting value, it is called the **probability of success in one trial.** Thus, if we conceive of repeating indefinitely the drawing of a ball from a thorough mixture of balls, three-tenths of which are white, we may assume that the relative frequency of white balls would approach three-tenths and we say three-tenths is the probability of obtaining a white ball in one trial. This illustrates the following definition of the probability of success in one trial:

If the relative frequency of successes approaches a limit when the trial is repeated indefinitely under the same set of circumstances, this limit is called the probability of success in one trial.

Since the sum of the relative frequency of successes and of failures is 1, it readily follows that *the sum of the probability of success and of failure is* 1.

In framing this definition we idealize our actual experience. We say the probability that a penny will fall "heads up" is one half. This may be looked upon as an answer to the following question: What should we expect in the long run for the ratio of the number of heads to the total number of pennies tossed?

When applying the above definition of probability, a question very naturally arises about the meaning of the expression, "the same set of circumstances"; for we may in a sense question whether two or more dice could be tossed under the same circumstances, or again whether two or more men of the same age could live under the same set of circumstances. Without taking the space to discuss at length this question, some light may be thrown on it by saying that the expression implies the absence of specific differences. For example, since we can specify the difference between loaded dice and unloaded dice, between healthy and diseased men, between old and young men, we do not include two such kinds in the same group.

172. Approximate Probability Derived from Observation

After we have obtained a relative frequency of successes m/n in n trials (n a large number); then in the absence of further knowledge, it is usually assumed that $\dfrac{m}{n}$ *is a good estimate of probability of success in a given trial and that confidence in this estimate increases as n increases.*

Such estimates of probability are of much practical value in insurance and statistics. For example, if we observe 80,000 men of a well-defined class, say of age 30, and find that 480 deaths occurred during the year, we give, $\dfrac{480}{80,000} = .006$ as an estimate of probability that a man of this class will die within a year.

173. Probability Derived from an Analysis into Equally Likely Ways

In certain cases, notably in games of chance, the probability may be obtained by an analysis of all trials into a certain number of equally likely ways. For example, consider the case of a bag containing three white and seven black balls. What is the probability that a ball to be drawn will be white? To answer this question, we may analyze all possible drawings into 10 equally likely cases of which three will give white balls. We give 3/10 as the probability of drawing a white ball. This simple case illustrates the following process of arriving at a probability:

If all the successes and failures can be analyzed into r + s possible ways each of which is equally likely; and if r of these ways give successes, and s of them failures, the probability of success in a single trial is $\dfrac{r}{r + s}$ *and the probability of failure in the trial is* $\dfrac{s}{r + s}.$

In this connection, the fact should not be overlooked that the ways were assumed to be "equally likely." To illustrate the need of precaution in this matter, consider the following

Example. What is the probability that a man, A, in good health will die within the next 24 hours?

We might argue that the event can happen in only one way and fail in only one way, and that the probability that A will die in the next 24 hours is therefore $\dfrac{1}{2}.$ What is the flaw in this argument?

The expression "equally likely" indicates that we have no more reason to expect the event to take place in one way than in any other.

In the above analysis into equally likely ways, the **odds** are said to be r to s in favor of the event if $r > s$, r to s against it if $r < s$, **even** if $r = s$.

ORAL EXERCISES

1. What is the probability that a coin tossed at random will fall "heads up"?

2. What is the probability of obtaining an ace in throwing a single die?

3. If the probability of losing a game is 0.55, what is the probability of winning it?

4. From a class of 25 students of whom 10 are girls, one student is to be selected by lot. What is the probability that a girl will be selected?

5. Out of 40 children born in a village in a given year, 22 were boys and 18 were girls. What is the relative frequency of girls among the children born in the village in the year?

6. The odds are even that A will win a game. What is the probability that he will win it?

174. Mathematical Expectation of Money

If p is the probability that a person will win a sum of **money** m, we may define his **mathematical expectation** as pm.

175. Expected Number of Occurrences

The **expected number of occurrences** of an event in n trials is defined to be np, where p is the probability of occurrence of the event in a single trial. It is an immediate and useful consequence of this definition that the probability of occurrence of an event is the ratio, $\dfrac{np}{n} = p$, of the expected number of occurrences to the number of trials.

PROBLEMS

1. A bag contains 3 white balls, 2 red balls, and 4 black balls. What is the probability that a ball drawn at random will be white? Will be red? Will be black? Will be either black or red?

2. If the odds are 4 to 3 in favor of a man winning a prize of $50, find (a) his probability of winning, and (b) his mathematical expectation.

3. In a lottery, the prize is $25 and 250 tickets have been issued What is the mathematical expectation of a man with 20 tickets?

4. It is suggested that each student in the class throw a coin at random 50 times and record the number of heads. Combine the results for the class and find the relative frequency of heads. Compare the result with the probability, $\frac{1}{2}$, of throwing a head with a single coin.

5. Six coins are tossed. What is the probability that exactly two of them are heads?

Solution: Since each coin can fall in two ways, the six can fall in $2^6 = 64$ ways. The two coins can be selected from the six in $C(6, 2) = 15$ ways. Hence the probability is $\frac{15}{64}$.

6. From a bag containing 8 white balls and 4 black balls, 2 balls are drawn at random. Find the probability that (a) both are white; (b) one is black and one is white; (c) both are black.

7. From 12 men and 6 women a committee of 5 is chosen by lot. Find the probability that the committee will consist of 3 men and 2 women.

8. At a bridge party attended by four married couples, each man is to be assigned a woman partner chosen by lot. Find the probability that each man will draw his own wife as a partner.

9. From a deck of 52 playing cards, 5 cards are drawn at random. What is the probability that 2 aces and 3 kings will be drawn?

10. From a deck of 52 playing cards, what is the probability of drawing 5 spades at random?

11. What is the probability of throwing a seven in a single throw of two dice?

12. If the probability of death within one year of a man aged 24 is 0.008, what would be the expected number of deaths within a year among 50,000 such men?

13. According to the "American Experience Table of Mortality" (constructed in 1868 when relatively little experience was available on insured lives in America), out of 89,032 persons living at age 25, there are 57,917 who reach age 60. From these data, estimate, correct to three significant figures, the probability that a man aged 25 would not live to reach age 60.

14. According to the "American Men Mortality Table" (constructed from an immense number of insured lives in the United States and Canada exposed to risk between January 1, 1900 and January 1, 1915), out of 96,203 men living at age 25, there are 69,555 who reach age 60. From these data, estimate, correct to three significant figures, the probability that a man aged 25 would not live to reach age 60. Compare this result with that derived from the older table in problem 13.

15. According to the "Commissioners 1941 Standard Ordinary Table of Mortality" (compiled from mortality experience between 1930 and 1940 by a committee of the National Association of Insurance Commissioners), out of 939,197 persons alive at age 25, there are 677,771 who reach age 60. From these data, estimate, correct to three significant figures, the probability that a man aged 25 would not live to reach age 60. Compare this result with those derived in problems 13 and 14.

176. Theorems of Total and Compound Probability

Consider the questions: What is the probability of throwing either an ace or a deuce in a single throw with a die? What is the probability of throwing two aces in a single throw with two dice? The first question belongs to a class of questions answered by applications of a proposition called the theorem of total probability, the second to a class answered by applications of a proposition called the theorem of compound probability.

Let E_1, E_2, $\cdots$, E_r be a set of r events whose probabilities of occurrence in any single trial are p_1, p_2, $\cdots$, p_r respectively. The expected number of occurrences (Art. **175**) of the several events in n trials is np_1, np_2, $\cdots$, np_r respectively.

Exclusive events. The events of a set are said to be **mutually exclusive** when the occurrence of any one of them in a trial excludes the occurrence of any other in that trial. Thus, the throwing of an ace and a deuce with a single die are mutually exclusive events.

When the events E_1, E_2, $\cdots$, E_r are mutually exclusive, the expected number of occurrences for the total set of r events in n trials is

$$np_1 + np_2 + \cdots + np_r, \tag{1}$$

the sum of the expected values for the separate events.

Since the total probability P for an occurrence is the ratio of the expected number of occurrences (Art. **175**) for the whole set to the number of trials, we have

$$P = \frac{np_1 + np_2 + \cdots + np_r}{n} = p_1 + p_2 + \cdots + p_r, \qquad (2)$$

which may be stated as the

Theorem of total probability. *The probability that some one or other of a set of mutually exclusive events will happen in a single trial is the sum of the probabilities for the separate events.*

Thus, the probability of throwing either an ace or a deuce with one die is $\frac{1}{6} + \frac{1}{6} = \frac{1}{3}$.

Independent events. The events of a set are said to be **mutually independent** or **dependent** according as the occurrence of one of them does not or does affect the probability of occurrence of others in the set.

In n trials, where n is a large number, the expected number of occurrences of event E_1 is np_1 (Art. **175**). Out of this number, np_1, the expected number of occurrences of event E_2 is $p_2(np_1) = np_1p_2$. That is, both are expected to occur np_1p_2 times in the n trials. Continuing this process, the expected number of occurrences of all of the r events is

$$np_1p_2 \cdots p_r.$$

Then from Article **175,** the probability, P, that all of the r events will happen in one trial is the ratio

$$P = \frac{np_1p_2 \cdots p_r}{n} = p_1p_2 \cdots p_r,$$

which may be stated as the

Theorem of compound probability for independent events. *The probability that all of a set of independent events will occur on a given occasion when all of them are in question is the product of their separate probabilities.*

Thus, the probability of throwing two aces in a single throw with two dice is $\frac{1}{6} \cdot \frac{1}{6} = \frac{1}{36}$.

Theorem for dependent events. *If the probability of a first event is p_1, and if, after this has happened, the probability of a second event* *is p_2; then the probability that both events will happen in the order stated is p_1p_2. The extension to any number of events is obvious.*

PROBLEMS

1. If three coins are tossed, what is the probability of either three heads or three tails?

2. If three coins are tossed, what is the probability of exactly one head and two tails?

3. If three coins are tossed, what is the probability of at least two heads?

4. A bag contains 6 white, 4 red, and 2 black balls. A ball is drawn. What is the probability that it is either white or red?

5. Two dice are thrown once. What is the probability of two aces? An ace and a deuce?

6. A die is thrown twice. What is the probability of throwing two aces? An ace and then a deuce?

7. The probability that A will win a game is $\frac{3}{7}$, and the probability that B will win another independent game is $\frac{2}{5}$. Find the probability that both will win. What is the probability that either A or B but not both will win?

8. Find the probability of drawing a white ball and then a black ball in succession from a bag containing 6 white and 4 black balls, if the first ball is not replaced before the second drawing is made. What is the probability of drawing a white and then a black ball from the bag if the first ball is replaced before the second drawing is made?

9. If the probability is 0.188 that the height of a man selected at random from a certain group is between 5 feet 8 inches and 5 feet 9 inches and if the probability is 0.181 that his height is between 5 feet 9 inches and 5 feet 10 inches, what is the probability that a man selected at random from this group is between 5 feet 8 inches and 5 feet 10 inches?

10. A bag contains six balls marked 1, 2, 3, 4, 5, 6. A ball is drawn and not replaced, then a second ball is drawn and not replaced, and finally a third ball is drawn. Find the probability that the balls drawn bear the numbers 1, 2, 3 in some order.

11. Solve problem 10, assuming the ball drawn is replaced before the next drawing is made.

12. A purse contains 9 coins consisting of 4 dimes, 3 quarters, and 2 half dollars. If a coin is drawn from the purse, what is the probability of its being either a dime or a half dollar? Do you think one is just as likely to draw a dime as a half dollar?

177. Repeated Trials

If p is the probability that an event will happen in any single trial, then $C(n, r)p^r q^{n-r}$ is the probability that this event will happen exactly r times in n trials, where $q = 1 - p$ is the probability that the event will fail in any single trial.

For, the probability that it will happen in each of r specified trials and fail in all the remaining $n - r$ trials is $p^r q^{n-r}$ (Art. **176**), and r trials can be selected from n trials in $C(n, r)$ ways. These ways being mutually exclusive, we have by Article **176**, that the probability in question is

$$C(n, r)p^r q^{n-r}.$$

It will be observed that $C(n, r)p^r q^{n-r}$ is the $(n - r + 1)$th term of the binomial expansion of $(p + q)^n$.

Illustration: A die is thrown three times. What is the probability of obtaining exactly two aces?

Solution: The probability, given by the second term of the binomial expansion $\left(\dfrac{1}{6} + \dfrac{5}{6}\right)^3$, is $\dfrac{5}{72}$.

We next inquire into the probability that an event such as is described above happens at least r times in n trials. The event happens *at least r* times if it happens exactly $n, n - 1, n - 2, \cdots,$ or r times in n trials.

Hence, we have the following

THEOREM. *The probability that an event will happen at least r times in n trials is $p^n + C(n, \ n - 1)p^{n-1}q + C(n, \ n - 2)p^{n-2}q^2 + \cdots + C(n, r)p^r q^{n-r}$.*

This expression is the first $n - r + 1$ terms of the binomial expansion of $(p + q)^n$.

Illustration: A die is thrown three times. What is the probability of obtaining at least two aces?

Solution: The probability, given by the sum of the first and second terms of the expansion $\left(\dfrac{1}{6} + \dfrac{5}{6}\right)^3$, is $\dfrac{2}{27}$.

PROBLEMS

1. A coin is tossed five times. What is the probability that heads appear exactly three times? What is the probability that heads appear at least three times?

2. Five coins are tossed once. What is the probability that exactly three heads appear? What is the probability that at least three heads appear? Compare your results with those of problem 1.

3. What is the probability of throwing either a 7 or an 11 with a single throw of two dice?

4. In tossing eight coins, what is the probability for each of the following number of heads: (*a*) eight; (*b*) seven; (*c*) six; (*d*) five; (*e*) four; (*f*) three; (*g*) two; (*h*) one; (*i*) zero?

In 256 trials, each of which consists in tossing eight coins, what is the expected number of occurrences of (*a*) eight heads; (*b*) seven heads; (*c*) six heads; (*d*) five heads; (*e*) four heads; (*f*) three heads; (*g*) two heads; (*h*) one head; (*i*) no heads?

5. In teams of two students, throw eight coins and make a mark in a scheme such as the following to score the number of heads:

8 heads . . .	3 heads . . .
7 heads . . .	2 heads . . .
6 heads . . .	1 head . . .
5 heads . . .	0 heads . . .
4 heads . . .	

Continue the experiment until you have secured 256 tossings of the eight coins. With what frequencies did you get 8 heads, 7 heads, 6 heads, and so on, out of a total of 256 tossings? Discuss the deviations of the experimental results from the corresponding results of problem 4.

6. A coin is tossed seven times. (*a*) What is the probability of an even number of heads? (*b*) What is the probability of four heads appearing? (*c*) What is the probability of a head appearing on the first, third, fifth, and seventh toss?

7. A bag contains 5 red and 4 white balls. If 4 balls are drawn one at a time and not replaced, find the probability that they are alternately of different colors.

8. Solve problem 7, if after each drawing the ball is replaced.

9. If the odds are 3 to 2 that a man will win a certain game when he plays, find the probability that in a sequence of 6 games he will win (a) exactly half the games; (b) at least half the games; (c) at most half the games.

10. If q be the probability of failure in a single trial, show that $1 - q^n$ is the probability of at least one success in n trials.

11. Find the probability of heads occurring at least once in tossing a coin ten times.

12. Find the probability of throwing a six with a single die at least once in six trials.

13. An Italian nobleman, interested in gambling, had noticed, by continued observation of a game with three dice, that the sum 10 appeared more often than the sum 9. He expressed his surprise at this to Galileo and asked for an explanation. Find the probability of (a) the sum 10, (b) the sum 9, and explain the difficulty of the nobleman.

14. Which is the greater, the probability of throwing at least one ace in six trials of throwing a die, or the probability of throwing at least one head in two tosses of a coin?

15. A machinist works 300 days in a year. If the probability of his meeting with an accident on any particular day is 0.001, show that the probability of his entirely escaping injury during a year is approximately 0.75.

20 DETERMINANTS

178. Extension of the Determinant Notation

Determinants of the second and third orders were used in Chapter 6 in the solution of systems of linear equations in two and three variables; and a determinant of the second order was so defined that the pair of values

$$x = \frac{\begin{vmatrix} c_1 & b_1 \\ c_2 & b_2 \end{vmatrix}}{\begin{vmatrix} a_1 & b_1 \\ a_2 & b_2 \end{vmatrix}}, \qquad y = \frac{\begin{vmatrix} a_1 & c_1 \\ a_2 & c_2 \end{vmatrix}}{\begin{vmatrix} a_1 & b_1 \\ a_2 & b_2 \end{vmatrix}} \qquad (1)$$

satisfies the system of equations,

$$a_1 x + b_1 y = c_1,$$
$$a_2 x + b_2 y = c_2,$$

provided
$$\begin{vmatrix} a_1 & b_1 \\ a_2 & b_2 \end{vmatrix} \neq 0. \qquad (2)$$

Analogously, a determinant of the third order was so defined that the set of values

$$x = \frac{\begin{vmatrix} d_1 & b_1 & c_1 \\ d_2 & b_2 & c_2 \\ d_3 & b_3 & c_3 \end{vmatrix}}{\begin{vmatrix} a_1 & b_1 & c_1 \\ a_2 & b_2 & c_2 \\ a_3 & b_3 & c_3 \end{vmatrix}}, \quad y = \frac{\begin{vmatrix} a_1 & d_1 & c_1 \\ a_2 & d_2 & c_2 \\ a_3 & d_3 & c_3 \end{vmatrix}}{\begin{vmatrix} a_1 & b_1 & c_1 \\ a_2 & b_2 & c_2 \\ a_3 & b_3 & c_3 \end{vmatrix}}, \quad z = \frac{\begin{vmatrix} a_1 & b_1 & d_1 \\ a_2 & b_2 & d_2 \\ a_3 & b_3 & d_3 \end{vmatrix}}{\begin{vmatrix} a_1 & b_1 & c_1 \\ a_2 & b_2 & c_2 \\ a_3 & b_3 & c_3 \end{vmatrix}} \qquad (3)$$

satisfies the system of equations

$$a_1x + b_1y + c_1z = d_1,$$
$$a_2x + b_2y + c_2z = d_2,$$
$$a_3x + b_3y + c_3z = d_3,$$

provided
$$\begin{vmatrix} a_1 & b_1 & c_1 \\ a_2 & b_2 & c_2 \\ a_3 & b_3 & c_3 \end{vmatrix} \neq 0. \tag{4}$$

The determinant notation is extended in the present chapter to the solution of systems of linear equations containing more than three variables, and to certain problems of elimination.

It will be observed that each term in the expansions,

$$\begin{vmatrix} a_1 & b_1 \\ a_2 & b_2 \end{vmatrix} = a_1b_2 - a_2b_1, \tag{5}$$

$$\begin{vmatrix} a_1 & b_1 & c_1 \\ a_2 & b_2 & c_2 \\ a_3 & b_3 & c_3 \end{vmatrix} = a_1b_2c_3 + a_2b_3c_1 + a_3b_1c_2 - a_3b_2c_1 - a_2b_1c_3 - a_1b_3c_2, \tag{6}$$

of determinants of orders 2 and 3 respectively, consists (except for sign) of the product formed by taking one and only one element from each row and column. This fact suggests the extension of determinants to represent certain expressions in n^2 elements by means of an array,

$$\begin{vmatrix} a_1 & b_1 & c_1 & d_1 & \cdots & l_1 \\ a_2 & b_2 & c_2 & d_2 & \cdots & l_2 \\ a_3 & b_3 & c_3 & d_3 & \cdots & l_3 \\ a_4 & b_4 & c_4 & d_4 & \cdots & l_4 \\ \cdot & \cdot & \cdot & \cdot & \cdot & \\ a_n & b_n & c_n & d_n & \cdots & l_n \end{vmatrix} \tag{7}$$

where the expansion is to consist of terms which are products formed by taking one and only one element from each row and column, and where the signs of terms are to be consistent with the special cases of $n = 2$ and $n = 3$ (Art. **178**).

A square array such as (7) is called a determinant of the nth order. The diagonal from the upper left-hand to the lower right-hand corner of the square array is called the **principal diagonal** of the determinant, and the product, $a_1b_2c_3 \cdots l_n$, of the n numbers in this diagonal is called the **principal term** of the determinant.

179. Meaning of a Determinant.

In order to give the meaning of a determinant, we introduce the notion of an inversion. If, in an arrangement of positive integers, a greater precedes a less, there is said to be an **inversion**. Thus, in the order 12543, there are three inversions: 5 before 4, 5 before 3, 4 before 3. In 2341576, there are four inversions. When applied to any term in the expansion of a determinant such as (7), we say there is an inversion if the order of the subscripts presents an inversion when the letters (apart from subscripts) have the order $abcd \cdots l$ of the principal diagonal. With respect to determinants of orders 2 and 3, it may be observed that the number of inversions is even when the term is positive, and that the number of inversions is odd when the term is negative.

Consistent with these conditions, we lay down the following

DEFINITION. *A square array of n^2 elements is called a* **determinant of the nth order.** *It is an abbreviation for the algebraic sum of all the products that can be formed*

(1) *by taking as factors one and only one element from each column and each row of the array, and*

(2) *by giving to each term a positive or a negative sign according as the number of inversions of the subscripts of the term is even or odd, when the letters have the same order as in the principal diagonal.*

It may be added that if in any case the number of inversions in the principal diagonal is different from zero, the sign of a term is + or − according as the number of inversions in its subscripts differs from the number in the principal diagonal by an even or odd number. Since the subscripts fix the signs of terms, it may appear necessary to carry subscripts along in any numerical case, but we shall derive other modes of expansion (Arts. **180, 181**) which make this unnecessary. We shall, in general, use the Greek letter Δ to represent a determinant.

THEOREM. *The expansion of a determinant Δ of order n contains $n!$ terms.*

Since the number of terms is the same as the number of permutations of the subscripts $1, 2, 3, \cdots, n$, the number is $n!$ (Art. **164**).

ORAL EXERCISES

How many inversions are there in each of the following arrangements?

1. 1432.   **3.** 24135.   **5.** 14253768.
2. 4321.   **4.** 31452.   **6.** 15243867.

180. Useful Properties of Determinants

The following theorems embody useful properties of determinants.

THEOREM I. *If in a determinant* Δ *corresponding rows and columns are interchanged, the expansion is unchanged.*

Thus, if $\quad \Delta = \begin{vmatrix} a_1 & b_1 & c_1 \\ a_2 & b_2 & c_2 \\ a_3 & b_3 & c_3 \end{vmatrix}$ and $\Delta' = \begin{vmatrix} a_1 & a_2 & a_3 \\ b_1 & b_2 & b_3 \\ c_1 & c_2 & c_3 \end{vmatrix}$,

then $\Delta = \Delta'$.

The expansion of Δ will contain terms with the letters in natural order but with possible inversion of the subscripts. The expansion of Δ' will contain terms with the subscripts in natural order but with possible inversion of the letters.

Consider the term, $a_3 b_1 c_2$, in the expansion of Δ and the corresponding term, $b_1 c_2 a_3$, in the expansion of Δ'. The number of inversions on the subscripts in the first case is the same as the number of inversions of the letters from their natural order in the second case.

Interchanging two adjacent columns of a determinant will simply interchange two adjacent subscripts in each term of the expansion. This will change the sign of every term in the expansion. The number of adjacent interchanges necessary to bring the subscripts of any term into their natural order is the same as the number of adjacent interchanges introduced on the letters, since every adjacent interchange of subscripts introduces an interchange of letters. Hence, the signs of the terms in the expansion of Δ are the same as the signs of the corresponding terms in the expansion of Δ'. These statements hold for determinants of any order.

THEOREM II. *If two rows (or columns) of a determinant* Δ *are interchanged, the sign of the determinant is changed.*

Let us take for simplicity a determinant of the third order, but the argument used will clearly apply to any determinant. Thus,

$$\begin{vmatrix} a_1 & b_1 & c_1 \\ a_2 & b_2 & c_2 \\ a_3 & b_3 & c_3 \end{vmatrix} = - \begin{vmatrix} a_3 & b_3 & c_3 \\ a_2 & b_2 & c_2 \\ a_1 & b_1 & c_1 \end{vmatrix}.$$

In the first place, interchanging two adjacent rows will simply interchange two adjacent subscripts in each term of the expansion. This will change the sign of every term of the expansion. Consider next the effect of interchanging any two rows (or columns) separated by m intermediate rows. The lower row can be brought just below the upper one by m interchanges of adjacent rows. To bring likewise the upper row into the original position of the lower row, $m + 1$ further interchanges are necessary. Hence, interchanging the two rows in question is equivalent to $2m + 1$ interchanges of adjacent rows. Since $2m + 1$ is an odd number, this process changes the sign of the determinant.

THEOREM III. *If a determinant Δ has two rows (or columns) identical, its value is zero.*

If we interchange two rows, we obtain, by Theorem II, $-\Delta$. But since the interchange of two identical rows does not alter the determinant we have $\qquad \Delta = -\Delta,$

that is, $\qquad\qquad\qquad 2\Delta = 0,$

or $\qquad\qquad\qquad\qquad \Delta = 0.$

THEOREM IV. *If all the elements of a row (or column) of Δ are multiplied by the same number m the determinant is multiplied by m.*

For, one element from the column multiplied by m must enter into each term of the expansion of Δ.

THEOREM V. *If one row (or column) of Δ has as elements the sum of two or more numbers, Δ can be written as the sum of two or more determinants.* That is,

$$\Delta = \begin{vmatrix} a_1 + a_1' + a_1'' & b_1 & c_1 \\ a_2 + a_2' + a_2'' & b_2 & c_2 \\ a_3 + a_3' + a_3'' & b_3 & c_3 \end{vmatrix} = \begin{vmatrix} a_1 & b_1 & c_1 \\ a_2 & b_2 & c_2 \\ a_3 & b_3 & c_3 \end{vmatrix} + \begin{vmatrix} a_1' & b_1 & c_1 \\ a_2' & b_2 & c_2 \\ a_3' & b_3 & c_3 \end{vmatrix} + \begin{vmatrix} a_1'' & b_1 & c_1 \\ a_2'' & b_2 & c_2 \\ a_3'' & b_3 & c_3 \end{vmatrix}.$$

This theorem is evident for this special case, since each term in the expansion of Δ is evidently equal to the sum of the corresponding terms of the three determinants. Similarly, we can prove the general case.

THEOREM VI. *The value of any determinant Δ is not changed if each element of any row (or column), or each element multiplied by any given number, m, be added to the corresponding element of any other row (or column).*

By Theorems IV and V,

$$\begin{vmatrix} a_1 + ma_3 & a_2 & a_3 \\ b_1 + mb_3 & b_2 & b_3 \\ c_1 + mc_3 & c_2 & c_3 \end{vmatrix} = \begin{vmatrix} a_1 & a_2 & a_3 \\ b_1 & b_2 & b_3 \\ c_1 & c_2 & c_3 \end{vmatrix} + m * \begin{vmatrix} a_3 & a_2 & a_3 \\ b_3 & b_2 & b_3 \\ c_3 & c_2 & c_3 \end{vmatrix},$$

$$= \begin{vmatrix} a_1 & a_2 & a_3 \\ b_1 & b_2 & b_3 \\ c_1 & c_2 & c_3 \end{vmatrix} + 0, \text{ by Theorem III.}$$

Likewise, the theorem can be proved for a determinant of any order.

The theorems of this article can often be used to good advantage in the simplification and evaluation of determinants.

Illustration 1.   Evaluate $\begin{vmatrix} 20 & 17 & 2 \\ 15 & 12 & 8 \\ 25 & 22 & -6 \end{vmatrix}$.

Solution: Factor out 5 from the first column, and 2 from the third and we have $5 \cdot 2 \begin{vmatrix} 4 & 17 & 1 \\ 3 & 12 & 4 \\ 5 & 22 & -3 \end{vmatrix}$ (Theor. IV)

Next, subtract 4 times the first column from the second and we have $5 \cdot 2 \begin{vmatrix} 4 & 1 & 1 \\ 3 & 0 & 4 \\ 5 & 2 & -3 \end{vmatrix}$ (Theor. VI).

Subtract the second column from the first and factor 3 out of the resulting first column and we have $5 \cdot 2 \cdot 3 \begin{vmatrix} 1 & 1 & 1 \\ 1 & 0 & 4 \\ 1 & 2 & -3 \end{vmatrix} = 30.$

Illustration 2.   Evaluate $\begin{vmatrix} a & b + c & 1 \\ b & a + c & 1 \\ c & a + b & 1 \end{vmatrix}$.

Solution: Add the first column to the second and we have

$$\begin{vmatrix} a & a+b+c & 1 \\ b & a+b+c & 1 \\ c & a+b+c & 1 \end{vmatrix} \qquad \text{(Theor. VI).}$$

Factor out $(a + b + c)$ from the second column and we have

$$(a+b+c) \begin{vmatrix} a & 1 & 1 \\ b & 1 & 1 \\ c & 1 & 1 \end{vmatrix} = 0 \qquad \text{(Theor. III)}$$

* This notation means that the determinant is multiplied by m.

EXERCISES

Find the value of each determinant.

1.
$$\begin{vmatrix} 6 & 4 & -6 \\ 6 & 5 & -5 \\ -3 & 0 & 6 \end{vmatrix}.$$

3.
$$\begin{vmatrix} -3 & 16 & 6 \\ 5 & -2 & -10 \\ 7 & 4 & -16 \end{vmatrix}.$$

2.
$$\begin{vmatrix} 0 & 1 & 1 & 1 \\ 1 & 0 & 2 & 2 \\ 1 & 2 & 0 & 3 \\ 1 & 2 & 3 & 0 \end{vmatrix}.$$

4.
$$\begin{vmatrix} 4 & 1 & -3 & 8 \\ -1 & 4 & 5 & 10 \\ 2 & 1 & -1 & -5 \\ 7 & 3 & -4 & 13 \end{vmatrix}.$$

181. Expansion by Minors

If we suppress both the row and column to which any element, say c_k, of the determinant belongs, the unsuppressed elements form a determinant called the first minor of c_k, which we shall denote by the capital letter C_k. Thus, in

$$\begin{vmatrix} a_1 & b_1 & c_1 \\ a_2 & b_2 & c_2 \\ a_3 & b_3 & c_3 \end{vmatrix},$$

the minor of b_2 is
$$\begin{vmatrix} a_1 & c_1 \\ a_3 & c_3 \end{vmatrix}.$$

A determinant Δ may be expressed in terms of the elements $c_1, c_2, \cdots, c_n$ of a column (or row) and their first minors as follows:

1. *Form the product of each element such as c_k in the column by the corresponding minor C_k.*

2. *Give each of the products thus formed a positive or a negative sign according as the sum of the number of the row and the number of the column containing c_k is even or odd.*

3. *Take the algebraic sum of these results. This sum is equal to Δ.*

Thus,
$$\begin{vmatrix} a_1 & b_1 & c_1 \\ a_2 & b_2 & c_2 \\ a_3 & b_3 & c_3 \end{vmatrix} = a_1 \begin{vmatrix} b_2 & c_2 \\ b_3 & c_3 \end{vmatrix} - a_2 \begin{vmatrix} b_1 & c_1 \\ b_3 & c_3 \end{vmatrix} + a_3 \begin{vmatrix} b_1 & c_1 \\ b_2 & c_2 \end{vmatrix}.$$

If we can establish this theorem, we have a systematic method for expanding any determinant, since the first minors of Δ are again determinants which can be expressed in terms of their own minors. This process can be continued until we have the expansion of Δ.

The proof of the theorem follows:

Part I. The terms in the expansion of Δ can be separated into n groups, the first having the factor a_1, the second the factor a_2, and so on. The coefficient of a_1 contains a term for each permutation of the numbers 2, 3, 4, $\cdots$, n, and hence is the expansion of a determinant A_1 which is the first minor of a_1. The signs of the terms are not changed by prefixing the factor a_1 since no inversion of the subscripts results.

The coefficient of a_2 contains a term for each permutation of the numbers 1, 3, 4, $\cdots$, n and hence is the expansion of the determinant A_2 which is the first minor of a_2. By prefixing the factor a_2, one inversion of the subscripts results in each term and hence the terms of Δ containing a_2 as a factor are given by $-a_2A_2$.

If the same argument is continued, we reach the conclusion that

$$\Delta = a_1A_1 - a_2A_2 + a_3A_3 - a_4A_4 + \cdots + (-1)^{n+1}a_nA_n.$$

Part II. Next we shall prove that we shall get the same value for Δ if we multiply each element of the kth column by its minor, affix the proper sign, and add.

Suppose the elements in the kth columm are e_1, e_2, $\cdots$, e_n. By successive interchanges of this column with each column preceding it, the column e_1, e_2, $\cdots$, e_n may be moved to the left until it is the first column in the determinant, and all the remaining columns will retain the same relative positions.

$$\begin{vmatrix} e_1 & a_1 & b_1 & c_1 \cdots l_1 \\ e_2 & a_2 & b_2 & c_2 \cdots l_2 \\ \cdot & \cdot & \cdot & \cdot \\ \cdot & \cdot & \cdot & \cdot \\ \cdot & \cdot & \cdot & \cdot \\ e_n & a_n & b_n & c_n \cdots l_n \end{vmatrix}$$

Call this determinant Δ'. By Theorem II (Art. **180**),

$$\Delta' = (-1)^{k-1}\Delta,$$
or
$$\Delta = (-1)^{k+1}\Delta'.$$

By part I of this proof,

$$\Delta' = e_1E_1 - e_2E_2 + e_3E_3 - e_4E_4 + \cdots + (-1)^{n+1}e_nE_n.$$

Hence,

$$\Delta = (-1)^{k+1}e_1E_1 + (-1)^{k+2}e_2E_2 + \cdots + (-1)^{k+n}e_nE_n.$$

Part III. By Theorem I (Art. **180**), the value of Δ is not changed if the rows and columns of the determinant are interchanged. Hence, all that has been said above about expanding Δ by going down a column applies equally to going across a row.

EXERCISES

1. Expand the following determinant by multiplying each element in the first row by its first minor. Then expand by multiplying each element in the third column by its first minor. The results should verify the theorem of Article **181.**

$$\begin{vmatrix} 1 & 0 & 3 & 1 \\ 1 & -4 & 0 & 1 \\ 2 & 3 & 1 & 1 \\ 1 & 2 & 2 & -1 \end{vmatrix}.$$

Use the theorems of Article **180** to reduce all the elements except one in some row or column to zero and then expand.

2.
$$\begin{vmatrix} 1 & 2 & 0 & 1 \\ 3 & 4 & -1 & 2 \\ 1 & 1 & 2 & 1 \\ 2 & 1 & 3 & 1 \end{vmatrix}.$$

Solution: Add twice the second row to the third and three times the second row to the fourth and get

$$\begin{vmatrix} 1 & 2 & 0 & 1 \\ 3 & 4 & -1 & 2 \\ 7 & 9 & 0 & 5 \\ 11 & 13 & 0 & 7 \end{vmatrix} = \begin{vmatrix} 1 & 2 & 1 \\ 7 & 9 & 5 \\ 11 & 13 & 7 \end{vmatrix}.$$

If, in this third-ordered determinant, twice the first column is subtracted from the second column and the first column is subtracted from the third, we have

$$\begin{vmatrix} 1 & 0 & 0 \\ 7 & -5 & -2 \\ 11 & -9 & -4 \end{vmatrix} = \begin{vmatrix} 5 & 2 \\ 9 & 4 \end{vmatrix} = 20 - 18 = 2.$$

3.
$$\begin{vmatrix} -4 & 3 & 2 & 3 \\ -3 & 0 & -1 & 2 \\ 1 & 2 & 0 & 1 \\ 1 & 1 & 0 & -3 \end{vmatrix}.$$

4.
$$\begin{vmatrix} 2 & 7 & 6 & 5 \\ 6 & 5 & 7 & 4 \\ 1 & 1 & 7 & 3 \\ 4 & 3 & 5 & 1 \end{vmatrix}.$$

5. $\begin{vmatrix} 1 & 2 & 3 & -3 \\ 2 & 1 & 3 & 4 \\ -5 & 7 & 2 & 6 \\ 4 & -3 & -9 & 7 \end{vmatrix}.$ **6.** $\begin{vmatrix} 2 & 0 & -3 & 4 \\ 9 & -2 & 5 & 8 \\ 3 & 3 & -3 & 5 \\ -4 & 7 & 2 & -3 \end{vmatrix}.$

7. Show that $\Delta = \begin{vmatrix} 1 & 1 & 1 \\ a & b & c \\ a^2 & b^2 & c^2 \end{vmatrix} = (a-b)(b-c)(c-a).$

Hint: When $a = b$, two columns are identical so that Δ vanishes, and by the factor theorem, Article **113**, $a - b$ is a factor of Δ.

Factor each of the following determinants:

8. $\begin{vmatrix} 1 & a & b \\ 1 & a^2 & b^2 \\ 1 & a^3 & b^3 \end{vmatrix}.$ **9.** $\begin{vmatrix} a & b & c \\ a^2 & b^2 & c^2 \\ a^3 & b^3 & c^3 \end{vmatrix}.$ **10.** $\begin{vmatrix} a & a & a \\ a & b & b \\ a & b & c \end{vmatrix}.$

Expand.

11. $\begin{vmatrix} 0 & a & b \\ a & 0 & c \\ b & c & 0 \end{vmatrix}.$ **14.** $\begin{vmatrix} 1 & a & b \\ -a & 1 & c \\ -b & -c & 1 \end{vmatrix}.$

12. $\begin{vmatrix} 0 & a & b \\ -a & 0 & c \\ -b & -c & 0 \end{vmatrix}.$ **15.** $\begin{vmatrix} 0 & a & b & 1 \\ a & 0 & c & 1 \\ b & c & 0 & 1 \\ 1 & 1 & 1 & 0 \end{vmatrix}.$

13. $\begin{vmatrix} 1 & a & b \\ a & 1 & c \\ b & c & 1 \end{vmatrix}.$ **16.** $\begin{vmatrix} 1 & a & b & 1 \\ a & 1 & c & 1 \\ b & c & 1 & 1 \\ 1 & 1 & 1 & 1 \end{vmatrix}.$

182. A Vanishing Determinant

We shall now establish a theorem of determinants which is useful in performing the eliminations required in the solutions of equations in two or more variables.

THEOREM. *In expanding a determinant by minors with respect to a certain column (or row), if the elements of this column (or row) are replaced by the corresponding elements of some other column (or row), the resulting expression vanishes.*

For example, we have, by Article **181**,

$$\Delta = \begin{vmatrix} a_1 & b_1 & c_1 & d_1 \\ a_2 & b_2 & c_2 & d_2 \\ a_3 & b_3 & c_3 & d_3 \\ a_4 & b_4 & c_4 & d_4 \end{vmatrix} = a_1A_1 - a_2A_2 + a_3A_3 - a_4A_4.$$

We are to prove that

$$b_1A_1 - b_2A_2 + b_3A_3 - b_4A_4 = 0. \tag{1}$$

The left member of (1) is equal to the expansion of the determinant derived from Δ by replacing the column of a's by the b's with corresponding subscripts. But this gives a determinant with two columns identical, which therefore vanishes (Art. **180**, Theorem III). The same method of proof can manifestly be applied to a determinant of any order.

183. Systems of Linear Equations Containing the Same Number of Equations as Variables

In Chapter 6, we used determinants to express the solution of simultaneous equations containing two and three variables. We are now in a position to make use of determinants to solve a system of n linear equations of n variables.

For simplicity of notation, take $n = 4$, and consider the system of equations

$$a_1x + b_1y + c_1z + d_1w = k_1, \tag{1}$$
$$a_2x + b_2y + c_2z + d_2w = k_2, \tag{2}$$
$$a_3x + b_3y + c_3z + d_3w = k_3, \tag{3}$$
$$a_4x + b_4y + c_4z + d_4w = k_4, \tag{4}$$

to be solved for x, y, z, and w if a solution exists. It is convenient to call the determinant of the coefficients of the variables,

$$\Delta = \begin{vmatrix} a_1 & b_1 & c_1 & d_1 \\ a_2 & b_2 & c_2 & d_2 \\ a_3 & b_3 & c_3 & d_3 \\ a_4 & b_4 & c_4 & d_4 \end{vmatrix},$$

the *determinant of the system* of equations.

Case I. When $\Delta \neq 0$.

As above, let $A_1, A_2, \cdots, B_1, B_2, \cdots$ be the minors of $a_1, a_2, \cdots, b_1, b_2, \cdots$ respectively. Multiplying both members of (1), (2), (3), and (4) by A_1, $-A_2$, A_3, and $-A_4$, respectively, we obtain

$$A_1a_1x + A_1b_1y + A_1c_1z + A_1d_1w = \quad A_1k_1, \tag{5}$$
$$- A_2a_2x - A_2b_2y - A_2c_2z - A_2d_2w = - A_2k_2, \tag{6}$$
$$A_3a_3x + A_3b_3y + A_3c_3z + A_3d_3w = \quad A_3k_3, \tag{7}$$
$$- A_4a_4x - A_4b_4y - A_4c_4z - A_4d_4w = - A_4k_4. \tag{8}$$

Adding (5), (6), (7), (8), we obtain Δ for the coefficient of x (Art. **181**), and zero for coefficients of the other variables (Art. **182**). That is,

$$\Delta \cdot x = \quad A_1k_1 - A_2k_2 + A_3k_3 - A_4k_4. \tag{9}$$
Similarly, $$\Delta \cdot y = - B_1k_1 + B_2k_2 - B_3k_3 + B_4k_4, \tag{10}$$
$$\Delta \cdot z = \quad C_1k_1 - C_2k_2 + C_3k_3 - C_4k_4, \tag{11}$$
and $$\Delta \cdot w = - D_1k_1 + D_2k_2 - D_3k_3 + D_4k_4. \tag{12}$$

If, in Δ, we replace the a's by k's and expand, we have the right-hand member of (9). Similarly, replacing the b's, c's, and d's respectively by k's, we have the right-hand members of (10), (11), and (12). It follows that

$$x = \frac{\begin{vmatrix} k_1 & b_1 & c_1 & d_1 \\ k_2 & b_2 & c_2 & d_2 \\ k_3 & b_3 & c_3 & d_3 \\ k_4 & b_4 & c_4 & d_4 \end{vmatrix}}{\Delta}, \qquad y = \frac{\begin{vmatrix} a_1 & k_1 & c_1 & d_1 \\ a_2 & k_2 & c_2 & d_2 \\ a_3 & k_3 & c_3 & d_3 \\ a_4 & k_4 & c_4 & d_4 \end{vmatrix}}{\Delta}$$

$$z = \frac{\begin{vmatrix} a_1 & b_1 & k_1 & d_1 \\ a_2 & b_2 & k_2 & d_2 \\ a_3 & b_3 & k_3 & d_3 \\ a_4 & b_4 & k_4 & d_4 \end{vmatrix}}{\Delta}, \qquad w = \frac{\begin{vmatrix} a_1 & b_1 & c_1 & k_1 \\ a_2 & b_2 & c_2 & k_2 \\ a_3 & b_3 & c_3 & k_3 \\ a_4 & b_4 & c_4 & k_4 \end{vmatrix}}{\Delta}$$

is a solution, and the only solution, of (1), (2), (3), (4).

Hence, to obtain the solution of any system of n linear equations containing n variables when Δ, the determinant of the system, is not zero, we apply the

THEOREM. *Any variable is equal to a fraction (1) whose denominator is the determinant of the system, and (2) whose numerator is the determinant formed from the determinant of the system by substituting for the coefficients of the variable sought the corresponding constant terms with that sign attached to each constant term which it has when on the side of the equation opposite the variables.*

Case II. When $\Delta = 0$.

If a solution exists when $\Delta = 0$, it cannot take the preceding form, since division by zero is excluded from algebraic operations. While the theory becomes too complicated in this case to be presented in full here, certain particular cases may well be considered.

As a rule (subject to certain exceptions), a system of equations has no solution when $\Delta = 0$. For example, the system

$$3x + 4y = 5,$$
$$6x + 8y = 9$$

has no solution. Likewise the system

$$x + y - z = 5,$$
$$4x + y - 2z = 9,$$
$$5x + 2y - 3z = 1$$

has no solution.

A system may, however, have an infinite number of solutions when $\Delta = 0$. For instance, the equations

$$x + y - z = 0, \tag{13}$$
$$4x + y - 2z = 0, \tag{14}$$
$$5x + 2y - 3z = 0 \tag{15}$$

constitute such a system. These equations are manifestly satisfied by $x = y = z = 0$. This is called the **trivial solution**. To obtain other solutions solve (13) and (14) for x and y in terms of z. This gives

$$x = \frac{1}{3} z, \qquad y = \frac{2}{3} z. \tag{16}$$

These values of x and y satisfy (15) as well as (13) and (14). Hence any value assigned to z with the corresponding values x and y obtained from $x = \frac{1}{3} z$, $y = \frac{2}{3} z$ satisfies (13), (14), and (15). Since z may have any value, there is an infinite number of solutions of the system in question.

Systems with an infinite number of solutions may be more generally illustrated by the **homogeneous** * equations

$$a_1x + b_1y + c_1z = 0, \tag{17}$$
$$a_2x + b_2y + c_2z = 0, \tag{18}$$
$$a_3x + b_3y + c_3z = 0, \tag{19}$$

* A homogeneous equation is one in which all terms are of the same degree in the variables.

when $$\Delta = \begin{vmatrix} a_1 & b_1 & c_1 \\ a_2 & b_2 & c_2 \\ a_3 & b_3 & c_3 \end{vmatrix} = 0, \tag{20}$$

but some minor of Δ is not zero, say $\begin{vmatrix} a_1 & b_1 \\ a_2 & b_2 \end{vmatrix} \neq 0. \tag{21}$

To prove that (17), (18), (19) have an infinite number of solutions, substitute in (19) the values

$$x = \frac{\begin{vmatrix} -c_1z & b_1 \\ -c_2z & b_2 \end{vmatrix}}{\begin{vmatrix} a_1 & b_1 \\ a_2 & b_2 \end{vmatrix}}, \qquad y = \frac{\begin{vmatrix} a_1 & -c_1z \\ a_2 & -c_2z \end{vmatrix}}{\begin{vmatrix} a_1 & b_1 \\ a_2 & b_2 \end{vmatrix}},$$

which satisfy (17) and (18) when condition (21) is fulfilled. This substitution gives, after clearing of fractions,

$$-za_3 \begin{vmatrix} c_1 & b_1 \\ c_2 & b_2 \end{vmatrix} - zb_3 \begin{vmatrix} a_1 & c_1 \\ a_2 & c_2 \end{vmatrix} + zc_3 \begin{vmatrix} a_1 & b_1 \\ a_2 & b_2 \end{vmatrix} \equiv z \begin{vmatrix} a_1 & b_1 & c_1 \\ a_2 & b_2 & c_2 \\ a_3 & b_3 & c_3 \end{vmatrix},$$

which, by (20), vanishes whatever value be assigned to z. Hence, z can take an infinite number of values, each of which with the corresponding x and y satisfies (17), (18), and (19).

184. Systems of Equations Containing More Variables Than Equations

Consider first the single equation

$$3x + 5y - 6 = 0 \tag{1}$$

with two variables. It is clear from our work on graphs of equations (Art. **36**) that there are an infinite number of pairs of values of x and y which satisfy this equation.

Consider next the two equations,

$$3x - 4y - 2z + 1 = 0, \tag{2}$$
$$4x + 3y - z - 6 = 0 \tag{3}$$

with three variables.

We may solve (2) and (3) for x and y in terms of z. This gives

$$x = \frac{\begin{vmatrix} 2z-1 & -4 \\ z+6 & 3 \end{vmatrix}}{\begin{vmatrix} 3 & -4 \\ 4 & 3 \end{vmatrix}} = \frac{10z+21}{25}, \tag{4}$$

$$y = \frac{\begin{vmatrix} 3 & 2z - 1 \\ 4 & z + 6 \end{vmatrix}}{\begin{vmatrix} 3 & -4 \\ 4 & 3 \end{vmatrix}} = \frac{-5z + 22}{25}. \tag{5}$$

Any value assigned to z and the corresponding x and y obtained from (4) and (5) satisfy (2) and (3). Hence, the system has an infinite number of solutions.

The main point to be brought out by these illustrations is that, in general, from n equations containing more than n variables, we may solve (Art. **183**) for some selected n of the variables in terms of the remaining variables. We are then at liberty to assign any values to these remaining variables, and thus obtain an infinite number of solutions. The problem in the exceptional cases in which it is impossible to solve for a selected set of n variables is too complicated to be treated here.

185. Systems of Equations Containing Fewer Variables Than Equations. Elimination

In a system of n linear equations taken at random, with m variables, $m < n$, the equations are usually inconsistent, that is, the solution of m of the equations will not satisfy the remaining equations. However, under certain conditions, all of the n equations are consistent.*

ORAL EXERCISES

1. Give three linear equations in x and y that are inconsistent.
2. Give three linear equations in x and y that are consistent.

We shall restrict our discussion of systems containing fewer variables than equations to the important case in which the number of equations is one greater than the number of variables.

Consider the equations

$$a_1x + b_1y + c_1 = 0, \tag{1}$$
$$a_2x + b_2y + c_2 = 0, \tag{2}$$
$$a_3x + b_3y + c_3 = 0. \tag{3}$$

---

* Two or more equations are *consistent* (Art. **36**) when they have a common solution.

If these three equations are consistent in case $a_1 b_2 - a_2 b_1 \neq 0$, then

$$x = -\frac{\begin{vmatrix} c_1 & b_1 \\ c_2 & b_2 \end{vmatrix}}{\begin{vmatrix} a_1 & b_1 \\ a_2 & b_2 \end{vmatrix}}, \qquad y = -\frac{\begin{vmatrix} a_1 & c_1 \\ a_2 & c_2 \end{vmatrix}}{\begin{vmatrix} a_1 & b_1 \\ a_2 & b_2 \end{vmatrix}},$$

which satisfy (1) and (2) must satisfy (3). This requires that

$$-a_3 \frac{\begin{vmatrix} c_1 & b_1 \\ c_2 & b_2 \end{vmatrix}}{\begin{vmatrix} a_1 & b_1 \\ a_2 & b_2 \end{vmatrix}} - b_3 \frac{\begin{vmatrix} a_1 & c_1 \\ a_2 & c_2 \end{vmatrix}}{\begin{vmatrix} a_1 & b_1 \\ a_2 & b_2 \end{vmatrix}} + c_3 = 0.$$

Clearing of fractions, and interchanging columns in $\begin{vmatrix} c_1 & b_1 \\ c_2 & b_2 \end{vmatrix}$, we obtain

$$a_3 \begin{vmatrix} b_1 & c_1 \\ b_2 & c_2 \end{vmatrix} - b_3 \begin{vmatrix} a_1 & c_1 \\ a_2 & c_2 \end{vmatrix} + c_3 \begin{vmatrix} a_1 & b_1 \\ a_2 & b_2 \end{vmatrix} = 0,$$

or,

$$\begin{vmatrix} a_1 & b_1 & c_1 \\ a_2 & b_2 & c_2 \\ a_3 & b_3 & c_3 \end{vmatrix} = 0, \quad \text{(Art. 181)} \tag{4}$$

as a condition to be satisfied in order that equations (1), (2), and (3) be consistent. The variables x and y are eliminated, and the determinant in (4) is called the **eliminant** of the equations (1), (2), and (3). Stated in words, in order that three linear equations in two variables have a common solution, it is necessary that the eliminant of the system shall be equal to zero.

The method used for three linear equations in two variables can be extended to any number n of linear equations in $n-1$ variables. Thus, we have the

THEOREM. *The determinant (eliminant) formed of the coefficients of the variables and of the constant terms must vanish in order that the n equations in $n-1$ variables have a common solution.*

While the vanishing of the eliminant is a necessary condition for the existence of a common root, it is not a sufficient condition as is shown by the following example.

Take the system of equations

$$x + y - 4 = 0, \tag{5}$$
$$2x + 2y + 5 = 0, \tag{6}$$
$$x + y - 6 = 0. \tag{7}$$

Here,
$$\begin{vmatrix} 1 & 1 & -4 \\ 2 & 2 & 5 \\ 1 & 1 & -6 \end{vmatrix} = 0,$$

but any two of the equations are inconsistent.

In establishing the above necessary condition, we assumed that two of the equations have a solution. This condition is satisfied by no two of equations (5), (6), (7).

EXERCISES

Solve by using determinants.

1. $4x - 5y = 7,$
$3y - 7x = 23.$

2. $5x - y + 2z = 17,$
$2x + 3y - 8z + 23 = 0,$
$x + 11y + 3z = 0.$

3. $3x + 2y + 5z - w = 1,$
$4x - y + z + 2w = 3,$
$6x + 5y - 8z - 9w = 15,$
$5x + y - 3z - 10 = 0.$

4. $x + y + z + u + v = 6,$
$2x + 3z - v - 4 = 0,$
$2y + 3u + 3v - 8 = 0,$
$3x - 4y + 8u - 9 = 0,$
$4x + 6y - 2z + 3u + v = 0.$

5. Find a value of k such that

$$2x + 7y = 1,$$
$$x + y = k,$$
$$2x - ky = 11,$$

are consistent equations. Can k take more than one value? Find the solution of the system for each possible value of k.

6. By Article **185**, it follows that $\begin{vmatrix} a_1 & b_1 \\ a_2 & b_2 \end{vmatrix} = 0$ is a necessary condition that the two equations

$$a_1x + b_1 = 0, \quad (a_1 \neq 0)$$
$$a_2x + b_2 = 0, \quad (a_2 \neq 0)$$

be consistent. Show that this condition is also sufficient for this special case.

7. Discuss the number of values of x, y, z, which satisfy

$$2x + y + 3z = 0,$$
$$9x - 3y + z = 0,$$
$$x - 4y - 6z = 0,$$

and find the ratios $x : y : z$ of corresponding values apart from the trivial solution $x = y = z = 0$.

Prove each system of equations inconsistent or find a solution of the system.

8. $5x + 2y = \quad 4,$
$\quad 3x - 2y = \quad 12,$
$\quad\quad x + 2y = -3.$

9. $3x + 4y = 25,$
$\quad x + \quad y = \quad 7,$
$\quad x + 2y = \quad 8.$

10. $\quad x - \quad y + \quad z = \quad 6,$
$\quad 2x + 3y - \quad z = \quad 1,$
$\quad 3x + 2y + 4z = 15,$
$\quad\quad x + \quad y - \quad z = \quad 0.$

11. $\quad x + \quad y - \quad z = 0,$
$\quad 2x - 3y - 5z = 7,$
$\quad 3x + 2y + 2z = 8,$
$\quad 4x + 3y + 2z = 5.$

12. Eliminate x and y from the equations $y = m_1 x + b_1,$ $y = m_2 x + b_2,$ $y = m_3 x + b_3,$ and show that the eliminant is zero if $b_1 = b_2 = b_3.$

13. Discuss the solution of the system

$$2x + 3y + \quad z = \quad 4,$$
$$3x - \quad y + 2z = 13.$$

21 PARTIAL FRACTIONS

186. Introduction

Early in the study of algebra we added together algebraic fractions and found the sum to be a single fraction whose denominator is the lowest common multiple of the denominators. Thus,

$$\frac{6}{x+1} + \frac{2}{2x+3} = \frac{14x+20}{2x^2+5x+3}.$$

It is often necessary to perform the inverse operation, that is, to decompose a given fraction into a sum of other fractions (called "partial" fractions) having denominators of lower degree. Thus, it is easily shown that $\dfrac{2x}{x^2-1}$ can be decomposed into $\dfrac{1}{x+1} + \dfrac{1}{x-1}$.

An algebraic fraction is said to be **proper** when its numerator is of lower degree than its denominator. In this chapter it is necessary to consider only proper fractions; for if the degree of the numerator is not lower than that of the denominator, the fraction may be reduced by division to the sum of an integral part and a proper fraction. Thus,

$$\frac{3x^4 - 3x^2 + 2x}{x^2 - 1} = 3x^2 + \frac{2x}{x^2 - 1}.$$

We shall *assume* the possibility of decomposing any proper fraction whose denominator contains factors prime to each other into the partial fractions of the types

$$\frac{A}{ax+b}, \quad \frac{B}{(ax+b)^p}, \quad \frac{Cx+D}{ax^2+bx+c}, \quad \frac{Ex+F}{(ax^2+bx+c)^q}$$

306

where A, B, C, D, E, F, a, b, c are real numbers, p, q positive integers and $ax^2 + bx + c$ an expression without real linear factors.* With this assumption we shall show how to decompose certain classes of fractions.

187. Case I. *When the denominator can be resolved into factors of the first degree, all of which are real and different.*

Example. Resolve $\dfrac{1 - x + 6x^2}{x - x^3}$ into its simplest partial fractions.

The sum of three fractions

$$\frac{A}{x} + \frac{B}{1 - x} + \frac{C}{1 + x}$$

will give a fraction whose denominator is $x - x^3$. We, therefore, try to determine A, B, and C so that

$$\frac{1 - x + 6x^2}{x - x^3} \equiv \frac{A}{x} + \frac{B}{1 - x} + \frac{C}{1 + x}$$

$$\equiv \frac{A(1 - x)(1 + x) + Bx(1 + x) + Cx(1 - x)}{x(1 + x)(1 - x)}.$$

Then,

$$1 - x + 6x^2 \equiv A(1 - x)(1 + x) + Bx(1 + x) + Cx(1 - x). \quad (1)$$

The two members of (1) are equal for all values of x except possibly for $x = 0$, $x = 1$, $x = -1$. Hence, by Article **118**, Corollary II, they are equal for these values. In (1), making

$$x = 0, \quad \text{we obtain } A = 1;$$

making $\quad\quad x = 1, \quad \text{we obtain } B = 3;$

making $\quad\quad x = -1, \text{we obtain } C = -4.$

Therefore, $\quad \dfrac{1 - x + 6x^2}{x - x^3} \equiv \dfrac{1}{x} + \dfrac{3}{1 - x} - \dfrac{4}{1 + x}.$

Exercise. Verify by adding terms of second member.

The values of A, B, and C could also have been obtained by arranging the right-hand member of (1) in powers of x and equating coefficients of like powers (Art. **118**, Corollary I); thus,

$$1 - x + 6x^2 \equiv A + (B + C)x + (-A + B - C)x^2.$$
$$A = 1,$$
$$B + C = -1,$$
$$-A + B - C = 6.$$

* See Chrystal's *Algebra*, Fifth edition, Part I, Chapter VIII.

These equations when solved yield $A = 1$, $B = 3$, $C = -4$.

In resolving a fraction into partial fractions, for every factor $(ax + b)$ occurring in the denominator there is a single partial fraction of the form $\dfrac{A}{(ax + b)}$ where A is a constant.

EXERCISES

Resolve each of the following into its simplest partial fractions and verify your result when the answer is not given:

1. $\dfrac{1}{x(x + 1)}$.

2. $\dfrac{5x + 1}{x^2 + x - 2}$.

3. $\dfrac{x - 3}{6x^2 - x - 1}$.

4. $\dfrac{x}{2x^2 - 9x + 9}$.

5. $\dfrac{10x + 24}{5 - 24x - 5x^2}$.

6. $\dfrac{14 - 47x}{4x - 14x^2}$.

7. $\dfrac{x^3 - 4x - 4}{x^2 - 4}$.

8. $\dfrac{12x^2 + 12x + 1}{4x^2 - 1}$.

9. $\dfrac{x^2 + 13x + 6}{(x + 1)(x + 2)(x - 2)}$.

10. $\dfrac{6x^3 - 7x^2 - 13x - 20}{3x^2 - 8x - 3}$.

11. $\dfrac{6x^2 + 22x + 18}{x^3 + 6x^2 + 11x + 6}$.

12. $\dfrac{18x^2 + 10x + 1}{6x^3 + 5x^2 + x}$.

188. Case II. *When the denominator can be resolved into real linear factors, some of which are repeated.*

Example: Resolve $\dfrac{6x^3 - 8x^2 - 4x + 1}{x^2(x - 1)^2}$ into its simplest partial fractions.

The sum of four fractions

$$\frac{A}{x} + \frac{B}{x^2} + \frac{C}{x - 1} + \frac{D}{(x - 1)^2}$$

will give a fraction whose denominator is $x^2(x - 1)^2$; we therefore try to determine A, B, C, D so that

$$\frac{6x^3 - 8x^2 - 4x + 1}{x^2(x - 1)^2} \equiv \frac{A}{x} + \frac{B}{x^2} + \frac{C}{x - 1} + \frac{D}{(x - 1)^2}.$$

Then,

$$6x^3 - 8x^2 - 4x + 1 \equiv Ax(x - 1)^2 + B(x - 1)^2 + Cx^2(x - 1) + Dx^2$$
$$\equiv (A + C)x^3 + (-2A + B - C + D)x^2$$
$$+ (A - 2B)x + B.$$

Equating coefficients of like powers (Art. **118**, Corollary I) we have,

$$A + C = 6,$$
$$-2A + B - C + D = -8,$$
$$A - 2B = -4,$$
$$B = 1.$$

Solving these equations for A, B, C, D, we find

$$A = -2, \quad B = 1, \quad C = 8, \quad D = -5.$$

Hence,

$$\frac{6x^3 - 8x^2 - 4x + 1}{x^2(x-1)^2} \equiv \frac{-2}{x} + \frac{1}{x^2} + \frac{8}{x-1} - \frac{5}{(x-1)^2}.$$

In this case, for every factor $(ax + b)$ which occurs r times there are r partial fractions of the form

$$\frac{A_1}{ax+b}, \quad \frac{A_2}{(ax+b)^2}, \quad \cdots, \quad \frac{A_r}{(ax+b)^r},$$

where A_1, A_2, $\cdots$, A_r are constants.

EXERCISES

Resolve each of the following into its simplest partial fractions and verify the result.

1. $\dfrac{2x + 5}{(x+3)(x+1)^2}.$

2. $\dfrac{x^2 + 1}{2x(x-1)^2}$

3. $\dfrac{5x^2 - x - 1}{x^2(x-1)}.$

4. $\dfrac{2x - 8}{x^2(3x-4)}.$

5. $\dfrac{12x^2 - 27x + 16}{x(3x-4)^2}.$

6. $\dfrac{x^3 - 3x^2 + 10x - 2}{(x+1)(x-1)^2}.$

7. $\dfrac{2x^4 + 3x^3 - 7x^2 + x + 4}{x^2(x+1)}.$

8. $\dfrac{2x^2 + 2}{(x+1)^2(x-1)^2}$

9. $\dfrac{2x^3 + 2x^2 - 2x + 2}{(x+1)^2(x-1)^2}.$

10. $\dfrac{10x^3 - 29x^2 + 19x - 4}{x^2(1-2x)^2}.$

189. Case III. *When the denominator contains quadratic factors which are not repeated and which cannot be separated into real linear factors.*

Example: Resolve $\dfrac{11x^2 + 11x - 2}{(2x^2 + x + 1)(3x - 2)}$ into a sum of partial fractions.

Let $\dfrac{11x^2 + 11x - 2}{(2x^2 + x + 1)(3x - 2)} \equiv \dfrac{Ax + B}{2x^2 + x + 1} + \dfrac{C}{3x - 2}.$

Then $11x^2 + 11x - 2 \equiv (Ax + B)(3x - 2) + C(2x^2 + x + 1)$
$$\equiv (3A + 2C)x^2 + (-2A + 3B + C)x - 2B + C$$

Equating coefficients of like powers of x, we have

$$3A + 2C = 11,$$
$$-2A + 3B + C = 11,$$
$$-2B + C = -2,$$

whence $\qquad A = 1, \quad B = 3, \quad C = 4,$

and $\qquad \dfrac{11x^2 + 11x - 2}{(2x^2 + x + 1)(3x - 2)} = \dfrac{x + 3}{2x^2 + x + 1} + \dfrac{4}{3x - 2}.$

In this case, for every factor $ax^2 + bx + c$ occurring once, there is a single partial fraction of the form $\dfrac{Ax + B}{ax^2 + bx + c}$, where A and B are real numbers.

EXERCISES

Resolve each of the following into its simplest partial fractions and verify the result.

1. $\dfrac{3x^2 - 2}{(x^2 + x + 1)(x + 1)}.$

2. $\dfrac{x + 1}{(x - 1)(x^2 + 1)}.$

3. $\dfrac{5}{x^3 + 5x}.$

4. $\dfrac{3}{x^3 - 1}.$

5. $\dfrac{3}{x^3 + 1}.$

6. $\dfrac{x^2 + 4x + 10}{x^3 + 2x^2 + 5x}.$

7. $\dfrac{x^2 + 1}{(x^2 + 2)(2x^2 + 1)}.$

8. $\dfrac{2x^4 + x^2 + 2x - 1}{x^3 + x}.$

9. $\dfrac{x^5 + x^4 + 5x^3 + 4x^2 + 3x + 2}{(x^2 + 1)(x^2 + x + 1)}.$

10. $\dfrac{x^2 + 2x + 9}{1 - x^4}.$

190. Case IV. *When the denominator contains quadratic factors which are repeated.*

Example: Resolve $\dfrac{16x^4 - 20x^3 + 14x^2 - 6x + 2}{(1 - 2x)(2x^2 - x + 1)^2}$ into partial fractions.

Solution: Let

$$\frac{16x^4 - 20x^3 + 14x^2 - 6x + 2}{(1 - 2x)(2x^2 - x + 1)^2} = \frac{A}{1 - 2x} + \frac{Bx + C}{2x^2 - x + 1} + \frac{Dx + E}{(2x^2 - x + 1)^2}.$$

Then $16x^4 - 20x^3 + 14x^2 - 6x + 2$
$$\equiv A(2x^2 - x + 1)^2 + (Bx + C)(1 - 2x)(2x^2 - x + 1) + (Dx + E)(1 - 2x)$$
$$\equiv (4A - 4B)x^4 + (-4A + 4B - 4C)x^3 + (5A - 3B + 4C - 2D)x^2$$
$$+ (-2A + B - 3C + D - E)x + (C + E).$$

Equating coefficients of like powers of x, we have

$$4A - 4B = 16$$
$$-4A + 4B - 4C = -20$$
$$5A - 3B + 4C - 2D = 14$$
$$-2A + B - 3C + D - 2E = -6$$
$$A + C + E = 2.$$

Solving these equations for A, B, C, D, E, we find $A = +1$, $B = -3$, $C = 1$, $D = 2$, $E = 0$.
Hence,

$$\frac{16x^4 - 20x^3 + 14x^2 - 6x + 2}{(1 - 2x)(2x^2 - x + 1)^2} = \frac{1}{1 - 2x} - \frac{3x - 1}{2x^2 - x + 1} + \frac{2x}{(2x^2 - x + 1)^2}.$$

In this case, for every factor $(ax^2 + bx + c)$ occurring r times there are r partial fractions of the form

$$\frac{A_1 x + B_1}{(ax^2 + bx + c)}, \quad \frac{A_2 x + B_2}{(ax^2 + bx + c)^2}, \quad \cdots, \quad \frac{A_r x + B_r}{(ax^2 + bx + c)^r},$$

where $A_1, A_2, \cdots, A_r, B_1, B_2, \cdots, B_r$ are real numbers.

From the corollary of Article **121**, page 210 we know that any polynomial $f(x)$ with real coefficients can be expressed as a product of real linear and quadratic factors. Hence, if the factors of the denominator are known, any quotient of two polynomials with real coefficients can be decomposed into its partial fractions by the methods of this chapter.

EXERCISES

Resolve each of the following into its simplest partial fractions and verify your result when the answer is not given:

1. $\dfrac{2x^4 + 4x^2 + x + 2}{x(x^2 + 1)^2}.$

2. $\dfrac{x^4 + 2x^3 + 2x^2 + 5x + 1}{x(x^2 + 1)^2}.$

3. $\dfrac{x^4 + x^3 - 2x^2 - 5x - 4}{(x - 1)(x^2 + x + 1)^2}$.

5. $\dfrac{x^3 + 2x^2 + 2}{(x^2 + 1)^2}$.

4. $\dfrac{x^4 + 18x^2 - 28x}{(x + 2)(x^2 - 2x + 4)^2}$.

6. $\dfrac{6x^4 + 15x^3 + 29x^2 + 23x + 16}{x(2x^2 + 3x + 4)^2}$.

7. $\dfrac{3x^5 - x^4 + 4x^3 + x^2 + 1}{(1 + x^2)^2(1 - x + x^2)}$.

8. $\dfrac{x^6 - x^5 + 5x^4 - 4x^3 + 3x^2 + 5x + 16}{x(1 - x)^2(x^2 + 4)^2}$.

9. $\dfrac{3x^4 + 3x^2 - x + 1}{x^3(x^2 + 1)^2}$.

10. $\dfrac{- 3x^4 + 2x^2 + 1}{x^3(x^2 + 1)^2}$.

22 LIMITS

191. Absolute Values

The numerical value of x, that is, the value of x without regard to sign, is often represented by the symbol $|x|$ which is read "absolute value of x." In dealing with absolute values in this chapter it is convenient to emphasize two properties of absolute values.

1. The absolute value of a sum is never greater than the sum of the absolute values of the numbers. (See Art. **92,** exercise 15.)

For example, $|-7 + 3| \leq |-7| + |3|$,
or $4 \leq 10$.

2. The product of absolute values is equal to the absolute value of the product.

For example $|-7| \cdot |3| = |-7 \cdot 3|$
or $21 = 21$.

192. Definition of a Limit

A variable x is said to approach a constant a as a limit if $|a - x|$ becomes and remains less than any assigned positive number d when the variable x takes all values for which it is defined in the neighborhood of a.

We have had many illustrations of limits in elementary mathematics. Thus, in geometry the area of a circle is considered as the limiting value of the area of the inscribed regular polygon as the number of sides is indefinitely increased. In this case, the values of the variable are the areas of the inscribed polygons as the number of sides is increased. Again, as we annex 3's to the decimal .3333 · · ·, its value runs through the sequence of numbers .3, .33, .333, etc., which can be made to approach as near to $\frac{1}{3}$ as we please. In the geometrical progression

$$1 + \frac{1}{2} + \frac{1}{4} + \frac{1}{8} + \cdots,$$

S_n, the sum of the first n terms, runs through the sequence

$$1, \frac{3}{2}, \frac{7}{4}, \frac{15}{8}, \cdots,$$

and approaches the limiting value 2.

The essence of the definition of a limit lies in the words "becomes and remains less." For example, if x runs through the sequence of values $\frac{1}{2}, -\frac{1}{2}, \frac{2}{3}, -\frac{2}{3}, \frac{3}{4}, -\frac{3}{4}, \cdots$, the difference $|1 - x|$ takes on the values

$$\frac{1}{2}, \frac{3}{2}, \frac{1}{3}, \frac{4}{3}, \frac{1}{4}, \frac{5}{4}, \cdots$$

and becomes less than any assigned number but it does not remain so. In this case we cannot say that x approaches 1 as a limit.

To indicate that x approaches a as a limit, we use the notation

$$x \rightarrow a, \quad \text{or} \quad \lim x = a.$$

193. Infinitesimals

A very important class of variables consists of those which have the limit zero. They are called **infinitesimals.** The area between a circle and the inscribed regular polygon as the number of sides increases, the weight of the air in the receiver of a perfectly working air pump, and the difference $2 - S_n$, where S_n is the sum of the first n terms of the series $1 + \frac{1}{2} + \frac{1}{4} \cdots$, are examples of infinitesimals.

THEOREM. *If $u \rightarrow 0$ and $v \rightarrow 0$, and $|X|$ and $|Y|$ are always less than some positive constant k, then $Xu + Yv \rightarrow 0$.*

In other words, *if u and v are infinitesimals, then $Xu + Yv$ is an infinitesimal.*

Let d be any positive number however small. Since $\lim u = 0$, and $\lim v = 0$, $|u|$ and $|v|$ will ultimately become and remain less than $\frac{d}{2k}$. For these values of u and v, we have

$$|X| \cdot |u| < |X|\frac{d}{2k}$$

and from (2), Article **191**

$$|Xu| < \frac{|X|d}{2k}.$$

In a similar way

$$|Yv| < \frac{|Y|d}{2k}.$$

Adding these two inequalities,

$$|Xu| + |Yv| < \frac{(|X| + |Y|)d}{2k}.$$

By hypothesis, $|X| + |Y| < 2k$,

hence, $|Xu| + |Yv| < d.$

But from (1), Article **191**

$$|Xu + Yv| \leqq |Xu| + |Yv|$$

or $|Xu + Yv| < d.$

Since d may be chosen as small as we please,

$$Xu + Yv \rightarrow 0.$$

This theorem may be extended to any number of variables.

COROLLARY. *If $u \rightarrow 0$ and $v \rightarrow 0$, and C is a constant, then*

$$Xu + Yv + C \rightarrow C$$

Examples: If $u \rightarrow 0$ and $v \rightarrow 0$, then

(1) $7u + 3v \rightarrow 0,$

(2) $8 - 3u + 5v \rightarrow 8,$

(3) $a + b - (u + v) \rightarrow a + b,$

(4) $(a - u)(b - v) = ab - bu - av + uv = ab - (a - u)v - bu \rightarrow ab$

194. Theorems Concerning Limits

The following theorems follow directly from the theorem of Article **193**.

THEOREM I. *The limit of the sum of two variables is the sum of their limits.*

Let the variables be x and y, and let

$$\lim x = a, \quad \lim y = b.$$

Then $x = a - u, \quad y = b - v,$

where $u \to 0, \quad v \to 0.$

Adding, we have $x + y = a + b - (u + v).$

From the corollary of Article **193**, $a + b - (u + v) \to a + b,$

or $\lim (x + y) = a + b = \lim x + \lim y.$

COROLLARY I. *The limit of the sum of any finite number of variables is the sum of their limits.*

COROLLARY II. *The limit of the difference of two variables is the difference of their limits.*

THEOREM II. *The limit of the product of two variables is the product of their limits.*

Using the notation of Theorem I,

$$xy = (a - u)(b - v) = ab - [(a - u)v + bu].$$

From the theorem of Article **193**,

$$(a - u)v + bu \to 0.$$

Hence, $\lim xy = ab = \lim x \lim y.$

COROLLARY I. *The limit of the product of any finite number of variables is the product of their limits.*

COROLLARY II. *If n is a positive integer,*

$$\lim x^n = a^n = (\lim x)^n.$$

COROLLARY III. *If c is any constant,*

$$\lim cx = c \lim x.$$

195. Both Numerator and Denominator with Limit Zero

If both the numerator and the denominator of a fraction $\dfrac{x}{y}$ approach the limit zero, we have a rather curious result, as is shown by the cases which occur in the following example.

In the fraction $\dfrac{x}{y}$ let y approach 0 through the sequence of values

$$\frac{1}{2}, \frac{1}{2^2}, \frac{1}{2^3}, \cdots, \frac{1}{2^n}, \cdots.$$

Let x approach 0 through one of the four sequences:

(a)
$$\frac{1}{4}, \frac{1}{4^2}, \frac{1}{4^3}, \cdots, \frac{1}{4^n}, \cdots.$$

(b)
$$\frac{1}{\sqrt{2}}, \frac{1}{\sqrt{4}}, \frac{1}{\sqrt{8}}, \cdots, \frac{1}{\sqrt{2^n}}, \cdots.$$

(c)
$$\frac{k}{2}, \frac{k}{2^2}, \frac{k}{2^3}, \cdots, \frac{k}{2^n}, \cdots. \quad (k = \text{any constant.})$$

(d)
$$\frac{1}{2}, -\frac{1}{2^2}, \frac{1}{2^3}, -\frac{1}{2^4}, \cdots, \pm\frac{1}{2^n}, \cdots.$$

Case (a). We have here $\lim \dfrac{x}{y} = $ limit of $\dfrac{\frac{1}{4^n}}{\frac{1}{2^n}}$ as n increases with-

out limit. Since $\dfrac{\frac{1}{4^n}}{\frac{1}{2^n}}$ reduces to $\dfrac{1}{2^n}$, $\lim \dfrac{x}{y}$ becomes $\lim \dfrac{1}{2^n} = 0$.

Case (b). Here $\dfrac{x}{y}$ passes through the sequences of values

$$\sqrt{2}, \sqrt{2^2}, \sqrt{2^3}, \cdots, \sqrt{2^n}, \cdots$$

which increases without limit.

Case (c). In this case $\lim \dfrac{x}{y} = k$.

Case (d). Here $\dfrac{x}{y}$ takes alternately the values $+1$ or -1 and approaches no limit.

We see then that if x and y both approach 0 as a limit, their ratio may approach any number whatever including 0, may increase without limit, or may oscillate between two fixed numbers.

196. Infinity

If the numerator of the fraction is constant, or has the limit $a(a \neq 0)$, while the denominator has the limit 0, then $\dfrac{x}{y}$ increases without limit and is said to become **infinite**. This is usually expressed by writing $\lim\limits_{y \to 0} \dfrac{x}{y} = \infty$.

It is not, however, to be inferred that infinity is a limit. The variable $\frac{x}{y}$ in the case just given does not approach a limit. If z is a variable which increases without limit, the various expressions "$\lim z = \infty$," "$z \to \infty$," "$z = \infty$," should not be read "z approaches infinity" or "z equals infinity," but "z becomes infinite," "z increases without limit." Infinity is not a number in the sense in which we are using the term.

THEOREM I. $$\lim_{n \to \infty} \frac{1}{n} = 0.$$

Let d be any assigned small positive number. Let $n \geqq \frac{x}{d}$ where x is any number greater than 1. Then $\frac{1}{n} \leqq \frac{d}{x} < d$ (Art. **92,** exercise 4). That is, $\frac{1}{n}$ becomes and remains less than any assigned number.

THEOREM II. If $|r| < 1$, $\lim\limits_{n \to \infty} r^n = 0$.

Since $|r| < 1$, it can be written in the form $|r| = \frac{1}{1 + h}$ where h is positive. Hence,

$$|r^n| = \frac{1}{(1 + h)^n} = \frac{1}{1 + nh + \text{positive terms}}.$$
(By Binomial Theorem.)

Therefore $$|r^n| < \frac{1}{1 + nh} < \frac{1}{nh}.$$

By Theorem I of the present article and Corollary III, Article **194,**

$$\lim_{n \to \infty} \frac{1}{nh} = 0.$$

Hence, $$\lim_{n \to \infty} |r^n| = 0.$$

Since $r^n = \pm |r^n|$, we have

$$\lim_{n \to \infty} r^n = 0.$$

COROLLARY. *If $|r| < 1$,* $\lim\limits_{n \to \infty} \dfrac{ar^n}{1 - r} = 0.$

Exercise. Let y approach 0 through the sequence

$$0.1, 0.01, 0.001, \cdots.$$

Show that the fraction $\dfrac{x}{y}$ may be made to approach any number as a limit, may increase without limit, or may oscillate between two numbers.

197. Limiting Value of a Function

Let $f(x)$ represent any function of x. If x approaches a limit a and at the same time $f(x)$ takes on corresponding values such that

$$\lim f(x) = A,$$

we may abbreviate and write

$$\lim_{x \to a} f(x) = A,$$

which reads, "As x approaches a as a limit, $f(x)$ approaches the limit A"; or, more briefly, "The limit of $f(x)$, when x approaches a, is A."

If
$$f(a) = \lim_{x \to a} f(x),$$

the function is said to be **continuous** for $x = a$.

198. Indeterminate Forms

To find the value of the fraction $\dfrac{x^2 + x - 2}{x - 1}$ when $x = 2$, we substitute and find the value to be 4. But when $x = 1$, by substitution we find $\dfrac{0}{0}$, a meaningless symbol.

We may write
$$\frac{x^2 + x - 2}{x - 1} = x + 2,$$

but since division by zero is excluded from our operations, this simplification does not hold for $x = 1$. But for every other value of x, however near to 1, the division is possible. Hence, letting x approach 1, we have

$$\lim_{x \to 1} \frac{x^2 + x - 2}{x - 1} = \lim_{x \to 1} (x + 2) = 3.$$

Although substitution of $x = 1$ in $\dfrac{x^2 + x - 2}{x - 1}$ gives us a meaningless symbol, it is convenient to assign a value to the fraction. When $x = 1$, we *define* $\dfrac{x^2 + x - 2}{x - 1}$ to be $\lim\limits_{x \to 1} \dfrac{x^2 + x - 2}{x - 1} = 3$.

Giving this value to the fraction makes $\dfrac{x^2 + x - 2}{x - 1} = x + 2$ true for all values of x. In general, if $f(x)$ is a fraction which for $x = a$ takes the form $\dfrac{0}{0}$, we define $f(a)$ to be $\lim\limits_{x \to a} f(x)$.

The student should note that this is not a *necessary* definition of $f(a)$, but merely a convenient one. The convenience arises from the fact that with such a definition of $f(a)$, the function

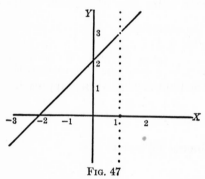

becomes continuous at $x = a$.

The above argument may be put in geometrical language. If we represent $y = \dfrac{x^2 + x - 2}{x - 1}$ graphically we have the result shown in Figure 47, which is a straight line with a gap in it for $x = 1$.

Since the function $\dfrac{x^2 + x - 2}{x - 1}$

FIG. 47

is not defined for $x = 1$ we are at liberty to choose any one of the dots in the vertical line through $x = 1$ to represent $\dfrac{x^2 + x - 2}{x - 1}$ for $x = 1$. It is most convenient to choose the point which fills up the gap and makes the graph continuous. This is a geometrical version of the statement that it is convenient to define $f(a)$ as the $\lim\limits_{x \to a} f(x)$ when $f(x)$ takes on the form $\dfrac{0}{0}$ when $x = a$.

We wish sometimes to find the limit of the value of a function as the variable increases without limit. The following example illustrates the method.

Find the limit of $\dfrac{x^2 + 2}{3x^2 + 2x - 1}$ for $x \to \infty$.

By the theorems on limits this will take the meaningless form $\dfrac{\infty}{\infty}$, but dividing numerator and denominator by x^2, we can write the fraction as

$$\frac{1 + \dfrac{2}{x^2}}{3 + \dfrac{2}{x} - \dfrac{1}{x^2}},$$

and since $\dfrac{2}{x^2}, \dfrac{2}{x}, \dfrac{1}{x^2}$ are infinitesimals by Theorem I, Article **196**, we have $\dfrac{1}{3}$ for the limit of the fraction.

The symbols $\dfrac{0}{0}, \dfrac{\infty}{\infty}$ are called **indeterminate forms.** Among other such forms which may arise are $0 \cdot \infty$ and $\infty - \infty$, but the expressions which give rise to these forms may be reduced to the form $\dfrac{0}{0}$, as shown in the following examples.

Example 1. $(x^2 + x - 2) \cdot \dfrac{1}{x - 1}$ takes the form $0 \cdot \infty$ when $x = 1$. For any other value of x we may write

$$(x^2 + x - 2) \cdot \frac{1}{x - 1} = \frac{x^2 + x - 2}{x - 1} = x + 2.$$

Hence, $\lim\limits_{x \to 1} (x^2 + x - 2) \cdot \dfrac{1}{x - 1} = \lim\limits_{x \to 1} (x + 2) = 3.$

Example 2. $\dfrac{x - 1}{x^2 - 9} - \dfrac{x^2 + x - 6}{x(x^2 - 9)}$ takes the form $\infty - \infty$ when $x = 3$. For any other value of x, we may write

$$\frac{x - 1}{x^2 - 9} - \frac{x^2 + x - 6}{x(x^2 - 9)} = \frac{-2(x - 3)}{x(x^2 - 9)} = \frac{-2}{x(x + 3)}.$$

Hence, $\lim\limits_{x \to 3} \left(\dfrac{x - 1}{x^2 - 9} - \dfrac{x^2 + x - 6}{x(x^2 - 9)} \right) = \lim\limits_{x \to 3} \dfrac{-2}{x(x + 3)} = -\dfrac{1}{9}.$

EXERCISES

What values should be given to the following expressions in order to make them continuous for the values of x indicated?

1. $\dfrac{x^2 - 9}{x - 3}$ when $x = 3$.

2. $\dfrac{3x^2 - 4x + 1}{x^2 - 1}$ when $x = 1$.

3. $\dfrac{x^3 - 27}{x - 3}$ when $x = 3$.

4. $\dfrac{x^3 - 27}{x^2 - 9}$ when $x = 3$.

5. $\dfrac{x^3 + a^3}{x^2 - a^2}$ when $x = -a$.

7. $\dfrac{x^2 - 8x - 9}{\sqrt{x} - 3}$ when $x = 9$.

6. $\dfrac{2x^2 - 5x - 12}{x^2 - 5x + 4}$ when $x = 4$.

8. $\dfrac{2x^2 + 13x - 7}{x^2 + 9x + 14}$ when $x = -7$.

9. $(2x^2 - 3x) \cdot \left(\dfrac{2x + 3}{x}\right)$ when $x = 0$.

10. $\dfrac{5 - 2x}{1 - x^2} - \dfrac{3}{x(1 - x^2)}$ when $x = 1$.

As n increases without limit find the limits of the following fractions.

11. $\dfrac{3 + 4n}{n}$.

13. $\dfrac{5n^3 - n}{3n^3 + 7n^2}$.

12. $\dfrac{3n}{2n^2 - 1}$.

14. $\dfrac{2n^2 + 3n - 7}{0.3n^2 - n + 9}$

23 INFINITE SERIES

199. Definition

Let $u_1, u_2, \cdots, u_n, \cdots$ be any unending sequence of real numbers positive or negative. The expression

$$u_1 + u_2 + \cdots + u_n + u_{n+1} + \cdots,$$

when the terms are formed according to some law of succession, is called an **infinite series**.

In the discussion of geometric progressions (Art. **153**) we have met such series, for example,

$$1 + \frac{1}{2} + \frac{1}{4} + \frac{1}{8} + \cdots.$$

200. Convergence and Divergence

In the series

$$u_1 + u_2 + \cdots + u_n + \cdots,$$

let S_n represent the sum of the first n terms; that is, let

$$S_1 = u_1,$$
$$S_2 = u_1 + u_2,$$
$$S_3 = u_1 + u_2 + u_3,$$
$$\cdot \quad \cdot \quad \cdot \quad \cdot \quad \cdot \quad \cdot$$
$$S_n = u_1 + u_2 + \cdots + u_n.$$

Example 1. In the series $1 + \frac{1}{2} + \frac{1}{4} + \frac{1}{8} + \cdots$ given in Article **199,** we have

$$S_1 = 1,$$

$$S_2 = 1 + \frac{1}{2} = \frac{3}{2},$$

$$S_3 = 1 + \frac{1}{2} + \frac{1}{4} = \frac{7}{4},$$

. . . .

$$S_n = 1 + \frac{1}{2} + \frac{1}{4} + \cdots + \frac{1}{2^{n-1}} = 2 - \frac{1}{2^{n-1}}.$$

Example 2. In the series, $1 + 2 + 3 + 4 + \cdots$, we have

$$S_1 = 1,$$
$$S_2 = 1 + 2 = 3,$$
$$S_3 = 1 + 2 + 3 = 6,$$

. . . .

$$S_n = 1 + 2 + 3 + \cdots + n = \frac{n}{2}(1 + n).$$

Example 3. In the series, $1 - 1 + 1 - 1 + 1 - \cdots$, we have

$$S_1 = 1,$$
$$S_2 = 0,$$
$$S_3 = 1,$$

. . . .

$S_n = 1$ or 0, according as n is odd or even.

These three examples illustrate three cases which may occur.

Case I. S_n approaches a limit, say S, as n increases without limit. In the first example above, S_n is never greater than 2, no matter how large a number n represents, and approaches 2 as a limit, when n increases without limit.

Case II. S_n is numerically larger than any assigned number for a sufficiently large value of n.

This case is illustrated in example 2.

Case III. S_n remains finite but does not approach a limit as n increases without limit.

This case is illustrated in example 3, where S_n may have either of the values 0 or 1, according as n is even or odd.

Series which come under Case I are called **convergent** series and are by far the most important. Series which are included in Cases II and III are called **divergent** series. We have then the

DEFINITION. *When in an infinite series the sum of the first n terms approaches a limit as n increases without limit, the series is said to be convergent; otherwise it is divergent.*

The *limit, S, of the sum* of n terms of a convergent series, written $\lim_{n \to \infty} S_n$, is often called the *sum* * of the series. In connection with convergent series we shall also use the expression "limiting value of the series" to mean $\lim S_n$.

From the definition of convergence and certain theorems on limits (Art. **194**), the following theorems may be stated.

THEOREM I. *A necessary condition for the convergence of an infinite series is that its nth term shall approach zero as a limit when $n \to \infty$.*

For,
$$u_n = S_n - S_{n-1}.$$
$$\lim_{n \to \infty} u_n = \lim_{n \to \infty} S_n - \lim_{n \to \infty} S_{n-1}, \quad \text{(Cor. II, Theor. I, Art. 194.)}$$
$$= S - S = 0.$$

That the necessary condition $\lim_{n \to \infty} u_n = 0$ is not a sufficient condition for convergence is well illustrated by the series

$$1 + \frac{1}{2} + \frac{1}{3} + \cdots + \frac{1}{n} + \cdots.$$

In this case, $\lim_{n \to \infty} \frac{1}{n} = 0$, but the series is divergent as will be shown in example 6, Article **203**.

COROLLARY. If $\lim_{n \to \infty} u_n$ is not zero, the series is divergent.

For example, the series $\frac{1}{3} + \frac{2}{5} + \cdots + \frac{n}{2n + 1} + \cdots$ is divergent, for the nth term has the limit $\frac{1}{2}$ as $n \to \infty$.

THEOREM II. *The convergence of a series is not changed by the omission of a finite number of terms.*

For the sum of the terms omitted is a definite number which added to the sum of the new series gives a definite number for the sum of the entire series.

For an illustration, see examples 2 and 3, Article **203**.

---

* The word "sum" is here used in a purely conventional sense. It is not to be understood as the sum of an infinite number of terms, but as the limit of the sum of n terms as n increases without limit.

EXERCISES

In exercises 1–3, the nth term of a series is given. Write the first three terms and the $(n + 1)$st term.

1. $\dfrac{1}{n}$.   **2.** $\dfrac{n}{n + 1}$.   **3.** $\dfrac{(-1)^n x^n}{n!}$.

Write the nth term of each of the following series:

4. $1 + \dfrac{1}{3} + \dfrac{1}{9} + \dfrac{1}{27} + \cdots$.   **6.** $1 + \dfrac{1}{2!} + \dfrac{1}{3!} + \dfrac{1}{4!} + \cdots$.

5. $1 + \dfrac{1}{\sqrt{2}} + \dfrac{1}{\sqrt{3}} + \dfrac{1}{\sqrt{4}} + \cdots$.   **7.** $x - \dfrac{x^3}{3!} + \dfrac{x^5}{5!} - \dfrac{x^7}{7!} + \cdots$.

Show that each of the following series is divergent:

8. $\dfrac{1}{3} + \dfrac{2}{5} + \cdots + \dfrac{n}{2n + 1} + \cdots$.

9. $\dfrac{1}{3} - \dfrac{2}{5} + \dfrac{3}{7} - \dfrac{4}{9} + \cdots$.

10. $a + ar + ar^2 + ar^3 + \cdots$ where $r > 1$.

SERIES OF POSITIVE TERMS

201. Fundamental Assumption

An infinite series of positive terms is convergent if S_n is always less than some definite number, however great n may be.[*]

Let K be a number such that $S_n < K$ for all values of n. Since the series contains positive terms only, S_n is a variable which increases as n increases. Since it can never attain so great a value as K, we assume that there is some number less than K which S_n approaches as a limit.

To illustrate this assumption, consider the series

$$1 + \frac{1}{2^2} + \frac{1}{3^3} + \frac{1}{4^4} + \cdots,$$

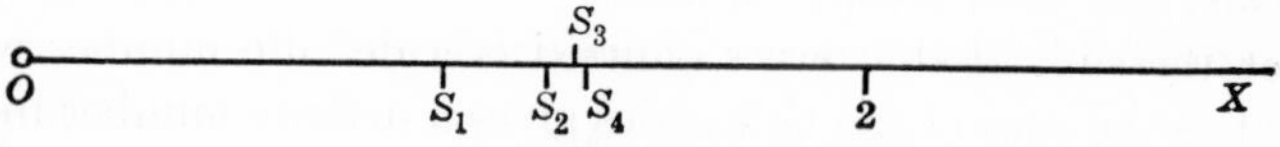

Fig. 48

and take points on the line OX (Fig. 48), to represent $S_1, S_2, S_3, \cdots$ so that the measure of OS_1, is S_1, of OS_2, is S_2, etc.

[*] For proof see Pierpont's *Theory of Functions of a Real Variable*, Article 109.

$$S_1 = 1,$$

$$S_2 = 1 + \frac{1}{2^2} = 1.2500,$$

$$S_3 = 1 + \frac{1}{2^2} + \frac{1}{3^3} = 1.2870,$$

$$S_4 = 1 + \frac{1}{2^2} + \frac{1}{3^3} + \frac{1}{4^4} = 1.2909,$$

. . . .

We can show that the sum of n terms of this series is less than 2. (See Art. **203**, example 2.) Hence, according to the assumption of this section, there is some point not farther to the right than 2 which S_n approaches as a limit when $n \to \infty$.

An analogous assumption exists for a series all of whose terms are negative. An infinite series of negative terms is convergent if S_n is always algebraically greater than some definite number, however great n may be.

EXERCISES

1. It can be shown that the sum of the series,

$$1 + \frac{1}{1!} + \frac{1}{2!} + \frac{1}{3!} + \frac{1}{4!} + \cdots + \frac{1}{(n-1)!} + \cdots,^*$$

is always less than 3. Illustrate the assumption of this section graphically by means of this series.

2. Illustrate graphically the assumption for a series of negative terms by means of the series,

$$-1 - \frac{1}{2^2} - \frac{1}{3^3} - \frac{1}{4^4} - \cdots.$$

202. Comparison Tests for Convergence and Divergence

THEOREM I. *Given a series of positive terms*

$$u_1 + u_2 + \cdots + u_n + \cdots$$

to be tested for convergence. Suppose we find a series of positive terms

$$v_1 + v_2 + \cdots + v_n + \cdots$$

* For meaning of 1!, 2!, 3!, etc. see Article **97**.

known to be convergent, and such that each term of the v-series is equal to or greater than the corresponding term of the u-series, then the u-series is convergent.

Let $\qquad S_n = u_1 + u_2 + \cdots + u_n \qquad\qquad (1)$

and $\qquad S_n' = v_1 + v_2 + \cdots + v_n. \qquad\qquad (2)$

By hypothesis,

$$u_1 \leqq v_1,\ u_2 \leqq v_2,\ \cdots,\ u_n \leqq v_n. \qquad\qquad (3)$$

Adding members of (3), and using (1) and (2), we have

$$S_n \leqq S_n'.$$

Then $\qquad\qquad \lim_{n\to\infty} S_n \leqq \lim_{n\to\infty} S_n'.$

Since by hypothesis $\lim S_n'$ exists, it follows that S_n is always less than a definite number, and by the assumption of Article **201** the series $u_1 + u_2 + \cdots + u_n + \cdots$ is convergent.

THEOREM II. *Given a series of positive terms*

$$u_1 + u_2 + \cdots + u_n + \cdots$$

to be tested for divergence. Suppose we find a series of positive terms

$$v_1 + v_2 + \cdots + v_n + \cdots$$

known to be divergent, and such that each term of the v-series is equal to or less than the corresponding term of the u-series, then the u-series is divergent.

Since $v_1 \leqq u_1,\ v_2 \leqq u_2,\ \cdots,\ v_n \leqq u_n$, if the u-series were convergent, the v-series would be convergent by Theorem I, but this is contrary to the hypothesis. Hence, the u-series is divergent.

203. Some Examples of Series Useful in Making Comparison Tests

Example 1. The infinite geometric progression

$$a + ar + ar^2 + \cdots + ar^{n-1} + \cdots$$

is one of the most useful comparison series for testing convergence and divergence. This series converges if $|\,r\,| < 1$ and diverges if $|\,r\,| \geqq 1$. That it converges if $|\,r\,| < 1$ was proved in Articles **153** and **196**. By the corollary of Theorem I, Article **200**, the series diverges if $|\,r\,| \geqq 1$, since in this case ar^{n-1} does not approach zero as a limit as $n \to \infty$.

Example 2. Prove the series

$$2 + 1 + \frac{1}{2^2} + \frac{1}{3^3} + \frac{1}{4^4} + \cdots + \frac{1}{(n-1)^{n-1}} + \cdots$$

to be convergent.

Solution: For purposes of comparison take as the *v*-series the geometric progression

$$1 + \frac{1}{2} + \frac{1}{2^2} + \cdots + \frac{1}{2^{n-1}} + \cdots.$$

Write the series to be tested under the comparison series, and we have

$$1 + \frac{1}{2} + \frac{1}{2^2} + \frac{1}{2^3} + \cdots + \frac{1}{2^{n-1}} + \cdots,$$

$$2 + 1 + \frac{1}{2^2} + \frac{1}{3^3} + \cdots + \frac{1}{(n-1)^{n-1}} + \cdots.$$

After the third term, each term in the second series is less than the corresponding term just above it. That this is true for every term after the third is shown by examining the two *n*th terms. If $n > 3$, then

$$\frac{1}{(n-1)^{n-1}} < \frac{1}{2^{n-1}}.$$

Beginning with the fourth term, the sum of n terms of the first series is always less than $\frac{1}{4}$. Hence, the sum of the second series can never exceed $2 + 1 + \frac{1}{2^2} + \frac{1}{4} = 3\frac{1}{2}$. In comparing two series it is not sufficient to compare a few terms at the beginning of the series. The *n*th terms should be compared.

Example 3. Test for convergence the series

$$\frac{3 \cdot 3^3}{1} + \frac{2 \cdot 3^2}{1} + \frac{3}{1} + 1 + \frac{1}{3} + \frac{1}{2 \cdot 3^2} + \frac{1}{3 \cdot 3^3} + \cdots.$$

If we drop out the first three terms of this series and prove the remainder to be convergent, the given series must converge by Theorem II, Article **200**. Thus, if the series beginning with the fourth term has a sum, the sum of the entire series will be the sum of terms after the third plus $3 \cdot 3^3 + 2 \cdot 3^2 + 3 = 102$. Beginning then with the fourth term and comparing with the series,

$$1 + \frac{1}{3} + \frac{1}{9} + \cdots$$

which is known to converge to $\dfrac{3}{2}$ (Art. **153**), we have

$$1 + \frac{1}{3} + \frac{1}{3^2} + \frac{1}{3^3} + \cdots + \frac{1}{3^{n-1}} + \cdots,$$

and $\quad 1 + \dfrac{1}{3} + \dfrac{1}{2 \cdot 3^2} + \dfrac{1}{3 \cdot 3^3} + \cdots + \dfrac{1}{(n-1) \cdot 3^{n-1}} + \cdots.$

Each term in the second row is equal to or less than the corresponding term in the first. Hence, the second series converges to some number not greater than $\dfrac{3}{2}$ and the sum of the entire series in question is not greater than 103.5.

Example 4. Find the sum of the series

$$\frac{1}{1 \cdot 2} + \frac{1}{2 \cdot 3} + \frac{1}{3 \cdot 4} + \frac{1}{4 \cdot 5} + \cdots.$$

Solution: Write S_n in the form

$$S_n = \left(1 - \frac{1}{2}\right) + \left(\frac{1}{2} - \frac{1}{3}\right) + \left(\frac{1}{3} - \frac{1}{4}\right) + \cdots + \left(\frac{1}{n} - \frac{1}{n+1}\right) = 1 - \frac{1}{n+1}.$$

Hence, $\qquad\qquad \lim_{n \to \infty} S_n = 1,$

and thus the series is convergent.

Example 5. Show that $1 + \dfrac{1}{2^p} + \dfrac{1}{3^p} + \cdots$, where $p > 1$, is convergent.

Solution: Write down the inequalities,

$$\frac{1}{2^p} + \frac{1}{3^p} < \frac{2}{2^p} = \frac{1}{2^{p-1}},$$

$$\frac{1}{4^p} + \frac{1}{5^p} + \frac{1}{6^p} + \frac{1}{7^p} < \frac{4}{4^p} = \frac{1}{4^{p-1}},$$

$$\frac{1}{8^p} + \frac{1}{9^p} + \cdots + \frac{1}{15^p} < \frac{8}{8^p} = \frac{1}{8^{p-1}}.$$

$$\cdots \cdots \cdots \cdots \cdots \cdots$$

Add the members of the inequalities, thus

$$\frac{1}{2^p} + \frac{1}{3^p} + \frac{1}{4^p} + \cdots < \frac{1}{2^{p-1}} + \frac{1}{4^{p-1}} + \frac{1}{8^{p-1}} + \cdots.$$

The right-hand side of this inequality is a geometric progression whose ratio is $\frac{1}{2^{p-1}}$, which is < 1 when $p > 1$. Hence, the series is convergent.

Example 6. Show that the harmonic series

$$1 + \frac{1}{2} + \frac{1}{3} + \frac{1}{4} + \cdots$$

is divergent.

Solution: Consider the inequalities:

$$1 + \frac{1}{2} > 1,$$

$$\frac{1}{3} + \frac{1}{4} > \frac{1}{4} + \frac{1}{4} = \frac{1}{2},$$

$$\frac{1}{5} + \frac{1}{6} + \frac{1}{7} + \frac{1}{8} > \frac{1}{8} + \frac{1}{8} + \frac{1}{8} + \frac{1}{8} = \frac{1}{2},$$

$$\frac{1}{9} + \frac{1}{10} + \cdots + \frac{1}{16} > \frac{1}{2},$$

$$\cdot \quad \cdot \quad \cdot \quad \cdot \quad \cdot \quad \cdot \quad \cdot \quad \cdot \quad \cdot \quad \cdot \quad \cdot$$

Adding members of the inequalities, we have

$$1 + \frac{1}{2} + \frac{1}{3} + \frac{1}{4} + \cdots > 1 + \frac{1}{2} + \frac{1}{2} + \frac{1}{2} + \cdots.$$

But the right-hand member of this inequality can be made as large as we please. The series in question is therefore divergent.

204. Summary of Standard Comparison Series

When any new series has been shown to be convergent or divergent, we evidently increase our supply of series for comparison purposes, but the standard series given in examples 1–6, Article **203** are so useful as to deserve special mention and are sometimes called **comparison series.**

Convergent series for comparsion.

1. $a + ar + ar^2 + \cdots + ar^{n-1} + \cdots \ (r < 1).$ (exercise 1, Art. **203**)

2. $\frac{1}{1 \cdot 2} + \frac{1}{2 \cdot 3} + \frac{1}{3 \cdot 4} + \cdots + \frac{1}{n(n+1)} + \cdots.$ (exercise 4, Art. **203**)

3. $1 + \frac{1}{2^p} + \frac{1}{3^p} + \cdots + \frac{1}{n^p} + \cdots \ (p > 1).$ (exercise 5, Art. **203**)

4. $1 + \frac{1}{2^2} + \frac{1}{3^3} + \cdots + \frac{1}{n^n} + \cdots.$ (exercise 2, Art. **203**)

Divergent series for comparsion.

1. $a + ar + ar^2 + \cdots + ar^{n-1} + \cdots \ (r \geqq 1)$. (exercise 1, Art. **203**)

2. $1 + \dfrac{1}{2} + \dfrac{1}{3} + \dfrac{1}{4} + \cdots + \dfrac{1}{n} + \cdots$. (exercise 6, Art. **203**)

EXERCISES

Show that each of the following series is convergent:

1. $1 + \dfrac{1}{4} + \dfrac{1}{2 \cdot 4^2} + \dfrac{1}{3 \cdot 4^3} + \dfrac{1}{4 \cdot 4^4} + \cdots$.

2. $1 + \dfrac{1}{3+1} + \dfrac{1}{3^2+1} + \dfrac{1}{3^3+1} + \cdots$.

3. $1 + \dfrac{1}{2^2} + \dfrac{1}{3^2} + \dfrac{1}{4^2} + \cdots$.   **8.** $\dfrac{1}{1!} + \dfrac{1}{2!} + \dfrac{1}{3!} + \cdots$.

4. $\dfrac{1}{1 \cdot 2} + \dfrac{1}{3 \cdot 4} + \dfrac{1}{5 \cdot 6} + \cdots$.   **9.** $\dfrac{1}{2!} + \dfrac{1}{4!} + \dfrac{1}{6!} + \cdots$.

5. $\dfrac{1}{2^2+3} + \dfrac{2}{3^3+3} + \dfrac{1}{4^4+3} + \cdots$.   **10.** $\dfrac{1}{1} + \dfrac{1}{3^3} + \dfrac{1}{5^5} + \cdots$.

6. $1 + \dfrac{1}{2^{\frac{3}{2}}} + \dfrac{1}{3^{\frac{3}{2}}} + \cdots$.   **11.** $\dfrac{1}{1^p} + \dfrac{1}{3^p} + \dfrac{1}{5^p} + \cdots \ (p > 1)$.

7. $\dfrac{1}{1^2} + \dfrac{1}{3^2} + \dfrac{1}{5^2} + \cdots$.   **12.** $\dfrac{1}{2^2} + \dfrac{1}{4^2} + \dfrac{1}{6^2} + \cdots$.

Show that each of the following series is divergent:

13. $\sqrt{1} + \sqrt{2} + \sqrt{3} + \cdots$.

14. $\dfrac{1}{1^p} + \dfrac{1}{2^p} + \dfrac{1}{3^p} + \cdots \ (0 < p < 1)$.

15. $\dfrac{1}{\sqrt{2}} + \dfrac{1}{\sqrt{3}} + \dfrac{1}{\sqrt{4}} + \cdots$.   **18.** $\dfrac{1}{2-\sqrt{2}} + \dfrac{1}{3-\sqrt{3}} + \dfrac{1}{4-\sqrt{4}} + \cdots$.

16. $\dfrac{1}{2} + \dfrac{1}{4} + \dfrac{1}{6} + \cdots$.   **19.** $\dfrac{1}{\sqrt[3]{2}} + \dfrac{1}{\sqrt[3]{3}} + \dfrac{1}{\sqrt[3]{4}} + \cdots$.

17. $\dfrac{1}{3} + \dfrac{2}{3} + \dfrac{2^2}{3} + \dfrac{2^3}{3} + \cdots$.   **20.** $\dfrac{1}{1-\dfrac{1}{2}} + \dfrac{3}{2-\dfrac{1}{3}} + \dfrac{3^2}{2^2-\dfrac{1}{4}} + \cdots$.

Test each series by comparison or by Theorem I, Article **200** to determine whether it converges or diverges.

21. $\dfrac{1}{2} + \dfrac{2}{3} + \dfrac{3}{4} + \cdots$.

25. $\dfrac{\log 2}{2} + \dfrac{\log 3}{3} + \dfrac{\log 4}{4} + \cdots$.

22. $\dfrac{1}{2+1} + \dfrac{1}{2^2+1} + \dfrac{1}{2^3+1} \cdots$.

26. $\dfrac{1}{1 \cdot 3} + \dfrac{1}{3 \cdot 5} + \dfrac{1}{5 \cdot 7} + \cdots$.

23. $\dfrac{2^4}{2!} + \dfrac{3^4}{3!} + \dfrac{4^4}{4!} + \cdots$.

27. $\dfrac{1}{\sqrt{2}} + \dfrac{1}{\sqrt{4}} + \dfrac{1}{\sqrt{6}} + \cdots$.

24. $\dfrac{\sqrt{2}}{2^2} + \dfrac{\sqrt{3}}{3^2} + \dfrac{\sqrt{4}}{4^2} + \cdots$.

28. $\dfrac{4}{2 \cdot 3} + \dfrac{5}{3 \cdot 4} + \dfrac{6}{4 \cdot 5} + \cdots$.

205. Ratio Test

Given an infinite series of positive terms

$$u_1 + u_2 + \cdots + u_n + u_{n+1} + \cdots. \tag{1}$$

Consider the ratio, $\dfrac{u_{n+1}}{u_n}$, of the $(n + 1)$th to the nth term. Suppose that this ratio approaches a limit as $n \to \infty$. Call this limit R. In other words, suppose $\lim\limits_{n \to \infty} \dfrac{u_{n+1}}{u_n} = R$. Then we may state the **ratio test** as follows:

(a) If $R < 1$, series (1) is convergent;
(b) if $R > 1$, series (1) is divergent;
(c) if $R = 1$, the test fails.

(a) $R < 1$. Since $\lim\limits_{n \to \infty} \dfrac{u_{n+1}}{u_n} = R$, we can make $\dfrac{u_{n+1}}{u_n}$ differ from R by as small a number as we please. Hence, if we plot values of

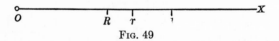

Fig. 49

$\dfrac{u_{n+1}}{u_n}$ on the line OX, Figure 49, as n increases the points representing $\dfrac{u_{n+1}}{u_n}$ will concentrate about the point R. If n is taken large enough, they will lie to the left of the point r, where $R < r < 1$. For these values of n, we have

$$\frac{u_{n+1}}{u_n} < r, \qquad u_{n+1} < ru_n,$$

$$\frac{u_{n+2}}{u_{n+1}} < r, \; u_{n+2} < r u_{n+1} < r^2 u_n,$$

$$\frac{u_{n+3}}{u_{n+2}} < r, \qquad u_{n+3} < r^3 u_n,$$

$$\cdot \quad \cdot \quad \cdot \quad \cdot \quad \cdot \quad \cdot \quad \cdot \quad \cdot$$

Since $r < 1$, the series

$$r u_n + r^2 u_n + r^3 u_n + \cdots = u_n(r + r^2 + r^3 + \cdots)$$

is convergent. But each term of the series

$$u_{n+1} + u_{n+2} + u_{n+3} + \cdots$$

is less than the corresponding term of the ru series. Hence, by Theorem I, Article **202,** the series $u_1 + u_2 + \cdots + u_n + \cdots$ is convergent.

(*b*) $R > 1$. In this case the points representing $\frac{u_{n+1}}{u_n}$ will ultimately concentrate about the point R on the line OX in Figure 50

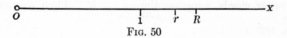

Fig. 50

and if n is large enough, they will lie to the right of the point r, where $1 < r < R$. Then

$$\frac{u_{n+1}}{u_n} > r,$$

or

$$u_{n+1} > r u_n,$$

and

$$u_{n+2} > r^2 u_n,$$

$$u_{n+3} > r^3 u_n,$$

$$\cdot \quad \cdot \quad \cdot \quad \cdot$$

Therefore, since the series

$$r u_n + r^2 u_n + r^3 u_n + \cdots$$

is divergent for $r > 1$,

the series $\qquad u_1 + u_2 + u_3 + \cdots + u_n + \cdots$

is divergent (Theorem II, Art. **202**).

(*c*) $R = 1$. If $\lim\limits_{n \to \infty} \frac{u_{n+1}}{u_n} = 1$, this test fails. This is illustrated in the two series,

$$\frac{1}{1 \cdot 2} + \frac{1}{2 \cdot 3} + \frac{1}{3 \cdot 4} + \cdots,$$

and
$$1 + \frac{1}{2} + \frac{1}{3} + \frac{1}{4} + \cdots.$$

The first has been shown to be convergent (exercise 4, Art. **203**), the second divergent (exercise 6, Art. **203**), but for each $\lim\limits_{n \to \infty} \dfrac{u_{n+1}}{u_n} = 1$.

Example 1.   Consider the series

$$\frac{1}{2} + \frac{2}{2^2} + \frac{3}{2^3} + \frac{4}{2^4} + \cdots.$$

Here, $u_{n+1} = \dfrac{n+1}{2^{n+1}}, \; u_n = \dfrac{n}{2^n},$

$$\frac{u_{n+1}}{u_n} = \frac{n+1}{2^{n+1}} \cdot \frac{2^n}{n} = \frac{n+1}{2n} = \frac{n}{2n} + \frac{1}{2n} = \frac{1}{2} + \frac{1}{2n}.$$

$$\lim_{n \to \infty} \frac{u_{n+1}}{u_n} = \lim_{n \to \infty} \left(\frac{1}{2} + \frac{1}{2n} \right) = \frac{1}{2}.$$

Hence, the series is convergent.

Example 2.   Consider the series

$$\frac{2}{2^2} + \frac{2^2}{3^2} + \frac{2^3}{4^2} + \frac{2^4}{5^2} + \cdots.$$

Here, $u_{n+1} = \dfrac{2^{n+1}}{(n+2)^2}, \; u_n = \dfrac{2^n}{(n+1)^2},$

$$\frac{u_{n+1}}{u_n} = \frac{2^{n+1}}{(n+2)^2} \cdot \frac{(n+1)^2}{2^n} = 2 \left(\frac{n+1}{n+2} \right)^2.$$

$$\lim_{n \to \infty} \frac{u_{n+1}}{u_n} = 2.$$

Hence, the series is divergent.

EXERCISES

Apply the ratio test to each series to determine its convergence or divergence.   In case the ratio test fails, apply other tests, or use previous knowledge to answer the question of convergence.

1. $\dfrac{1}{2} + \dfrac{1}{2^3} + \dfrac{1}{2^5} + \cdots.$ **3.** $1 + \dfrac{1}{2} + \dfrac{1}{3} + \cdots.$

2. $\dfrac{3^2}{2^3} + \dfrac{4^2}{2^4} + \dfrac{5^2}{2^5} + \cdots.$ **4.** $1 + \dfrac{1}{2!} + \dfrac{1}{3!} + \dfrac{1}{4!} + \cdots.$

5. $1 + \dfrac{2!}{2^2} + \dfrac{3!}{3^2} + \dfrac{4!}{4^2} + \cdots$.

13. $\dfrac{1}{2} + \dfrac{1}{4} + \dfrac{1}{6} + \cdots$.

6. $\dfrac{1}{2!} + \dfrac{1}{4!} + \dfrac{1}{6!} + \cdots$.

14. $\dfrac{1}{2\sqrt{2}} + \dfrac{1}{3\sqrt{3}} + \dfrac{1}{4\sqrt{4}} + \cdots$.

7. $1 + \dfrac{3}{2^2} + \dfrac{4}{2^3} + \dfrac{5}{2^4} + \cdots$.

15. $\dfrac{1}{3} + \dfrac{2}{4} + \dfrac{3}{5} + \dfrac{4}{6} + \cdots$.

8. $\dfrac{1}{10} + \dfrac{2!}{10^2} + \dfrac{3!}{10^3} + \cdots$.

16. $\dfrac{2}{3} \cdot \dfrac{1}{2} + \dfrac{3}{4} \cdot \dfrac{1}{2^2} + \dfrac{4}{5} \cdot \dfrac{1}{2^3} + \cdots$.

9. $\dfrac{3^1}{1!} + \dfrac{3^2}{2!} + \dfrac{3^3}{3!} + \cdots$.

17. $1 + \dfrac{1}{2^2} + \dfrac{1}{3^2} + \dfrac{1}{4^2} + \cdots$.

10. $\dfrac{1}{2+1} + \dfrac{2}{4+1} + \dfrac{3}{6+1} + \cdots$.

18. $1 + \dfrac{2^4}{2!} + \dfrac{3^4}{3!} + \dfrac{4^4}{4!} + \cdots$.

11. $\dfrac{1000}{1!} + \dfrac{1000^2}{2!} + \dfrac{1000^3}{3!} + \cdots$.

19. $1 + \dfrac{1}{3!} + \dfrac{1}{5!} + \dfrac{1}{7!} + \cdots$.

12. $1 + \dfrac{2^2}{1!} + \dfrac{3^2}{2!} + \dfrac{4^2}{3!} + \cdots$.

20. $\dfrac{1}{2!} + \dfrac{1}{4!} + \dfrac{1}{6!} + \cdots$.

21. $1 + \dfrac{2!}{2^p} + \dfrac{3!}{3^p} + \dfrac{4!}{4^p}$, where p may have any real value.

SERIES WITH BOTH POSITIVE AND NEGATIVE TERMS

206. The following theorem will throw light on the convergence of series whose terms are not all of the same sign.

THEOREM. *An infinite series of real terms which are not all of the same sign is convergent if the series formed by making all the terms positive is convergent.*

After all the minus signs have been changed to plus signs, let the series be $\qquad u_1 + u_2 + u_3 + \cdots$.

By hypothesis, this series is convergent and therefore has a limiting value S. The sum of the first n terms of this series is then less than S. Hence, the sum, S_n, of the first n terms of the original series is numerically less than S. Let these n terms consist of p positive and q negative terms. If P_p be the sum of the positive terms and N_q the sum of the negative terms, then

$$S_n = P_p - N_q.$$

But P_p and N_q are always less than S. Hence, by Article **201**, P_p and N_q approach fixed numbers P and N respectively as n

increases without limit. Then

$$\lim_{n \to \infty} S_n = P - N, \text{ a definite number,}$$

and the series is convergent.

207. Generalized Ratio Test

The ratio test can readily be extended to series whose terms are not all of the same sign. Since a series of positive terms is convergent if

$$\lim_{n \to \infty} \frac{u_{n+1}}{u_n} < 1,$$

it follows, from the theorem just proved in Article **206**, that any series is convergent if the numerical value of $\lim_{n \to \infty} \dfrac{u_{n+1}}{u_n}$ is less than 1. That is, if

$$\lim_{n \to \infty} \left| \frac{u_{n+1}}{u_n} \right| < 1.$$

If $\lim_{n \to \infty} \left| \dfrac{u_{n+1}}{u_n} \right| > 1$, the nth term cannot approach zero as a limit, hence, by the corollary of Theorem I, Article **200**, the series is divergent. We may then write the ratio test for *any* infinite series

$$u_1 + u_2 + u_3 + \cdots$$

as follows:

If $\lim_{n \to \infty} \left| \dfrac{u_{n+1}}{u_n} \right| < 1,$ *the series converges.*

If $\lim_{n \to \infty} \left| \dfrac{u_{n+1}}{u_n} \right| > 1,$ *the series diverges.*

If $\lim_{n \to \infty} \left| \dfrac{u_{n+1}}{u_n} \right| = 1,$ *the test fails.*

Example: Test for convergence and divergence the series

$$1 - 2x + 3x^2 - 4x^3 + \cdots.$$

Here,
$$\left| \frac{u_{n+1}}{u_n} \right| = \left| \frac{(n+1)x^n}{nx^{n-1}} \right| = \left| \left(\frac{n+1}{n} \right) x \right|,$$

and
$$\lim_{n \to \infty} \left| \frac{u_{n+1}}{u_n} \right| = |x|.$$

Hence, if x lies between $+1$ and -1, the series is convergent. For $|x| > 1$, the series is divergent. The interval between $+1$ and -1 is called the *interval of convergence* of the series, and is represented graphically by the heavy part of the line in Figure 51. For the points 1 and -1 the test tells us nothing.

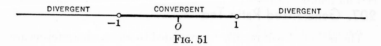

DIVERGENT   CONVERGENT   DIVERGENT

-1 O 1

FIG. 51

208. Alternating Series

A series whose terms are alternately positive and negative is convergent if each term is numerically less than the preceding term, and if the nth term approaches zero as a limit when n increases without limit.

Let the series be

$$u_1 - u_2 + u_3 - u_4 + \cdots + (-1)^{n-1} u_n \pm \cdots,$$

where $u_1, u_2, u_3, \cdots$ are positive,

and $u_2 < u_1, u_3 < u_2, \cdots,$

and where $\lim_{n \to \infty} u_n = 0.$

Let n be an even number. We may then write S_n in the form

$$S_n = (u_1 - u_2) + (u_3 - u_4) + \cdots + (u_{n-1} - u_n).$$

Since each parenthesis contains a positive number, S_n is positive and increases as n increases. We may also write S_n in the form

$$S_n = u_1 - (u_2 - u_3) - \cdots - (u_{n-2} - u_{n-1}) - u_n.$$

Since the number within each parenthesis is positive,

$$S_n < u_1.$$

By the assumption of Article **201**, as n increases beyond bound, S_n approaches a limit S. But

$$S_{n+1} = S_n + u_{n+1},$$

hence, $\lim S_{n+1} = \lim S_n + \lim u_{n+1}.$

By hypothesis, $\lim u_{n+1} = 0.$

Hence, $\lim S_{n+1} = \lim S_n = S,$

and the series is convergent.

209. Approximate Sum of a Series

In the case of some series, for example, a geometric progression, we are able to find exactly the limiting value of the sum of n terms as n increases without limit, but with many series we must be content to find an approximation to the limit, say correct to a certain number of decimal places.

Example: Calculate

$$1 - \frac{1}{3!} + \frac{1}{5!} - \frac{1}{7!} + \frac{1}{9!} + \cdots$$

correct to four decimal places.

$$1 = 1.00000$$

$$\frac{1}{5!} = 0.00833 \qquad\qquad -\frac{1}{3!} = -0.16667$$

$$\frac{1}{9!} = 0.00000 \qquad\qquad -\frac{1}{7!} = -0.00020$$

$$\begin{array}{r} \overline{1.00833} \\ -0.16687 \\ \hline 0.84146 \end{array} \qquad\qquad \begin{array}{r} -\dfrac{1}{11!} = -0.00000 \\ \hline -0.16687 \end{array}$$

To four decimal places then the sum is 0.8415. But the question arises as to just where we must stop adding terms. Even if $\frac{1}{11!}$ has no significant figure in the fifth place, we are dropping an infinite number of terms, a number of which when added together may affect the result materially. In the case of an alternating series, this question is easily answered by the

THEOREM. *The sum of the first n terms of a convergent, alternating decreasing series differs from the sum of the series by less than the $(n+1)$th term.*

Let S represent the limit of S_n, the sum of the first n terms as n becomes infinite, and R_n, the remainder. For n, even or odd, we have

$$|R_n| = u_{n+1} - u_{n+2} + u_{n+3} - \cdots.$$

From Article **208**, the sum of this alternating series, whose first term is u_{n+1}, is less than the first term. Hence,

$$|S - S_n| = |R_n| < u_{n+1}.$$

EXERCISES

Test the following series for convergence and divergence:

1. $1 - \dfrac{1}{2} + \dfrac{1}{3} - \dfrac{1}{4} + \cdots.$ **2.** $1 - \dfrac{1}{2} + \dfrac{2}{3} - \dfrac{3}{4} + \cdots.$

3. $1 - \dfrac{1}{\sqrt{2}} + \dfrac{1}{\sqrt{3}} - \dfrac{1}{\sqrt{4}} + \cdots.$

4. $\dfrac{2}{1 \cdot 3} - \dfrac{4}{3 \cdot 5} + \dfrac{6}{5 \cdot 7} - \cdots.$

5. $1 - \dfrac{1}{3} + \dfrac{1}{5} - \dfrac{1}{7} + \cdots.$

6. $\dfrac{1}{2} - \dfrac{1}{2 \cdot 2^2} + \dfrac{1}{3 \cdot 2^3} - \dfrac{1}{4 \cdot 2^4} + \cdots.$

7. $\dfrac{\sqrt{3}}{2} - \dfrac{\sqrt{4}}{3} + \dfrac{\sqrt{5}}{4} - \dfrac{\sqrt{6}}{5} + \cdots.$

8. $\dfrac{1}{2} + \dfrac{1}{2 \cdot 2^2} + \dfrac{1}{3 \cdot 2^3} + \dfrac{1}{4 \cdot 2^4} + \cdots.$

9. $\dfrac{1}{2} - \dfrac{1}{2 + a} + \dfrac{1}{2 + 2a} - \dfrac{1}{2 + 3a} + \cdots, \; (a > 0).$

10. $\dfrac{1}{1} + \dfrac{1 \cdot 2}{3 \cdot 4} + \dfrac{1 \cdot 2 \cdot 3}{4 \cdot 5 \cdot 6} + \dfrac{1 \cdot 2 \cdot 3 \cdot 4}{5 \cdot 6 \cdot 7 \cdot 8} + \cdots.$

Compute the value of each series, correct to four decimal places:

11. $1 - \dfrac{1}{2!} + \dfrac{1}{3!} - \dfrac{1}{4!} + \dfrac{1}{5!} - \cdots.$

12. $\dfrac{1}{10^2} - \dfrac{1}{20^2} + \dfrac{1}{30^2} - \dfrac{1}{40^2} + \cdots.$

13. $1 - \dfrac{2}{3!} + \dfrac{4}{5!} - \dfrac{6}{7!} + \cdots.$

14. $\dfrac{1}{10} - \dfrac{1}{20^2} + \dfrac{1}{30^3} - \dfrac{1}{40^4} + \cdots.$

210. Power Series

The series

$$a_0 + a_1 x + a_2 x^2 + \cdots + a_n x^n + \cdots, \tag{1}$$

in which $a_0, a_1, a_2, \cdots$ are constants, is called a **power series.** Such a series clearly converges for $x = 0$. It may converge for all values of x, may diverge for all values of x except for $x = 0$, or it may converge for some values of x and diverge for others.

The generalized ratio test (Art. **207**) is used to find the range of values of x for which such a power series as (1) converges.

When the values x for which a power series in x converges are represented graphically, they form an interval called the **interval of convergence.** The end points of the interval require special study to determine whether they are to be included in the interval of convergence.

If the series converges for all values of x, the interval is often said to extend from $-\infty$ to $+\infty$.

EXERCISES

Find the interval of convergence of the following series. Exhibit the results graphically.

1. $\dfrac{x}{2} + \dfrac{2^2 x^2}{2^2} + \dfrac{3^2 x^3}{2^3} + \cdots.$

Solution: $\qquad u_n = \dfrac{n^2 x^n}{2^n}, \quad u_{n+1} = \dfrac{(n+1)^2 x^{n+1}}{2^{n+1}}.$

$$\lim_{n \to \infty} \frac{u_{n+1}}{u_n} = \lim_{n \to \infty} \frac{(n+1)^2 x}{2n^2} = \lim_{n \to \infty} \left(\frac{n^2}{2n^2} + \frac{2n}{2n^2} + \frac{1}{2n^2} \right) x = \frac{x}{2}.$$

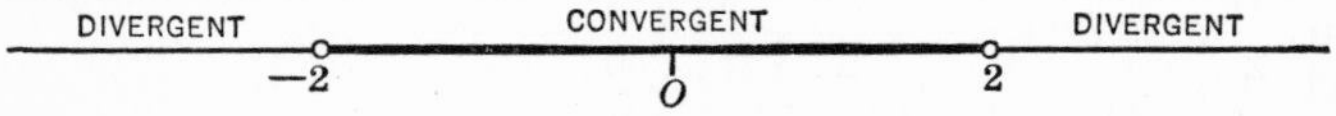

DIVERGENT $\qquad$ CONVERGENT $\qquad$ DIVERGENT

$$-2 \qquad\qquad O \qquad\qquad 2$$

Fig. 52

The series is therefore convergent for $|x| < 2$ (Fig. 52).

2. $x + \dfrac{x^2}{2} + \dfrac{x^3}{3} + \cdots.$

Solution: $\qquad u_n = \dfrac{x^n}{n}, \quad u_{n+1} = \dfrac{x^{n+1}}{n+1}.$

$$\lim_{n \to \infty} \frac{u_{n+1}}{u_n} = \lim_{n \to \infty} \frac{nx}{n+1} = x.$$

Hence, the series converges if $|x| < 1$, that is if $-1 < x < 1$. With respect to the end points, 1 and -1, the series diverges if $x = 1$ (example 6, Art. **203**). If $x = -1$, the series is an alternating decreasing series and thus converges. Hence, the interval of convergence is expressed by $-1 \leqq x < 1$.

3. $1 + \left(\dfrac{x}{2}\right) + \left(\dfrac{x}{2}\right)^2 + \left(\dfrac{x}{2}\right)^3 + \cdots.$

4. $1 + \dfrac{2x}{3^2} + \dfrac{3x^2}{4^2} + \dfrac{4x^3}{5^2} + \cdots.$

5. $\dfrac{x^2}{2 \cdot 2^2} - \dfrac{x^4}{3 \cdot 2^4} + \dfrac{x^6}{4 \cdot 2^6} - \cdots.$

6. $1 + \dfrac{x}{2!} + \dfrac{2x^2}{3!} + \dfrac{3x^3}{4!} + \cdots.$

7. $1 + 2!x + 3!x^2 + 4!x^3 + \cdots \ (x \neq 0).$

8. $\dfrac{1}{2} + \dfrac{3x}{2^2} + \dfrac{3^2x^2}{2^3} + \dfrac{3^3x^3}{2^4} + \cdots.$

By division expand the following fractions into series, and test for convergence.

9. $\dfrac{1}{1 + x}.$ **10.** $\dfrac{2}{1 - 2x}.$ **11.** $\dfrac{1 - x}{1 + x}.$ **12.** $\dfrac{(1 - x)(1 - 2x)}{1 + x}.$

The expansions of four functions of x are given below. Find the interval of convergence of each of the series.

13. $\sin x = x - \dfrac{x^3}{3!} + \dfrac{x^5}{5!} - \dfrac{x^7}{7!} + \cdots$, if x is measured in radians.

14. $\cos x = 1 - \dfrac{x^2}{2!} + \dfrac{x^4}{4!} - \dfrac{x^6}{6!} + \cdots$, if x is measured in radians.

15. $\dfrac{1}{2}\left(e^x + e^{-x}\right) = 1 + \dfrac{x^2}{2!} + \dfrac{x^4}{4!} + \dfrac{x^6}{6!} + \cdots.$

16. $\text{Arc} \sin x = x + \dfrac{1}{2} \cdot \dfrac{x^3}{3} + \dfrac{1}{2} \cdot \dfrac{3}{4} \cdot \dfrac{x^5}{5} + \dfrac{1}{2} \cdot \dfrac{3}{4} \cdot \dfrac{5}{6} \cdot \dfrac{x^7}{7} + \cdots.$

17. From trigonometry we know that $\text{arc} \sin \dfrac{1}{2} = \dfrac{\pi}{6}.$ Calculate the value of π to four decimal places from the series in exercise 16.

211. Binomial Series

The power series

$$1 + mx + \frac{m(m - 1)}{2!} x^2 + \frac{m(m - 1)(m - 2)}{3!} x^3 + \cdots$$

is called the **binomial series.** If m is a positive integer, the series ends with the $(m + 1)$th term and has been shown to be the expansion of $(1 + x)^m$. If m is not a positive integer, the series is an infinite series, but it can be shown that it converges toward $(1 + x)^m$ when x has any value which makes the series convergent. In other words, it can be shown that for these values of x, the binomial expansion holds for any exponent, integral or fractional, positive or negative.*

The binomial series is convergent for $|x| < 1$, and divergent for $|x| > 1$. For, we have, beginning with the term mx,

$$u_{n+1} = \frac{m(m-1)(m-2)\cdots(m-n)}{(n+1)!} x^{n+1},$$

$$u_n = \frac{m(m-1)(m-2)\cdots(m-n+1)}{n!} x^n,$$

$$\frac{u_{n+1}}{u_n} = \frac{m-n}{n+1} x,$$

$$\lim_{n\to\infty} \frac{u_{n+1}}{u_n} = \lim_{n\to\infty} \frac{m-n}{n+1} x = \lim_{n\to\infty} \frac{\frac{m}{n}-1}{1+\frac{1}{n}} x = -x.$$

Hence, from Art. **210**, the series converges for $-1 < x < 1$.

In expanding $(b + x)^m$ for fractional or negative values of m, we may write it in the form $b^m\left(1+\dfrac{x}{b}\right)^m$. The expansion will then proceed in powers of $\dfrac{x}{b}$, thus:

$$b^m\left(1+\frac{x}{b}\right)^m = b^m\left[1 + m\frac{x}{b} + \frac{m(m-1)}{2!}\left(\frac{x}{b}\right)^2 + \cdots\right].$$

This series converges when $\left|\dfrac{x}{b}\right| < 1$, that is, the interval of convergence for the expansion of $(b + x)^m$ is the interval between $-b$ and $+b$ (Fig. 53).

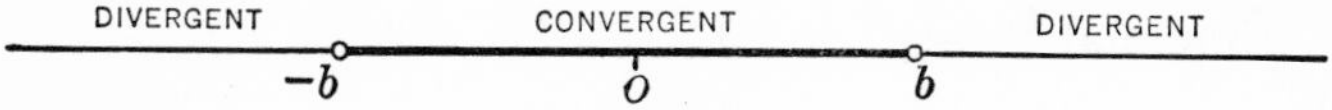

FIG. 53

EXERCISES

Expand the following binomials to five terms and indicate the interval for which the expansion holds.

---

* For a proof of the binomial expansion for any exponent, see Fine's *College Algebra*, p. 553.

1. $(1 + x)^{-3}$.
2. $(1 + 2x)^{-\frac{1}{2}}$.
3. $(1 - 2y)^{\frac{1}{2}}$.
4. $(1 - 3y)^{-\frac{1}{2}}$.
5. $(2 - 3x)^{-3}$.
6. $\sqrt{1 + x}$.
7. $\sqrt[3]{1 + 3x}$.

8. $\dfrac{1}{\sqrt{2 - 7y}}$.

9. $\dfrac{1}{\sqrt{7 - 2x}}$.

10. $(3 - 4y^2)^{\frac{4}{3}}$.

11. $\dfrac{1}{\sqrt[3]{1 + x^3}}$.

Extract the following roots to four places of decimals by the binomial expansion.

12. $\sqrt[3]{65}$.

Solution:
$$\sqrt[3]{65} = (4^3 + 1)^{\frac{1}{3}} = 4\left(1 + \frac{1}{4^3}\right)^{\frac{1}{3}}$$
$$= 4\left(1 + \frac{1}{3} \cdot \frac{1}{4^3} - \frac{1}{3} \cdot \frac{1}{3} \cdot \frac{1}{4^6} + \cdots\right)$$
$$= 4(1 + 0.00521 - 0.00003 + \cdots)$$
$$= 4.0207^+.$$

13. $\sqrt{10}$.	**16.** $\sqrt[3]{9}$.	**19.** $\sqrt[3]{26}$.
14. $\sqrt{17}$.	**17.** $\sqrt[3]{1.05}$.	**20.** $\sqrt[5]{0.99}$.
15. $\sqrt{8}$.	**18.** $\sqrt[6]{63}$.	**21.** $\sqrt[3]{0.341}$.

212. Logarithmic Series

The power series

$$x - \frac{x^2}{2} + \frac{x^3}{3} - \cdots + (-1)^{n-1}\frac{x^n}{n} + \cdots$$

is called the **logarithmic series**.

Since
$$u_{n+1} = \pm \frac{1}{n + 1} x^{n+1}, \ u_n = \mp \frac{1}{n} x^n,$$

we have
$$\lim_{n \to \infty} \frac{u_{n+1}}{u_n} = -x,$$

and the series is convergent for $|x| < 1$.

It will be shown in the calculus * that this series converges to $\log_e (1 + x)$ for any value of x for which the series is convergent, where e is the base of natural logarithms discussed in Article **69**.

* Townsend and Goodenough's *First Course in Calculus*, p. 326.

The series can then be used to find logarithms of numbers to the base e. Thus,

$$\log_e\left(\frac{3}{2}\right) = \log_e\left(1 + \frac{1}{2}\right)$$

$$= \frac{1}{2} - \frac{\left(\frac{1}{2}\right)^2}{2} + \frac{\left(\frac{1}{2}\right)^3}{3} - \frac{\left(\frac{1}{2}\right)^4}{4} + \cdots.$$

The logarithmic series can be used to calculate logarithms of positive numbers less than 2. However, it converges so slowly that it is not well adapted to numerical computation.

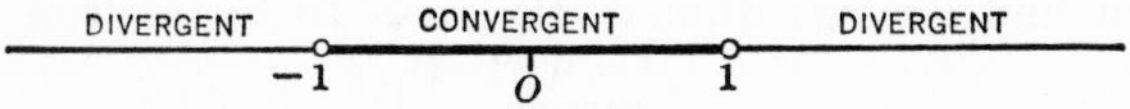

FIG. 54

To derive a more convenient series for the calculation of natural logarithms, we proceed as follows: *

$$\log_e(1 + x) = x - \frac{x^2}{2} + \frac{x^3}{3} - \frac{x^4}{4} + \cdots.$$

Hence, $$\log_e(1 - x) = -x - \frac{x^2}{2} - \frac{x^3}{3} - \frac{x^4}{4} + \cdots.$$

By subtraction,

$$\log_e(1 + x) - \log_e(1 - x) = \log_e\frac{1 + x}{1 - x} = 2\left(x + \frac{x^3}{3} + \frac{x^5}{5} + \cdots\right).$$

Let $$\frac{1 + x}{1 - x} = \frac{m + 1}{m},$$

whence $$x = \frac{1}{2m + 1}.$$

We have then

$$\log_e\frac{m + 1}{m} = 2\left(\frac{1}{2m + 1} + \frac{1}{3(2m + 1)^3} + \frac{1}{5(2m + 1)^5} + \cdots\right),$$

$$\log_e(m + 1) = \log_e m + 2\left(\frac{1}{2m+1} + \frac{1}{3(2m+1)^3} + \frac{1}{5(2m+1)^5} + \cdots\right).$$

If $m = 1$, we have

$$\log_e 2 = 0 + 2\left(\frac{1}{3} + \frac{1}{3^4} + \frac{1}{5 \cdot 3^5} + \cdots\right) = 0.6931 + \cdots.$$

* For a more detailed discussion, see Osgood's *Introduction to Infinite Series*, pp. 23 and 44.

Letting $m = 2$,

$$\log_e 3 = \log_e 2 + 2\left(\frac{1}{5} + \frac{1}{3 \cdot 5^3} + \cdots\right)$$

$$= 0.6931 + 0.4055 + \cdots = 1.0986 + \cdots.$$

In this way the logarithm of any number to the base e may be computed.

From Article **69**, if a is any positive number, we have

$$\log_{10} a = \frac{\log_e a}{\log_e 10} = \frac{1}{\log_e 10} \cdot \log_e a.$$

Hence, if we have computed the logarithm of a number to the base e, we can find its logarithm to the base 10 by multiplying by $\frac{1}{\log_e 10}$. To five significant figures, $\frac{1}{\log_e 10} = 0.43429$.

In computing a table of logarithms we need compute the logarithms of prime numbers only. The logarithms of composite numbers may then be found by means of the theorems on logarithms.

EXERCISES

1. Using the series for $\log_e (1 + x)$, compute $\log_e \frac{5}{4}$ to three places of decimals and then find $\log_{10} \frac{5}{4}$.

2. Calculate $\log_e 5$ to four significant figures.

3. Find $\log_e 9$ and $\log_e 10$ to four significant figures.

4. By computing the logarithms of 2, 3, 5, 7, construct a table of logarithms to the base 10 for the whole numbers 1 to 10, and verify by reference to a table.

TABLES

n	n^2	n^3	$\sqrt{n}$	$\sqrt[3]{n}$	$1/n$	n	n^2	n^3	$\sqrt{n}$	$\sqrt[3]{n}$	$1/n$
1	1	1	1.000	1.000	1.0000	51	2,601	132,651	7.141	3.708	.0196
2	4	8	1.414	1.260	.5000	52	2,704	140,608	7.211	3.733	.0192
3	9	27	1.732	1.442	.3333	53	2,809	148,877	7.280	3.756	.0189
4	16	64	2.000	1.587	.2500	54	2,916	157,464	7.348	3.780	.0185
5	25	125	2.236	1.710	.2000	55	3,025	166,375	7.416	3.803	.0182
6	36	216	2.449	1.817	.1667	56	3,136	175,616	7.483	3.826	.0179
7	49	343	2.646	1.913	.1429	57	3,249	185,193	7.550	3.849	.0175
8	64	512	2.828	2.000	.1250	58	3,364	195,112	7.616	3.871	.0172
9	81	729	3.000	2.080	.1111	59	3,481	205,379	7.681	3.893	.0169
10	100	1,000	3.162	2.154	.1000	60	3,600	216,000	7.746	3.915	.0167
11	121	1,331	3.317	2.224	.0909	61	3,721	226,981	7.810	3.936	.0164
12	144	1,728	3.464	2.289	.0833	62	3,844	238,328	7.874	3.958	.0161
13	169	2,197	3.606	2.351	.0769	63	3,969	250,047	7.937	3.979	.0159
14	196	2,744	3.742	2.410	.0714	64	4,096	262,144	8.000	4.000	.0156
15	225	3,375	3.873	2.466	.0667	65	4,225	274,625	8.062	4.021	.0154
16	256	4,096	4.000	2.520	.0625	66	4,356	287,496	8.124	4.041	.0152
17	289	4,913	4.123	2.571	.0588	67	4,489	300,763	8.185	4.062	.0149
18	324	5,832	4.243	2.621	.0556	68	4,624	314,432	8.246	4.082	.0147
19	361	6,859	4.359	2.668	.0526	69	4,761	328,509	8.307	4.102	.0145
20	400	8,000	4.472	2.714	.0500	70	4,900	343,000	8.367	4.121	.0143
21	441	9,261	4.583	2.759	.0476	71	5,041	357,911	8.426	4.141	.0141
22	484	10,648	4.690	2.802	.0455	72	5,184	373,248	8.485	4.160	.0139
23	529	12,167	4.796	2.844	.0435	73	5,329	389,017	8.544	4.179	.0137
24	576	13,824	4.899	2.884	.0417	74	5,476	405,224	8.602	4.198	.0135
25	625	15,625	5.000	2.924	.0400	75	5,625	421,875	8.660	4.217	.0133
26	676	17,576	5.099	2.962	.0385	76	5,776	438,976	8.718	4.236	.0132
27	729	19,683	5.196	3.000	.0370	77	5,929	456,533	8.775	4.254	.0130
28	784	21,952	5.292	3.037	.0357	78	6,084	474,552	8.832	4.273	.0128
29	841	24,389	5.385	3.072	.0345	79	6,241	493,039	8.888	4.291	.0127
30	900	27,000	5.477	3.107	.0333	80	6,400	512,000	8.944	4.309	.0125
31	961	29,791	5.568	3.141	.0323	81	6,561	531,441	9.000	4.327	.0123
32	1,024	32,768	5.657	3.175	.0312	82	6,724	551,368	9.055	4.344	.0122
33	1,089	35,937	5.745	3.208	.0303	83	6,889	571,787	9.110	4.362	.0120
34	1,156	39,304	5.831	3.240	.0294	84	7,056	592,704	9.165	4.380	.0119
35	1,225	42,875	5.916	3.271	.0286	85	7,225	614,125	9.220	4.397	.0118
36	1,296	46,656	6.000	3.302	.0278	86	7,396	636,056	9.274	4.414	.0116
37	1,369	50,653	6.083	3.332	.0270	87	7,569	658,503	9.327	4.431	.0115
38	1,444	54,872	6.164	3.362	.0263	88	7,744	681,472	9.381	4.448	.0114
39	1,521	59,319	6.245	3.391	.0256	89	7,921	704,969	9.434	4.465	.0112
40	1,600	64,000	6.325	3.420	.0250	90	8,100	729,000	9.487	4.481	.0111
41	1,681	68,921	6.403	3.448	.0244	91	8,281	753,571	9.539	4.498	.0110
42	1,764	74,088	6.481	3.476	.0238	92	8,464	778,688	9.592	4.514	.0109
43	1,849	79,507	6.557	3.503	.0233	93	8,649	804,357	9.644	4.531	.0108
44	1,936	85,184	6.633	3.530	.0227	94	8,836	830,584	9.695	4.547	.0106
45	2,025	91,125	6.708	3.557	.0222	95	9,025	857,375	9.747	4.563	.0105
46	2,116	97,336	6.782	3.583	.0217	96	9,216	884,736	9.798	4.579	.0104
47	2,209	103,823	6.856	3.609	.0213	97	9,409	912,673	9.849	4.595	.0103
48	2,304	110,592	6.928	3.634	.0208	98	9,604	941,192	9.899	4.610	.0102
49	2,401	117,649	7.000	3.659	.0204	99	9,801	970,299	9.950	4.626	.0101
50	2,500	125,000	7.071	3.684	.0200	100	10,000	1,000,000	10.000	4.642	.0100

n	0	1	2	3	4	5	6	7	8	9
10	0000	0043	0086	0128	0170	0212	0253	0294	0334	0374
11	0414	0453	0492	0531	0569	0607	0645	0682	0719	0755
12	0792	0828	0864	0899	0934	0969	1004	1038	1072	1106
13	1139	1173	1206	1239	1271	1303	1335	1367	1399	1430
14	1461	1492	1523	1553	1584	1614	1644	1673	1703	1732
15	1761	1790	1818	1847	1875	1903	1931	1959	1987	2014
16	2041	2068	2095	2122	2148	2175	2201	2227	2253	2279
17	2304	2330	2355	2380	2405	2430	2455	2480	2504	2529
18	2553	2577	2601	2625	2648	2672	2695	2718	2742	2765
19	2788	2810	2833	2856	2878	2900	2923	2945	2967	2989
20	3010	3032	3054	3075	3096	3118	3139	3160	3181	3201
21	3222	3243	3263	3284	3304	3324	3345	3365	3385	3404
22	3424	3444	3464	3483	3502	3522	3541	3560	3579	3598
23	3617	3636	3655	3674	3692	3711	3729	3747	3766	3784
24	3802	3820	3838	3856	3874	3892	3909	3927	3945	3962
25	3979	3997	4014	4031	4048	4065	4082	4099	4116	4133
26	4150	4166	4183	4200	4216	4232	4249	4265	4281	4298
27	4314	4330	4346	4362	4378	4393	4409	4425	4440	4456
28	4472	4487	4502	4518	4533	4548	4564	4579	4594	4609
29	4624	4639	4654	4669	4683	4698	4713	4728	4742	4757
30	4771	4786	4800	4814	4829	4843	4857	4871	4886	4900
31	4914	4928	4942	4955	4969	4983	4997	5011	5024	5038
32	5051	5065	5079	5092	5105	5119	5132	5145	5159	5172
33	5185	5198	5211	5224	5237	5250	5263	5276	5289	5302
34	5315	5328	5340	5353	5366	5378	5391	5403	5416	5428
35	5441	5453	5465	5478	5490	5502	5514	5527	5539	5551
36	5563	5575	5587	5599	5611	5623	5635	5647	5658	5670
37	5682	5694	5705	5717	5729	5740	5752	5763	5775	5786
38	5798	5809	5821	5832	5843	5855	5866	5877	5888	5899
39	5911	5922	5933	5944	5955	5966	5977	5988	5999	6010
40	6021	6031	6042	6053	6064	6075	6085	6096	6107	6117
41	6128	6138	6149	6160	6170	6180	6191	6201	6212	6222
42	6232	6243	6253	6263	6274	6284	6294	6304	6314	6325
43	6335	6345	6355	6365	6375	6385	6395	6405	6415	6425
44	6435	6444	6454	6464	6474	6484	6493	6503	6513	6522
45	6532	6542	6551	6561	6571	6580	6590	6599	6609	6618
46	6628	6637	6646	6656	6665	6675	6684	6693	6702	6712
47	6721	6730	6739	6749	6758	6767	6776	6785	6794	6803
48	6812	6821	6830	6839	6848	6857	6866	6875	6884	6893
49	6902	6911	6920	6928	6937	6946	6955	6964	6972	6981
50	6990	6998	7007	7016	7024	7033	7042	7050	7059	7067
51	7076	7084	7093	7101	7110	7118	7126	7135	7143	7152
52	7160	7168	7177	7185	7193	7202	7210	7218	7226	7235
53	7243	7251	7259	7267	7275	7284	7292	7300	7308	7316
54	7324	7332	7340	7348	7356	7364	7372	7380	7388	7396

n	0	1	2	3	4	5	6	7	8	9
55	7404	7412	7419	7427	7435	7443	7451	7459	7466	7474
56	7482	7490	7497	7505	7513	7520	7528	7536	7543	7551
57	7559	7566	7574	7582	7589	7597	7604	7612	7619	7627
58	7634	7642	7649	7657	7664	7672	7679	7686	7694	7701
59	7709	7716	7723	7731	7738	7745	7752	7760	7767	7774
60	7782	7789	7796	7803	7810	7818	7825	7832	7839	7846
61	7853	7860	7868	7875	7882	7889	7896	7903	7910	7917
62	7924	7931	7938	7945	7952	7959	7966	7973	7980	7987
63	7993	8000	8007	8014	8021	8028	8035	8041	8048	8055
64	8062	8069	8075	8082	8089	8096	8102	8109	8116	8122
65	8129	8136	8142	8149	8156	8162	8169	8176	8182	8189
66	8195	8202	8209	8215	8222	8228	8235	8241	8248	8254
67	8261	8267	8274	8280	8287	8293	8299	8306	8312	8319
68	8325	8331	8338	8344	8351	8357	8363	8370	8376	8382
69	8388	8395	8401	8407	8414	8420	8426	8432	8439	8445
70	8451	8457	8463	8470	8476	8482	8488	8494	8500	8506
71	8513	8519	8525	8531	8537	8543	8549	8555	8561	8567
72	8573	8579	8585	8591	8597	8603	8609	8615	8621	8627
73	8633	8639	8645	8651	8657	8663	8669	8675	8681	8686
74	8692	8698	8704	8710	8716	8722	8727	8733	8739	8745
75	8751	8756	8762	8768	8774	8779	8785	8791	8797	8802
76	8808	8814	8820	8825	8831	8837	8842	8848	8854	8859
77	8865	8871	8876	8882	8887	8893	8899	8904	8910	8915
78	8921	8927	8932	8938	8943	8949	8954	8960	8965	8971
79	8976	8982	8987	8993	8998	9004	9009	9015	9020	9025
80	9031	9036	9042	9047	9053	9058	9063	9069	9074	9079
81	9085	9090	9096	9101	9106	9112	9117	9122	9128	9133
82	9138	9143	9149	9154	9159	9165	9170	9175	9180	9186
83	9191	9196	9201	9206	9212	9217	9222	9227	9232	9238
84	9243	9248	9253	9258	9263	9269	9274	9279	9284	9289
85	9294	9299	9304	9309	9315	9320	9325	9330	9335	9340
86	9345	9350	9355	9360	9365	9370	9375	9380	9385	9390
87	9395	9400	9405	9410	9415	9420	9425	9430	9435	9440
88	9445	9450	9455	9460	9465	9469	9474	9479	9484	9489
89	9494	9499	9504	9509	9513	9518	9523	9528	9533	9538
90	9542	9547	9552	9557	9562	9566	9571	9576	9581	9586
91	9590	9595	9600	9605	9609	9614	9619	9624	9628	9633
92	9638	9643	9647	9652	9657	9661	9666	9671	9675	9680
93	9685	9689	9694	9699	9703	9708	9713	9717	9722	9727
94	9731	9736	9741	9745	9750	9754	9759	9763	9768	9773
95	9777	9782	9786	9791	9795	9800	9805	9809	9814	9818
96	9823	9827	9832	9836	9841	9845	9850	9854	9859	9863
97	9868	9872	9877	9881	9886	9890	9894	9899	9903	9908
98	9912	9917	9921	9926	9930	9934	9939	9943	9948	9952
99	9956	9961	9965	9969	9974	9978	9983	9987	9991	9996

ANSWERS

ANSWERS TO ODD-NUMBERED
EXERCISES AND PROBLEMS

Article 11. Pages 14, 15

1. $5a - b - 4c$.
      3. $2a + 2c$.

5. $2ab + 2ac + 2bc - a^2 - b^2 - c^2$.

7. $5q + 15$.
      11. $36 - (9x^2 - 9y^2)$.

9. $25 - (4y^2 - 12xy + 9y^2)$.
      13. 0.

15. Sum: $5x^2 - xy + 2y^2 + 5x - 3y - 15$;
    Difference: $x^2 - 7xy + 2y^2 - 5x - 3y + 5$.

17. $4a - 5b + 2$.

Article 12. Page 16

1. $4x^2 - 9$.
      7. $8x^3 + 60x^2 + 150x + 125$.

3. $x^2 + 3x - 10$.
      9. $16x^2 + 72xy + 81y^2$.

5. $x^3 - 6x^2 + 12x - 8$.

11. $x^2 + 4y^2 + 16z^2 - 4xy + 8xz - 16yz$.

13. 1764.
      15. 1184.

Article 13. Page 18

1. $10x^3y^2 - 6x^2y^3 + 8xy^4$.
      5. $a^3 + 2a^2b - 4ab^2 - 8b^3$.

3. $2a^3 - ab - 4a^2b^2 + 2b^3$.
      7. $27x^3 - 108x^2y + 144xy^2 - $

9. $9a^2 + b^2 + 4c^2 - 6ab + 12ac - 4bc$.

11. $3b$.
      17. $x - 2y + 3z$.

13. $\dfrac{x + 2y}{2}$.
      19. $x^2 - x - \dfrac{5}{x + 3}$.

15. $2a - 3b$.
      21. $3x^2 - 2xy + 4y^2$.

Article 14. Written Exercises. Pages 21, 22.

1. $ab(a - 2b)(a^2 + 2ab + 4b^2)$.

3. $(x + y)(x - y)(x^2 - xy + y^2)(x^2 + xy + y^2)$.

5. $(x - y)(x^6 + x^5y + x^4y^2 + x^3y^3 + x^2y^4 + xy^5 + y^6)$.

7. $(2x - y)(3x - 4y)$.
      13. $2a(a^2 + 4b^2)$.

9. $(3x + 1)(x - 3)$.
      15. $(x + 2y - 2)(x + 2y$

11. $(2x - 5)(x + 7)$.
      17. $(a - b)(a + b)(a^2 - $

19. $2x^2(x - 1)(9x^2 - x - 3)$.

21. $(a + 4b - 8)(a + 4b - 2)$.

23. $(x - y + u + v)(x - y - u - v)$.

25. $2b(a + b)(2a^2 + ab + b^2)$.

27. $(5a - 3b)^3$.

29. $(x + 3)(x + 2)(x^2 - 3x + 9)(x^2 - 2x + 4)$.

Article 15.   Page 22

1. 360.

3. $360a^3b^2c^3$.

5. $(a - 1)(a + 2)(a + 6)$.

7. $(x - y)^2(x + y)^2(x^2 + y^2)$.

9. $y^2(y - 3)^2(2y - 3)$.

11. $x^n(x^n - 3)(x^n + 3)(x^n + 2)$.

Article 17.   Written Exercises.   Pages 24, 25

1. $\dfrac{a - b}{3a}$.

3. $\dfrac{x^2 + y^2}{(x^2 + xy + y^2)(x^2 - xy + y^2)}$.

9. $\dfrac{ab + ac + bc - a^2 - b^2 - c^2}{(a - b)(b - c)(c - a)}$.

5. $\dfrac{a + b}{b(a - b)}$.

7. $\dfrac{1 - 4x}{x(3x + 2)}$.

11. $\dfrac{-4}{3x}$.

13. 0.

15. $\dfrac{a + 1}{(2a - 1)(3a - 1)}$.

Article 18.   Written Exercises.   Page 27

1. $\dfrac{7}{3}$.

3. $\dfrac{4}{21}$.

5. $\dfrac{2}{5}$.

7. $\dfrac{32}{45}$.

9. $\dfrac{32}{45}$.

11. $\dfrac{2(4x - 3)}{y - 5}$.

13. $x - y$.

15. $\dfrac{(3x - 1)(2x - 1)}{x(2x + 1)(3x + 1)}$.

17. $\dfrac{a^3b^2}{a - b}$.

Article 19.   Page 29

1. $\dfrac{5}{4}$.

3. $\dfrac{a}{b}$.

5. $\dfrac{-2xy}{x^2 + y^2}$.

7. $-\dfrac{9}{4}$.

9. $\dfrac{1}{x + 1}$.

Miscellaneous Exercises and Problems.   Pages 29–31

1. \$975.61.

3. 23.64.

5. 0.72.

7. 30.

9. 60.

Article 20.   Pages 34, 35

1. Length of side.

3. Length of time of call.

5. Age of insured.

7. Volume of container.

Article 21.   Pages 35, 36

1. 12; 8; 4; 0; − 4.

3. $\dfrac{1}{3}$; 0; $\dfrac{1 - 2x + x^2}{3 + x + 3x^2} = g(x)$; $\dfrac{x^2}{3x^2 + 7x + 7}$; $\dfrac{y^2}{3y^2 + 7y + 7}$.

7. 1.

9. $-\dfrac{1}{x}$.

11. $1 + 3 + 5 + \cdots + (2n - 1) + (2n + 1)$; $s(5) = 25$.

Article 22.   Pages 38, 39

3. III, IV.

5. $y = -3x$.

7. 17.

9. 17.

11. (3, 5).

Article 26. Page 47

1. $\dfrac{5}{4}$.

3. 1, 2.

5. 0, 2.5, -2.5.

7. $\dfrac{1}{2}$, $-\dfrac{2}{3}$.

9. 1.

11. 2.3, 1.1.

13. 1.4, -3.4.

Article 29. Page 51

1. Equivalent.

3. Not equivalent, defective.

5. Not equivalent, redundant.

7. Equivalent.

Article 33. Page 55

1. $\dfrac{12}{5}$.

3. An identity, x may assume any value.

5. 4.

7. $\dfrac{1}{5}$.

9. $-\dfrac{4}{7}$.

11. No solution.

Article 34. Pages 57–60

1. 39, 40.

3. 19, 21.

5. 30.93 hours.

7. Rate of current is 1 m.p.h.; each boat takes 1 hour and 20 minutes to make the trip; they meet 40 minutes after leaving port at a distance 6 miles from A.

9. 27.27 m.p.h.

11. 6 ounces of 3% solution.

13. 12.4%.

15. (a) $16\dfrac{4}{11}$ minutes past 3; (b) $49\dfrac{1}{11}$ minutes past 3;

(c) $32\dfrac{8}{11}$ minutes past 3.

17. 7.5 hours.

19. (a) 50.01925 cms.; (b) 0.000000795; (c) 10.08 feet.

Article 36. Page 63

9. $x = \dfrac{3}{2}, y = 2$.

5. $x = 9, y = -4$.

7. $x = 2, y = -3$.

9. $x = 1, y = -1$.

Article 37. Page 66

1. $x = 8, y = 5$.

3. $x = \dfrac{76}{41}, y = \dfrac{20}{41}$.

5. $x = -\dfrac{1}{4}, y = \dfrac{3}{2}$.

7. $x = 15, y = 6$.

9. $x = n, y = -m$.

Article 38. Pages 67, 68

3. $x = -\dfrac{1}{4}, y = -\dfrac{1}{3}.$

5. $x = -4, y = 2.$

7. $x = 2.7, y = 3.2.$

9. $x = \dfrac{7}{3}, y = -\dfrac{1}{2}.$

Article 39. Page 70

1. $x = 1, y = 0, z = -2.$

3. $x = 4, y = 2, z = 6.$

5. $x = -1, y = 3, z = 2.$

7. $x = 2, y = 3, z = 5.$

9. $A = -2, B = 0, C = 2, D = 4.$

Article 40. Pages 72, 73

1. $-47.$

3. $-4.$

5. $0.$

15. $\dfrac{7}{6}.$

Article 41. Pages 75, 76

1. $x = 2, y = -1, z = 3.$

3. $x = -5, y = 3, z = 2.$

5. $x = 1, y = -1, z = 1, w = -1.$

7. $x = 2, y = -1, z = 3, w = -4.$

Miscellaneous Problems. Pages 76–79

1. 232.

3. A is 81 and B is 33.

A's age $= \dfrac{na(1 - m) + mb(1 - n)}{n - m},$

B's age $= \dfrac{(m - 1)a + (n - 1)b}{m - n}.$

5. $-\dfrac{4}{3}x^2 + 27x - \dfrac{125}{3}.$

7. 22.7 oz. cereal, 35.1 oz. milk, 2.4 oz. eggs.

9. Angles are $40°, 60°, 100°, 160°.$

11. $2, -1, 3.$

13. \$18,000 at $2\frac{1}{2}\%$, \$12,000 at 3%.

15. $\dfrac{P}{2a}$ received a dollars,

$\dfrac{(a + c)P - 2nac}{2a(b - c)}$ received b dollars,

$\dfrac{(a + b)P - 2nab}{2a(c - b)}$ received c dollars.

17. $5\frac{1}{3}$ oz. of 4% solution, $2\frac{2}{3}$ oz. of 10% solution.

19. 77.5 oz. of pure silver added, 72.5 oz. of pure gold added.

21. 6.0 oz. copper, 14.00 oz. aluminum.

23. $b = 761.3 - 0.086h.$

Article 42.   Written Exercises.   Pages 81, 82

1. $40x^4y^3$.

3. $\dfrac{(a-2b)^2}{4a^4}$.

5. $x^sy^r(x^r+y^s)$.

7. $-\dfrac{a^2+ab+b^2}{(a-b)^2}$.

9. $(-1)^n(2a-b)^{2n}$.

11. $-\dfrac{x^2+xy+y^2}{(x-y)^2}$.

Article 47.   Written Exercises.   Pages 85–88

1. x^2.

3. $3a^4b^2c^3$.

5. $-\dfrac{a^5y^{15}}{z^{10}}$.

7. $p^{0\cdot14}$.

9. $\dfrac{1}{a^2}$.

11. $x^{\frac{13}{27}}$.

13. $\dfrac{y-x}{xy}$.

15. $x-1$.

17. $\dfrac{1}{x^4}+\dfrac{2}{x^3}+\dfrac{4}{x^2}+\dfrac{8}{x}+16$.

19. $x+\sqrt{x}$.

21. $2\cdot2^{\frac14}$.

23. $5\cdot2^{\frac13}$.

25. $10\cdot20^{\frac13}$.

29. $(162)^{\frac23}$.

31. $(24)^{\frac23}$.

33. $-\dfrac{1}{2}$.

35. $\dfrac{15}{4}$.

37. $-\dfrac{15}{4}$.

39. Does not exist.

41. $\dfrac{1}{x+y}$.

43. $\dfrac{6y^5}{x^3}$.

45. $\dfrac{x^3y^3}{(x+y)^3}$.

47. $\dfrac{3(1+x)}{(3+2x)^{\frac12}}$.

49. 14.

51. 80.

53. 113.4.

55. 1.4×10^{22}.

57. 6.66×10^{-8}.

59. 0.000000005305, 5.305×10^{-9}.

61. 7.809×10^8.

Article 49.   Pages 89–91

1. $\sqrt[4]{a^3}$.

3. $\sqrt[3]{9a^2}$.

5. $\sqrt[4]{a+b}$.

7. $\sqrt[6]{x^4y^5}$.

9. $\sqrt{\sqrt{a}+\sqrt{b}}$.

11. $a^{\frac23}$.

13. $a^{\frac13}b^{\frac12}$.

15. $\dfrac{x^3y^2}{a^4b}$.

17. $a^{\frac23}$.

19. $a^{\frac{11}{6}}b^{\frac76}$.

21. $\sqrt[4]{81}$.

23. $\sqrt[4]{x^4y}$.

25. $\sqrt[3]{0.01}$.

27. $\sqrt[3]{(2+x)^4}$.

29. $\sqrt[5]{(5-x)^6}$.

33. $\sqrt{3}$.

35. $\sqrt{0.1}$.

39. $\sqrt[10]{x^5}$, $\sqrt[10]{y^2}$.

41. $\sqrt[6]{x^4}$, $x\sqrt[6]{x^3}$.

43. $2\sqrt[12]{x^{16}y^8z^{20}}, 3\sqrt[12]{x^6y^9z^{15}}$.

45. $\sqrt[4]{18} > \sqrt[6]{72}$.

47. $\sqrt[7]{-5} > \sqrt[3]{-2}$.

49. $3\sqrt{6}$.

51. $-\dfrac{1}{5}\sqrt[3]{5}$.

53. $\dfrac{1}{2}\sqrt[3]{10}$.

55. $\sqrt[3]{25}$.

57. $\sqrt[3]{a+b}$.

59. $(x-y)\sqrt{x^2+y^2}$.

61. $\dfrac{1}{2c^2}\sqrt[5]{2a^3}$.

63. $6xy^2\sqrt[3]{x^2y}$.

65. $a^4b^{2n}c^{6n-2}$.

Article 51. Pages 93, 94

1. $8\sqrt{2}$.

3. $-7\sqrt{2}$.

5. $\sqrt[3]{4}$.

7. $\dfrac{7}{6}\sqrt{6}$.

9. $(3y - 2x^2y^2 + z^3)\sqrt[4]{y}$.

11. $ac\sqrt[5]{ab^2c^2}\,[(2c+3)b\sqrt[4]{2} - a]$.

13. 0.

15. $\dfrac{\sqrt{ab}(a-b)^2}{ab}$.

17. $-y\sqrt[3]{x+y}$.

19. $x^{\frac{1}{3}}y^{\frac{2}{3}}(xy - 3x + 2y)$.

21. $2^{\frac{1}{2}}a^{\frac{1}{2}}b^{\frac{1}{3}}(a^{\frac{1}{2}} - 3b^{\frac{1}{2}})(a^{\frac{1}{2}} - 2b^{\frac{1}{2}})$

23. $(a^{\frac{1}{3}} - b^{\frac{1}{3}})^3$.

Article 52. Pages 94, 95

1. $6\sqrt{35}$.

3. $16\sqrt{abc}$.

5. $x\sqrt[6]{x}$.

7. 3.

9. $b\sqrt[6]{a^5b}$.

11. $6\sqrt[15]{2^4 \cdot 3^6}$.

13. $x^3yz\sqrt[12]{x^4y^7z^5}$.

15. $40a^2\sqrt[4]{ab^3}$.

17. $x^{\frac{1}{3}} + y^{\frac{1}{3}}$.

19. $6 + 2\sqrt{6} - 24\sqrt{2}$.

21. 2.

23. $15 + 13\sqrt{15}$.

25. 1575.

27. $a^{\frac{1}{3}}[4a^{\frac{1}{6}} - 12a^{\frac{1}{12}} + 9]$.

29. $a - b$.

31. $x^3 - y^3$.

33. $a + 3a^{\frac{2}{3}}b^{\frac{1}{3}} + 3a^{\frac{1}{3}}b^{\frac{2}{3}} + b$.

35. -2.

Article 53. Pages 96, 97

1. $\sqrt{5}$.

3. 3.

5. $\sqrt[3]{5}$.

7. $3\sqrt{7}$.

9. $\dfrac{1}{3}\sqrt{2}$.

11. $\sqrt[4]{ab^3}$.

13. $\dfrac{\sqrt[15]{2^{14}a^8b^4c^{11}}}{2ac}$.

15. $\sqrt[12]{x}\,(\sqrt[6]{x} - 1)$.

17. $\dfrac{2a\sqrt{b} - 3b\sqrt{a}}{ab}$.

19. $-\dfrac{4\sqrt{3} + 5\sqrt{2}}{2}$.

21. $5 + 2\sqrt{6}$.

23. $\dfrac{\sqrt[3]{4} + \sqrt[3]{6}}{5}$.

25. $\dfrac{1}{6}(3 + \sqrt{6} + \sqrt{15})$.

27. $\dfrac{3}{7}(\sqrt{3} + \sqrt[3]{2})(3 + \sqrt{2})$.

29. 5.475.

31. 0.636.

33. 1.024.

35. 0.127.

37. 7.873.

Article 54.   Pages 98, 99

1. 4.   **5.** −4.   **9.** 5.   **13.** No solution.

3. −1.   **7.** −4.   **11.** 5.   **15.** 0.

17. $s = \dfrac{\pm\, 2\sqrt[3]{27A^2}}{3}$.   **21.** 1336.

23. 5.9 sec.

19. $i = \sqrt[i]{\dfrac{A}{P}} - 1$.

Article 55.   Page 102

1. $6i$.

3. $-2ai\sqrt{3}$.

5. $\dfrac{4xi}{11y}$.

9. $4 + 6i$.

11. $-4i$.

13. $2i\sqrt{3}$.

15. $2 - 6i\sqrt{7}$.

17. $-\dfrac{1 + i\sqrt{3}}{2}$.

19. 5.

21. $-\dfrac{5 + 12i}{13}$.

23. $5\sqrt{6}$.

25. $-46 - 9i$.

27. $x^2 - 2x + 5$.

29. 0.

Article 57.   Page 104

1. 2; 4; 0; −2; 1.

3. 3; $-\dfrac{1}{2}$; $\dfrac{1}{4}$; 1; any positive number a, $a \neq 1$.

Article 58.   Pages 105, 106

5. $2 \log 3 + \dfrac{1}{2} \log 5 - 3 \log 2 - \dfrac{1}{2} \log 7$.

7. $\dfrac{1}{2} (\log 7 - 3 \log 3)$.   **9.** $\dfrac{1}{2} (9 \log 2 + 5 \log 3)$.

11. $\dfrac{1}{2} \log 2$.   **17.** 0.2330.   **23.** 1.3512.

13. 1.7993.   **19.** − 0.2386.   **25.** 2.1373.

15. 5065.   **21.** 0.0732.   **27.** $0.1373 + k$.

Article 64.   Pages 111, 112

1. 71.4 means some number between 71.35 and 71.45; 71.40 means some number between 71.395 and 71.405; 71.400 means some number between 71.3995 and 71.4005.

3. 3.1415926536; 3.141592654; 3.14159265; 3.1415926; 3.141593; 3.14159; 3.1416; 3.142; 3.14; 3.1.

5. 60.5.

7. 5.4248125 and 5.9259375; 5.7.

9. 192.43⁻ and 193.18⁻; 193.

Article 67.   Page 114

1. 1.5682.
3. 2.8354.
5. 9.9990 − 10.
7. 0.4972.
9. 8.7254.
11. 0.7212 − 10.

13. 73.0.
15. 486.4.
17. 0.9986.
19. 3.142×10^4.
21. 6.523×10^{-9}.
23. 4.76×10^{-12}.

Article 68.   Pages 116–120

1. 4.107×10^4.
3. 1754.
5. 0.4142.
7. 2.032×10^{-6}.
9. 8.472×10^{-3}.
11. 15.83.
13. 0.1973.
15. 0.4094.
17. 1.259.
19. 0.9550.
21. 0.02409.
23. 265.4.
25. 13.20.
27. 1.746×10^{-7}.
29. 0.3655.
31. 1.215.
33. −0.422.

35. −0.0384.
37. 9.
39. $\dfrac{10^{12}}{49}$.
41. 25.
43. 10^3.
45. 2.407×10^4.
47. 5.891×10^{-3}.
49. 5.334 in.
51. 982.6 lbs.
53. 1.078 sec.
55. 57.40 sq. ft.
57. 5.139×10^{-11}.
59. 128 tons.
61. 0.9002 lbs.
63. 0.2564 cu. ft.
65. 4.161×10^{-3}.

Article 69.   Pages 121, 122

1. 0.6932.
3. 1.610.
5. 2.197.
7. −0.6932.

9. 0.3466.
11. −2.540.
13. 1.431.
15. 0.8614.

17. 0.5580.
19. 5.192.
21. −5.059.

Article 71.   Pages 124–126

5. −1.337.
7. 1.6.
17. 0.5.
23. 4 grams at the end of 4 minutes; 8 minutes.
25. 7.736 minutes.
27. 18450 feet.
29. 6.814 minutes.

9. 2.216
11. 2.709.

13. −0.3405.
15. 0.03981.
21. $x = 0.6695; y = -1.2203$.
31. $s = \dfrac{v_0}{2k} (e^{kt} - e^{-kt})$.

Article 72.   Page 128

1. $a = 1, b = -3, c = 5.$
3. $a = 94, b = 12, c = -39.$
5. $a = 1, b = m - n, c = -mn.$

7. $a = k, b = 8k, c = 3k - 2.$
9. $a = 1, b = 0, c = 0.$

Article 73.   Page 129

3. $\dfrac{1}{3}, -2.$

5. $\dfrac{4}{3}, -\dfrac{5}{2}.$

7. $0, \dfrac{8}{3}.$

9. $\dfrac{3}{2}, -\dfrac{4}{3}.$

11. $4i, -4i.$

13. $-3, -1.$

15. $\dfrac{1}{3} \pm \sqrt{5}.$

Article 74.   Pages 131–133

1. $\dfrac{2}{3}, -2.$

3. $4 \pm i\sqrt{5}.$
5. $-1 \pm i\sqrt{3}.$
7. $\dfrac{-v_0 \pm \sqrt{v_0{}^2 + 2gs}}{g}.$

9. $5, \dfrac{3}{2}.$

11. $1, -4.$

13. $\dfrac{2 \pm \sqrt{10}}{2}.$

15. $\dfrac{-5 \pm 2\sqrt{2}}{3}.$

17. $\dfrac{2}{3} \pm i.$

19. $a, -\dfrac{1}{a}.$

21. $\dfrac{5i}{3}, -\dfrac{3i}{2}.$

23. $\dfrac{5}{3}, -2.$

25. $9, 1.$

27. $b, \dfrac{2a^2 - b^2}{b}.$

29. $2, -5.$
31. $n(1 + n), n(1 - n).$
33. $mn, -(m + n).$
37. $1, -2.$

39. $\dfrac{4}{3}.$

41. $-1.612, -8.192.$
43. $1.815, -0.031.$
45. $5.$
47. $4.$
49. No solution.

Article 75.   Pages 133–135

3. $\pm 2, \pm \dfrac{5}{2}.$

7. $\pm 3, \pm 4.$

9. $1, 3, 6, -2.$

11. $2, -\dfrac{1}{2}, \dfrac{3 \pm i\sqrt{7}}{2}.$

13. $\dfrac{39}{2}.$

5. $\dfrac{1}{2}, \dfrac{-1 \pm i\sqrt{3}}{4}, -2, 1 \pm i\sqrt{3}.$

15. $\dfrac{8}{27}, -\dfrac{1}{8}.$

17. $\dfrac{15}{2}.$

19. $\dfrac{5}{4}.$

21. $1291.$

23. $100, 10^{-6}.$

25. $0.3010; 0.4771.$

27. $\log_e 2; \log_e (-3).$
29. $\pm 1.316.$

Article 76.   Pages 135, 136

3. $x^2 + 3x - 10 = 0$.

5. $x^2 + 7x + 10 = 0$.

11. $x^2 - 5x + \sqrt{3}x - \sqrt{2}x + 6 + 2\sqrt{2} - 3\sqrt{3} - \sqrt{6} = 0$.

13. $x^2 + 9 = 0$.

15. $x^2 - 2ax + a^2 - b^2 = 0$.

7. $x^2 - (2 - \sqrt{2})x - 2\sqrt{2} = 0$.

9. $20x^2 + 7x - 6 = 0$.

17. $abx^2 - (a + b)x + ab = 0$.

Article 78.   Page 137

3. $k = 3$ or $k = -4$; second root is $x = 4$.

5. $m = 3$, $k = 2$.

7. $k = 2$, roots are ± 3.

Article 80.   Pages 138–140

1. Real, rational, unequal.

3. Conjugate imaginary.

5. Real, rational, equal.

9. $k = 0$, roots are both equal to 0;

$k = \dfrac{12}{13}$, roots are both equal to $\dfrac{6}{5}$.

11. $k = -2$, roots are both equal to $\dfrac{3}{2}$;

$k = \dfrac{2}{5}$, roots are both equal to $\dfrac{15}{2}$.

13. $k = 2$, roots are both equal to $-\dfrac{1}{2}$;

$k = -1$, roots are both equal to 1.

15. $k = 1$, roots are both equal to 3;

$k = -1$, roots are both equal to -3.

17. No finite value of k exists to make roots equal.

19. Sum $= 8$, product $= 25$, roots are $4 \pm 3i$.

21. Sum $= -\dfrac{3}{4}$, product $= -\dfrac{1}{2}$, roots are $-\dfrac{3 \pm \sqrt{41}}{8}$.

23. Sum $= -\dfrac{R}{L}$, product $= \dfrac{1}{LC}$, roots are $\dfrac{-R \pm \sqrt{R^2 - \dfrac{4L}{C}}}{2L}$.

27. $k = 1$, roots are $\dfrac{9}{2}$, $\dfrac{1}{2}$;

$k = -\dfrac{16}{25}$, roots are $\dfrac{2}{5}$, $-\dfrac{18}{5}$.

29. $k = 42$, roots are $\dfrac{3}{5}$ and -9;

$k = -42$, roots are 9 and $-\dfrac{3}{5}$.

31. $M > 20$ grams.

Article 81. Page 141

1. ± 3.   **3.** Imaginary.   **5.** 0, 3.   **7.** 3, -1.

9. Between 0.6 and 0.7 and -1.5.

11. Between 4.2 and 4.3 and between -0.2 and -0.3.

13. Imaginary.

15. (*a*) The curve opens in a direction parallel to the negative direction along the Y-axis. (*b*) Symmetrical about the Y-axis. (*c*) Passes through the origin.

Problems. Pages 142–146

1. 21, 22.   **3.** 14, 16.

5. 40 minutes for large pipe, 60 minutes for small pipe.

7. A's rate is 65 m.p.h., B's rate is 60 m.p.h.

9. (*a*) When $t = \dfrac{3}{4}$ sec., as ball is going up, and again when $t = 3$ sec., as ball is falling;   (*b*) $t = \dfrac{15}{8}$ sec.;   (*c*) $56\dfrac{1}{4}$ feet;   (*d*) $t = 3\dfrac{3}{4}$ sec.;   (*e*) 20 feet downward;   (*f*) $12\dfrac{1}{2}$ feet.

11. About 1.6 sec. longer.   **13.** 1.792.   **15.** 12 in.

17. Depth is $\dfrac{1}{6}(a + b - \sqrt{a^2 - ab + b^2})$.   If the sheet were square, the depth would be $\dfrac{a}{6}$.

19. $x = ar_1(r_2{}^2 - r_1{}^2)^{-\frac{1}{2}}$.

21. Curve moves upward along Y-axis as c increases.

23. $R = \dfrac{1 \pm \sqrt{1 - 4g^2X^2}}{2g}$.

25. $x = \dfrac{-PX \pm \sqrt{P^2X^2 - 4R^2W(W - P)}}{2RW} \cdot r$.

27. $d = 0.56$.

29. 16 inches.

31. 8 feet per second.

33. 198°.

Article 84. Pages 152–154

1. $(9, 4)$; $(-12, -3)$.

3. $x = 6(-3 \pm i)$; $y = 3 \pm 4i$.

5. $(0, 2)$; $\left(\dfrac{72}{11}, -\dfrac{86}{11}\right)$.

7. $(1, 0)$; $(5, -4)$.

9. $\left(\dfrac{1}{2}, \dfrac{1}{2}\right)$; $\left(-\dfrac{3}{2}, -1\right)$.

11. $(2 + i, 3 - 2i)$; $(2 - i, 3 + 2i)$.

13. $(1, 1)$; $\left(-\dfrac{1}{3}, \dfrac{1}{7}\right)$.

15. $\left(\dfrac{1}{4}a, \dfrac{1}{4}a\right)$.

17. $x = \dfrac{-7 \pm 3\sqrt{31}}{20}$, $y = \dfrac{-17 \pm 3\sqrt{31}}{10}$.

19. 85.   **21.** 15, 36.

23. (1) Cuts if $r > \dfrac{4}{\sqrt{5}}$; (2) is tangent if $r = \dfrac{4}{\sqrt{5}}$; (3) fails to meet if $r < \dfrac{4}{\sqrt{5}}$.

25. (1) Cuts if $c > -6$; (2) is tangent if $c = -6$; (3) fails to meet if $c < -6$.

27. $y = mx \pm r\sqrt{1 + m^2}$.   **29.** $x = 4$, $y = \dfrac{9}{5}$.

Article 86.   Pages 155, 156

3. $x = 0$, $y = \pm 3\sqrt{2}$.   **9.** $x = \pm \dfrac{\sqrt{2}}{2}$, $y = \pm \dfrac{\sqrt{15}}{5}$.

5. $x = \pm 2\sqrt{3}$, $y = \pm 5$.   **11.** $x = \pm 3$, $y = 0$.

7. $x = \pm 8$, $y = \pm 15$.

Article 87.   Pages 158, 159

1. $\left(\dfrac{4}{5}, \dfrac{3}{5}\right)$; $\left(-\dfrac{4}{5}, -\dfrac{3}{5}\right)$; $\left(\dfrac{3}{5}, \dfrac{4}{5}\right)$; $\left(-\dfrac{3}{5}, -\dfrac{4}{5}\right)$.

3. $(5, 2)$; $(-5, -2)$. Draw a graph of the curves to see what happened to the other two points of intersection you would normally expect.

5. $(2, -2)$; $(-2, 2)$; $\left(\dfrac{6}{17}\sqrt{51}, \dfrac{4}{17}\sqrt{51}\right)$; $\left(-\dfrac{6}{17}\sqrt{51}, -\dfrac{4}{17}\sqrt{51}\right)$.

7. $\left(\dfrac{11\sqrt{17}}{34}, \dfrac{-\sqrt{17}}{34}\right)$; $\left(\dfrac{-11\sqrt{17}}{34}, \dfrac{\sqrt{17}}{34}\right)$; $(i, -2i)$; $(-i, 2i)$.

9. $(3, 2)$; $(-3, -2)$; $(i, 2i)$; $(-i, -2i)$.

Article 88.   Page 160

1. $(3, 2)$; $(2, 3)$; $\left(\dfrac{-7 + i\sqrt{23}}{2}, \dfrac{-7 - i\sqrt{23}}{2}\right)$;
$\left(\dfrac{-7 - i\sqrt{3}}{2}, \dfrac{-7 + i\sqrt{3}}{2}\right)$.

3. $(1, -2)$; $(-2, 1)$; $\left(\dfrac{7 + \sqrt{61}}{6}, \dfrac{7 - \sqrt{61}}{6}\right)$; $\left(\dfrac{7 - \sqrt{61}}{6}, \dfrac{7 + \sqrt{61}}{6}\right)$.

5. $(2 + \sqrt{3}, 2 - \sqrt{3})$; $(2 - \sqrt{3}, 2 + \sqrt{3})$; $(3 + \sqrt{2}, 3 - \sqrt{2})$; $(3 - \sqrt{2}, 3 + \sqrt{2})$.

Miscellaneous Exercises and Problems Involving Quadratics.   Pages 161–164

1. $\left(\dfrac{6 + 2i\sqrt{6}}{3}, \dfrac{6 - i\sqrt{6}}{3}\right)$; $\left(\dfrac{6 - 2i\sqrt{6}}{3}, \dfrac{6 + i\sqrt{6}}{3}\right)$.

3. $(3, 3)$; $\left[\dfrac{-3(1 + i\sqrt{3})}{2}, \dfrac{-3(1 - i\sqrt{3})}{2}\right]$;

$\left[\dfrac{-3(1 - i\sqrt{3})}{2}, \dfrac{-3(1 + i\sqrt{3})}{2}\right]$.

5. $(0, 0)$; $(-10, -10)$; $(-6, 2)$; $(2, -6)$.

7. $(1, -1)$; $(2, 4)$.

9. $\left(-\dfrac{1}{2}, \dfrac{1}{5}\right)$; $\left(\dfrac{1}{5}, -\dfrac{1}{2}\right)$.

11. $(3, 1)$; $(1, 3)$; $(-1, -3)$; $(-3, -1)$.

13. $(2i, 4i)$; $(-2i, -4i)$; $(i, -3i)$; $(-i, 3i)$.

15. $(1, -1)$; $\left(\dfrac{10}{9}, -\dfrac{5}{6}\right)$; $(-24, 18)$; $(-6, 6)$.

17. $(2, 0)$; $(0, -1)$.

19. $\left(\dfrac{1}{4}, \dfrac{1}{4}\right)$.

21. $(9, 4)$.

23. $(1, 2, 3)$; $(2, -2, 1)$.

25. $(2, 3, 5)$; $(-2, -3, -5)$.

27. 7 and 9; or -7 and -9.

29. Length is $\dfrac{1}{2}(29 + \sqrt{85})$ in.; breadth is $\dfrac{1}{2}(29 - \sqrt{85})$ in.

31. $l = \dfrac{1}{2}[\sqrt{d^2 + 2A} + \sqrt{d^2 - 2A}]$;

$w = \dfrac{1}{2}[\sqrt{d^2 + 2A} - \sqrt{d^2 - 2A}]$.

33. A's rate is 45 m.p.h.; B's rate is 40 m.p.h.

35. 180 m.p.h.; 4 hours.

37. $5 + 5\sqrt{5}$ days; $15 + 5\sqrt{5}$ days.

39. 8 in. $\times$ 8 in. $\times$ 6 in.

41. 660 feet square.

43. 90 ft., 120 ft., 150 ft.; or 80 ft., 150 ft., 170 ft.

45. 8 in. $\times$ 9 in. $\times$ 12 in.

Article 95. Pages 171, 172

1. $x > 3$.

3. $x < -1$.

5. $x > 6$.

7. $-\dfrac{1}{2} < x < \dfrac{2}{3}$.

9. $-3 < x < 3$.

11. $-1 < x < 0$; or $x > 2$.

13. $x < 0$ or $x > 4$.

15. $-1 < x < 2$.

17. $x < 0$ or $0 < x < 1$.

19. $-\dfrac{1}{2} < x < 0$ or $x > 1$.

21. Fraction is positive if $-2 < x < 1$ or $x > 3$;
fraction is negative if $x < -2$ or $1 < x < 3$.

23. Roots are real and unequal if $k < -\dfrac{14}{9}$ or $k > 2$.

Roots are imaginary if $-\dfrac{14}{9} < k < 2$.

25. $x < -4$.   **27.** $-1 < x < 2$.   **29.** $x < 0$.

Article 97. Page 176

1. $\dfrac{1}{336}$.   **5.** $\dfrac{1}{5}$.

3. 15.   **7.** $n^3 - 3n^2 + 2n$.

Article 100. Pages 178–180

3. $a^5 - 5a^4x + 10a^3x^2 - 10a^2x^3 + 5ax^4 - x^5$.

5. $\dfrac{1}{16} + \dfrac{1}{2}a^2 + \dfrac{3}{2}a^4 + 2a^6 + a^8$.

7. $\dfrac{64}{x^6} + \dfrac{96}{x^{\frac{9}{2}}} + \dfrac{60}{x^3} + \dfrac{20}{x^{\frac{3}{2}}} + \dfrac{15}{4} + \dfrac{3x^{\frac{3}{2}}}{8} + \dfrac{x^3}{64}$.

9. $\dfrac{x^{10}}{32} - \dfrac{15x^8}{16y} + \dfrac{45x^6}{4y^2} - \dfrac{135x^4}{2y^3} + \dfrac{405x^2}{2y^4} - \dfrac{243}{y^5}$.

11. $x^4 + 8x^{\frac{7}{2}}y^{\frac{1}{2}} + 28x^3y + 56x^{\frac{5}{2}}y^{\frac{3}{2}} + 70x^2y^2 + 56x^{\frac{3}{2}}y^{\frac{5}{2}} + 28xy^3 + 8x^{\frac{1}{2}}y^{\frac{7}{2}} + y^4$.

13. $91\dfrac{1}{8}$.

15. $a^{10}b^5 - 15a^8b^4 + 90a^6b^3 - 270a^4b^2 + 405a^2b - 243$.

17. $a^3 + b^3 + c^3 + 3a^2b + 3a^2c + 3ab^2 + 3b^2c + 3ac^2 + 3bc^2 + 6abc$.

19. $x^{\frac{3}{2}} + 3x + 6x^{\frac{1}{2}} + 7 + \dfrac{6}{x^{\frac{1}{2}}} + \dfrac{3}{x} + \dfrac{1}{x^{\frac{3}{2}}}$.

21. $1024x^{30} + 15{,}360x^{27}y^2 + 103{,}680x^{24}y^4 + 414{,}720x^{21}y^6 + \cdots$.

23. $1 - \dfrac{k-1}{k}x + \dfrac{(k-1)(k-2)}{k^2} \cdot \dfrac{x^2}{2} - \dfrac{(k-1)(k-2)(k-3)}{k^3} \cdot \dfrac{x^3}{3!} \cdots$.

25. $\cdots + 45 \cdot 2^8 \cdot \dfrac{y^4}{x^2} - 10 \cdot 2^9 \cdot \dfrac{y^{\frac{9}{2}}}{x} + 2^{10} \cdot y^5$.

29. $\dfrac{15!}{7!\,8!}(2x)^8(-3y)^7$.   **33.** 1104×10^2.

     35. 887.5.

31. $-\dfrac{19!}{6!\,13!} \cdot \dfrac{2^6}{3^{13}} \cdot \dfrac{1}{x^{\frac{1}{2}}}$.   **37.** 2.594.

     39. $1 - x + x^2 - x^3 + x^4 \cdots$.

41. 1.049.   **45.** 3.979.   **49.** 1.372.

43. 2.080.   **47.** 0.9426.

Article 103. Pages 183, 184

11. Not conjugates.   **15.** Conjugates.

13. Not conjugates.   **17.** $b = 0$.

19. $x = -3, y = 2.$

21. $x = \dfrac{1}{2}, y = 2;$ or $x = -4, y = 5.$

Article 104. Page 185

1. $7 + 5i.$

3. $2.$

5. $\dfrac{13}{12} + \dfrac{i}{3}.$

7. $2 - 8i.$

9. $-5 - i.$

11. $-3 + i.$

Article 105. Pages 186, 187

3. $-2 + 23i.$

5. $4.$

7. $-6 + 2i.$

9. $i.$

11. $36.$

13. $-119 - 120i.$

15. $8.$

19. $i.$

21. $\dfrac{4 - 19i}{13}.$

23. $-\dfrac{1 + i\sqrt{3}}{2}.$

25. $\dfrac{-1 + i}{2}.$

27. $\dfrac{-5 - 12i}{169}.$

29. Result is real if either $a = 0$ or $b = 0$; points lie on axis of reals or axis of imaginaries. Result is pure imaginary if $a = \pm b$; points lie on lines making angles of 45° with axis of reals and axis of imaginaries.

Article 106. Page 188

3. $r = 13, \tan\theta = -\dfrac{5}{12}, \sin\theta = -\dfrac{5}{13}.$

5. $r = \sqrt{2}, \theta = -\dfrac{\pi}{4}$ or $\dfrac{7\pi}{4}.$

7. $r = 2, \theta = \dfrac{3\pi}{2}.$

9. $r = 3, \theta = \dfrac{3\pi}{2}.$

11. $r = 2, \theta = \dfrac{\pi}{4}.$

13. $r = 2, \theta = -\dfrac{\pi}{12}.$

15. $3\sqrt{3} + 3i.$

17. $\sqrt{2}(1 - i).$

19. $\dfrac{i}{4}.$

21. $\theta = \dfrac{2\pi}{3}.$

Article 107. Pages 189, 190

3. $12i.$

5. $1.$

7. $2i.$

9. $-3\sqrt{2} + 3i\sqrt{2}.$

11. $\dfrac{\sqrt{2}}{2} - \dfrac{i\sqrt{2}}{2}.$

13. $-4i.$

15. $\cos 2\theta + i \sin 2\theta.$

Article 108. Pages 191, 192

3. $\frac{1}{2}(1 - i)$.

5. $\frac{1}{2}(-\sqrt{3} + i)$.

7. $-1 + i$.

9. $\frac{1}{2}(-1 + i\sqrt{3})$.

11. $\frac{1}{4}(3\sqrt{2} + 3i\sqrt{2})$.

13. $-\frac{1}{2}(1 + i\sqrt{3})$.

15. $\frac{1}{4}(1 - i)$.

17. i.

19. $\frac{1}{4}(\sqrt{3} + i)$.

21. $\frac{1}{8}(1 - i\sqrt{3})$.

Article 110. Pages 193–195

3. 4096.
5. 1.

7. $\frac{243}{2}(1 + i\sqrt{3})$.

9. $-\frac{1}{2}i$.

11. $\frac{1}{4}(-1 + i\sqrt{3})$.

15. $\sqrt{2}(\cos x + i \sin x)$, where $x = 82.5°, 172.5°, 262.5°, 352.5°$.
17. $\cos x + i \sin x$, where $x = 75°, 165°, 255°, 345°$.

19. $\dfrac{\sqrt{2}(1 + i)}{2}, \dfrac{-\sqrt{2}(1 + i)}{2}$.

21. $-2, 1 + i\sqrt{3}, 1 - i\sqrt{3}$.

23. $\cos x + i \sin x$, where $x = \dfrac{\pi}{8}, \dfrac{5\pi}{8}, \dfrac{9\pi}{8}, \dfrac{13\pi}{8}$.

25. $\cos x + i \sin x$, where $x = 30°, 102°, 174°, 246°, 318°$.

Article 114. Pages 199, 200

3. 0.
5. 1.
7. 7.

15. $k = 1$ or $k = -\dfrac{1}{2}$.

Article 116. Pages 202, 203

3. $x^3 + 2x^2 - 6x + 10$ with remainder $- 28$.
5. $6x^2 + 25x + 66$ with remainder 200.
7. $x^4 - x^3 + 2x^2 - 2x + 2$ with remainder $- 7$.
9. $f(-2) = -35; f(-1) = -30; f(1) = -14; f(2) = 45$.

Article 117. Pages 203, 204

3. $-3, 0, 2$.   **5.** $1, -4$.   **7.** $-2.5^+, 1^-, 3^-$.

Article 119. Pages 207, 208

1. $x = 1$ is a single root; $x = -2$ is a triple root; $x = 5$ is a double root.
3. $x = 1$ is a double root; $x = -1$ is a single root; $x = 3$ is a single root.

5. $x = 1, x = \dfrac{-1 + i\sqrt{3}}{2}, x = \dfrac{-1 - i\sqrt{3}}{2}$; all single roots.

9. (a) $x^3 - 2x^2 - 16x + 32 = 0$.
   (b) $x^4 - 9x^2 - 4x + 12 = 0$.
   (c) $x^3 - 6x^2 + 9x - 2 = 0$.
   (d) $x^4 - 10x^3 + 23x^2 + 32x - 182 = 0$.

11. $Q(x) \equiv 4x^2 + 9$; $r = -25, s = -50$.

Article 123. Page 213

1. $y^3 - 8y^2 - 28y + 80 = 0$.
3. $y^4 + 5y^3 - 18y^2 - 20y + 56 = 0$.
5. $y^3 + 16y^2 - y - 16 = 0$.
7. $y^4 + 5y^3 + 108y^2 + 720y - 5184 = 0$.
9. $y^3 - 16y^2 - 235y + 250 = 0$.
11. $y^4 - 2y^2 + 3y - 2 = 0$.

Article 124. Pages 214, 215

3. 2 positive, no negative, and 2 imaginary roots.
5. 1 positive, 1 negative, and 2 imaginary roots.
7. 1 positive, 2 negative, and 2 imaginary roots; or 1 positive, no negative, and 4 imaginary roots. A graph of the function shows that the second case is the correct one.
9. Possible cases are:
   4 positive, 2 negative, and no imaginary roots;
   4 positive, no negative, and 2 imaginary roots;
   2 positive, 2 negative, and 2 imaginary roots;
   2 positive, no negative, and 4 imaginary roots;
   no positive, 2 negative, and 4 imaginary roots;
   no positive, no negative, and 6 imaginary roots.
11. 1 positive, no negative, and $2n$ imaginary roots.
13. 3 positive and 1 negative roots.
15. 2 positive and 1 negative roots.
17. 1 positive, 1 negative, and 6 imaginary roots.

Article 126. Pages 216, 217

1. Lower bound -2, upper bound 5.
3. Lower bound -5, upper bound 8.
5. Lower bound -2, upper bound 5.
7. Lower bound -5, upper bound 0.
11. -2.   **13.** 1.   **15.** 1.   **17.** 0.

Article 127. Pages 218–220

5. $-2, -1, 1, 3$.
7. $-\dfrac{1}{2}, -\dfrac{1}{3}, \dfrac{2}{3}$.

9. $-1, -1, 2, 2i, -2i$.
11. $-2, 3, 2 + 3i, 2 - 3i$.

13. $-\dfrac{1}{2}, 1, 1, \dfrac{i\sqrt{3}}{2}, \dfrac{-i\sqrt{3}}{2}.$

19. $\dfrac{2}{3}, 2, -1 + i\sqrt{3}, -1 - i\sqrt{3}.$

15. $\dfrac{3}{2}, \dfrac{7 + \sqrt{69}}{2}, \dfrac{7 - \sqrt{69}}{2}.$

21. $-\dfrac{2}{5}, -\dfrac{3}{4}, 2 + i, 2 - i.$

17. $\dfrac{1}{4}, \dfrac{\sqrt{2}}{2}, \dfrac{-\sqrt{2}}{2}.$

23. No rational roots; one irrational root between 0 and 1; another irrational root between 3 and 4; two imaginary roots.

Article 128. Page 223

1. 1.24.   **3.** 0.250, 0.707, − 0.707.   **5.** 4.51.

Article 129. Pages 224, 225

3. $y^3 + 6y^2 + 5y + 1 = 0.$ **5.** $y^3 - 7y + 7 = 0.$

7. $3y^4 - 16y^3 + 49y^2 - 34y + 8 = 0.$

9. $y^5 - 10.8y^4 + 39.08y^3 - 54.1768y^2 + 20.8928y + 5.45536 = 0.$

Article 132. Pages 230–232

1. 1.20.   **5.** 2.48.   **9.** 2.90.   **13.** 3.98.

3. 5.24⁻.   **7.** 0.13.   **11.** − 3.40.   **15.** − 3.

17. 1.88, − 0.35, − 1.53.

19. 3.01, 0.63, − 2.02, − 0.95.   **25.** 0.606.

21. 2.36⁻, 2.69, − 2.05.   **27.** 0.32, 0.64.

23. 6.17.   **29.** 11.07.

31. 0.259.

33. $2\sqrt[3]{\dfrac{292}{3}} - 8 = 1.20, \dfrac{5}{2}\sqrt[3]{\dfrac{292}{3}} - 10 = 1.50, 3\sqrt[3]{\dfrac{292}{3}} - 12 = 1.80.$

Article 133. Page 234

1. $x^3 + 2x^2 - 5x - 6 = 0.$ **9.** $2x^4 - 3x^2 - 3x - 3 = 0.$

3. $6x^3 + 5x^2 - 12x + 4 = 0.$ **11.** $3, 2i, -2i.$

5. $2x^3 - 3x^2 - 5x + 6 = 0.$ **13.** $-4, 2, 6.$

7. $3x^3 + 8x^2 + x - 2 = 0.$

Article 135. Pages 237, 238

1. $-1, \dfrac{3 + i\sqrt{3}}{2}, \dfrac{3 - i\sqrt{3}}{2}.$ **5.** $-3, \omega, \omega^2.$

7. $\dfrac{1 + i\sqrt{3}}{2}, \dfrac{1 - i\sqrt{3}}{2}, \dfrac{-3 + i\sqrt{3}}{2}, \dfrac{-3 - i\sqrt{3}}{2}.$

9. $3, -1 + i, -1 - i.$

Article 138. Pages 240, 241

1. $x = \dfrac{8}{3}.$ **3.** $x = -\dfrac{16}{3}.$ **5.** $x = -\dfrac{36}{5}.$

7. (a) $x = -14$, (b) $x = -\dfrac{15}{11}$, (c) $x = \dfrac{15}{4}$.

9. (a) $x = \dfrac{9}{5}$, (b) $x = \dfrac{9}{5}$, (c) $x = \dfrac{25}{3}$, (d) $x = -\dfrac{16}{7}$.

Problems Involving Similar Figures

17. Increase shortest side by $1\frac{3}{4}$ inches and the third side by $2\frac{1}{2}$ inches.

19. 135 sq. in.   **21.** 459.375 miles.

Article 143. Pages 244–247

1. $V = ke^3$, $k = 1$.

3. $S = kr^2$, $k = 4\pi$.

5. $v = \dfrac{k}{p}$.

7. $h = kT$.

9. $1666\frac{2}{3}$; 2500; $4166\frac{2}{3}$; $4166\frac{2}{3}$; 7500 shares.

11. 800 pounds.

13. $L = \dfrac{kt^4}{l^2}$.

15. Yes.

17. The strength of a rectangular beam varies jointly as the product of the breadth and the depth and inversely as the length.

19. 144.9 feet.

21. Dropped from a height of 579.6 feet; struck the ground with velocity of 193.2 feet per second.

23. 0.9528 seconds.

25. 16,200.

27. 72 cu. in.

29. 42.420 m.p.h.

31. 40 pounds.

33. (a) $s - c = \dfrac{ks^3}{r^2}$, $s = 3.155$ by formula, actually $s = 3.142$. (b) $c = 1.465$ in. (c) $s = 2.04$ in.

Article 148. Pages 251, 252

1. 17, 22, 27.

3. $\dfrac{1}{6}$, 0, $-\dfrac{1}{6}$.

5. $a_8 = 52$, $s_8 = 220$.

7. $d = \dfrac{12}{5}$, $s_6 = 66$.

9. $d = \dfrac{5}{12}$, $n = 7$.

11. $a_1 = \dfrac{2}{5}$, $n = 10$; or $a_1 = 0$, $n = 11$.

13. $s_{10} = \dfrac{65}{18}$.

15. $\dfrac{35}{4}$, $\dfrac{25}{2}$, $\dfrac{65}{4}$.

17. 13,608.

19. $n(n + 1)$.

Article 152. Pages 254, 255

1. $\dfrac{2}{3}, \dfrac{4}{3}, 2.$

7. $a_1 = 2, n = 5.$

3. $-\dfrac{3}{8}, \dfrac{3}{16}, -\dfrac{3}{32}.$

9. $n = 6, a_6 = \dfrac{3}{16}.$

5. $a_6 = \dfrac{4}{243}, s_6 = \dfrac{665}{1954}.$

11. $s_7 = \dfrac{43}{4}.$

13. 4, 32, 256; or 4, -32, 256.

15. 5, 25, 125, 625, 3125; 5, -25, 125, -625, 3125; 5, 25i, -125, $-625i$, 3125; 5, $-25i$, -125, 625i, 3125.

17. $r = -2, 1.40.$

19. $r = 1.66.$

Article 154. Pages 257, 258

1. $\dfrac{2}{3}.$

5. $4(2 + \sqrt{2}).$

9. $\dfrac{40}{99}.$

13. $\dfrac{50863}{33300}.$

3. $\dfrac{3}{5}.$

7. $\dfrac{10}{3}.$

11. $\dfrac{3032}{4995}.$

Article 156. Page 258

1. $\dfrac{8}{3}, 4, 8.$

3. The fourth term of the progression is 12. It can be extended no further.

5. $\dfrac{5}{3}, \dfrac{5}{11}, \dfrac{5}{19}, \dfrac{5}{27}, \dfrac{1}{7}.$

7. $\dfrac{2ab}{a + b}.$

Problems. Pages 259, 260

1. 805.00 feet.

3. 627.9 feet during the twentieth second; 6440 feet during the entire 20 seconds.

5. $8,857.30.

7. 162.9 cm.

9. $\dfrac{1}{x}.$

11. 51.29%.

13. 4 and 16.

17. Roots are 1, 2, 4; $c = 14.$

Article 160. Pages 263, 264

1. (a) $302.96; (b) $303.00.

3. $1343. **5.** $1368. **7.** $1373. **9.** $728.5 **11.** $1503.

13. 5% compounded semiannually.

Article 161. Pages 266, 267

3. Amount is $4776, present value is $3233.

5. $3904. **7.** $382.8.

9. Four payments of $200 each, last payment $180.

Article 165.   Pages 271, 272

1. 3024.

3. 12,144.

5. 14,400.

7. 576.

9. 103,680.

11. 12.

13. 6.

Article 169.   Pages 274–276

1. 2024.

3. 30.

5. 16.

7. 35.

9. 65.

11. $n = 6,\ r = 3$.

13. $r = 4$.

15. 10; 35; 126.

17. 10.

19. 15.

21. $\dfrac{4!\,52!}{(13!)^4}$.

23. 31.

25. $(n - 2)\,(n^2 - 4n + 6)$.

27. $P(n - 2, r) + C(n - 3, r - 2)\,\dfrac{r!}{2!} + C(n - 3, r - 3)\,\dfrac{r!}{3!}$.

29. (a) 3; (b) $C(n - 1, 3) + n - 2 = \dfrac{1}{3!}\,(n - 2)\,(n^2 - 4n + 9)$;

(c) $C(n - 1, r) + C(n - 2, r - 2)$;

(d) $C(n - 2, r) + C(n - 3, r - 2) + C(n - 3, r - 3)$;

(e) $C(n - 2, 3) + C(n - 3, 1) + 1 = C(n - 2, 3) + n - 2$.

Article 175.   Pages 280–282

1. Probability of white is $\dfrac{1}{3}$, of red is $\dfrac{2}{9}$, of black $\dfrac{4}{9}$, of either red or black $\dfrac{2}{3}$.

3. $2.

7. $\dfrac{275}{714}$.

9. $\dfrac{1}{13 \cdot 17 \cdot 49 \cdot 10}$

11. $\dfrac{1}{6}$.

13. 0.3495.

15. 0.2784.

Article 176.   Pages 284, 285

1. $\dfrac{1}{4}$.

3. $\dfrac{1}{2}$.

5. Two aces, $\dfrac{1}{36}$; an ace and a deuce, $\dfrac{1}{18}$.

7. Probability of both winning is $\dfrac{6}{35}$; probability of either A or B winning is $\dfrac{17}{35}$.

9. 0.369.

11. $\dfrac{1}{36}$.

Article 117. Pages 286, 287

1. Probability of heads exactly three times is $\dfrac{5}{8}$; probability of heads at least three times is $\dfrac{13}{16}$.

3. $\dfrac{2}{9}$.

7. $\dfrac{10}{63}$.

9. (a) 0.27648; (b) 0.8208; (c) 0.45568.

11. $1 - \left(\dfrac{1}{2}\right)^{10} = 0.99902.$

13. Probability of 10 is $\dfrac{1}{8}$; probability of 9 is $\dfrac{25}{216}$.

Article 180. Page 294

1. 6.

3. 148.

Article 181. Pages 296, 297

3. 75.

5. $-1430.$

13. $1 + 2abc - a^2 - b^2 - c^2.$

15. $a^2 + b^2 + c^2 - 2ab - 2ac - 2bc.$

9. $abc(a - b)\,(b - c)\,(c - a).$

11. $2abc.$

Article 185. Pages 304, 305

1. $x = -2,\ y = 3.$

3. $x = 1,\ y = 2,\ z = -1,\ w = 1.$

5. $k = 3,\ x = 4,\ y = -1;\ k = -\dfrac{19}{2},\ x = -\dfrac{27}{2},\ y = 4.$

7. $x : y : z = -2 : -5 : 3.$

9. Inconsistent.

11. Inconsistent.

13. $x = \dfrac{43 - 7z}{11},\ y = \dfrac{z - 14}{11}.$

Article 187. Page 308

1. $\dfrac{1}{x} - \dfrac{1}{x + 1}.$

3. $\dfrac{2}{3x + 1} - \dfrac{1}{2x - 1}.$

5. $\dfrac{5}{1 - 5x} - \dfrac{1}{x + 5}.$

7. $x - \dfrac{1}{x - 2} + \dfrac{1}{x + 2}.$

9. $\dfrac{2}{x + 1} + \dfrac{3}{x - 2} - \dfrac{4}{x + 2}.$

11. $\dfrac{1}{x + 1} + \dfrac{2}{x + 2} + \dfrac{3}{x + 3}.$

Article 188.   Page 309

1. $\dfrac{-1}{4(x+3)} + \dfrac{1}{4(x+1)} + \dfrac{3}{2(x+1)^2}.$

5. $\dfrac{1}{x} + \dfrac{1}{3x-4} + \dfrac{1}{(3x-4)^2}.$

3. $\dfrac{2}{x} + \dfrac{1}{x^2} + \dfrac{3}{x-1}.$

7. $1 + 2x - \dfrac{3}{x} + \dfrac{4}{x^2} - \dfrac{5}{x+1}.$

9. $\dfrac{1}{x+1} + \dfrac{1}{(x+1)^2} + \dfrac{1}{x-1} + \dfrac{1}{(x-1)^2}.$

Article 189.   Page 310

1. $\dfrac{2x-3}{x^2+x+1} + \dfrac{1}{x+1}.$

7. $\dfrac{1}{3(x^2+2)} + \dfrac{1}{3(2x^2+1)}.$

3. $\dfrac{1}{x} - \dfrac{x}{x^2+5}.$

9. $x + \dfrac{x-1}{x^2+1} + \dfrac{2x+3}{x^2+x+1}.$

5. $\dfrac{1}{x+1} - \dfrac{x-2}{x^2-x+1}.$

Article 190.   Pages 311, 312

1. $\dfrac{2}{x} + \dfrac{1}{(x^2+1)^2}.$

3. $\dfrac{1}{1-x} + \dfrac{2x+3}{x^2+x+1} + \dfrac{x}{(x^2+x+1)^2}.$

5. $\dfrac{x+2}{x^2+1} - \dfrac{x}{(x^2+1)^2}.$

7. $\dfrac{1+x}{1+x^2} + \dfrac{1-x}{(1+x^2)^2} + \dfrac{2x-1}{1-x+x^2}.$

9. $\dfrac{1}{x} - \dfrac{1}{x^2} + \dfrac{1}{x^3} - \dfrac{x-1}{x^2+1} + \dfrac{x+1}{(x^2+1)^2}.$

Article 198.   Pages 321, 322

1. 6.

7. 60.

13. $\dfrac{5}{3}.$

3. 27.

9. $-9.$

5. $\dfrac{-3a}{2}.$

11. 4.

Article 200.   Page 326

1. $1 + \dfrac{1}{2} + \dfrac{1}{3},\ \dfrac{1}{n+1}.$

5. $\dfrac{1}{\sqrt{n}}.$

3. $-x + \dfrac{x^2}{2!} - \dfrac{x^3}{3!},\ \dfrac{(-1)^{n+1}x^{n+1}}{(n+1)!}.$

7. $\dfrac{(-1)^{n-1}x^{2n-1}}{(2n-1)}.$

Article 204.   Pages 332, 333

21. Divergent.   **23.** Convergent.   **25.** Divergent.   **27.** Divergent.

Article 205.　Pages 335, 336

1. Convergent.　**7.** Convergent.　**13.** Divergent.　**19.** Convergent.
3. Divergent.　**9.** Convergent.　**15.** Divergent.　**21.** Divergent.
5. Divergent.　**11.** Convergent.　**17.** Convergent.

Article 209.　Page 340

1. Convergent.　**5.** Convergent.　**9.** Convergent.　**13.** 0.6988.
3. Convergent.　**7.** Convergent.　**11.** 0.6321.

Article 210.　Pages 341, 342

3. Convergent for $|x| < 2$.
5. Convergent if $-2 \leqq x \leqq 2$, diverges if $x < -2$ or if $x > 2$.
7. Divergent for all values of x for which the series is defined.
9. Convergent for $|x| < 1$.
11. Convergent for $|x| < 1$.
13. Convergent for all values of x.
15. Convergent for all values of x.　**17.** 3.1416.

Article 211.　Pages 343, 344

1. $1 - 3x + 6x^2 - 10x^3 + 15x^4 - \cdots, \ |x| < 1.$

3. $1 - y - \dfrac{1}{2} y^2 - \dfrac{1}{2} y^3 - \dfrac{5}{8} y^4 - \cdots, \ |y| < \dfrac{1}{2}.$

5. $\dfrac{1}{8} \left(1 + \dfrac{9}{2} x + \dfrac{27}{2} x^2 + \dfrac{135}{4} x^3 + \dfrac{1215}{16} x^4 + \cdots \right), \ |x| < \dfrac{2}{3}.$

7. $1 + x - x^2 + \dfrac{5}{3} x^3 - \dfrac{10}{3} x^4 + \cdots, \ |x| < \dfrac{1}{3}.$

9. $\dfrac{\sqrt{7}}{7} \left(1 + \dfrac{1}{7} x + \dfrac{3}{98} x^2 + \dfrac{5}{686} x^3 + \dfrac{5}{2744} x^4 + \cdots \right), \ |x| < \dfrac{7}{2}.$

11. $1 - \dfrac{1}{3} x^3 + \dfrac{2}{9} x^6 - \dfrac{14}{81} x^9 + \dfrac{35}{243} x^{12} - \cdots, \ |x| < 1.$

13. 3.1623.　**15.** 2.8284.　**17.** 1.0164.　**19.** 2.9625⁻.　**21.** 0.6986.

Article 212.　Page 346

1. $\log_e \dfrac{5}{4} = 0.223$, $\log_{10} \dfrac{5}{4} = 0.097^-$.　**3.** 2.1972, 2.3026.

INDEX

[Numbers refer to pages.]

[Numbers refer to pages.]

[Numbers refer to pages.]

[Numbers refer to pages.]

[Numbers refer to pages.]

[Numbers refer to pages.]